Name ______________________

1 READINESS

Use the vocabulary **top, bottom, in, out, over** and **under.**

Use the vocabulary **on top of, off, above, below, beside, outside** and **inside.**

Name ______________________________

Use the vocabulary **first, last, middle** and **between.**

Use the vocabulary **front, behind, right** and **left.**

Name ____________________

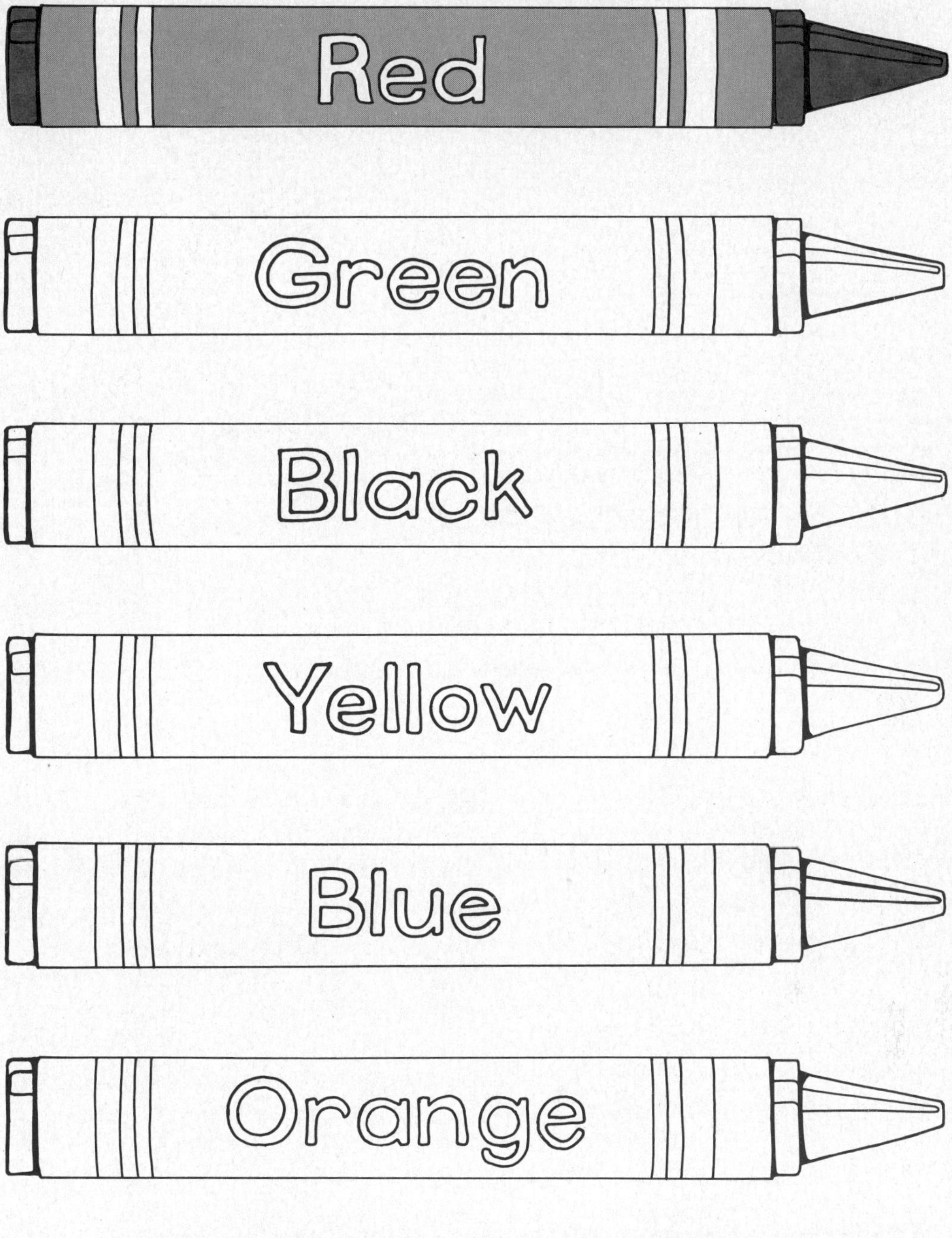

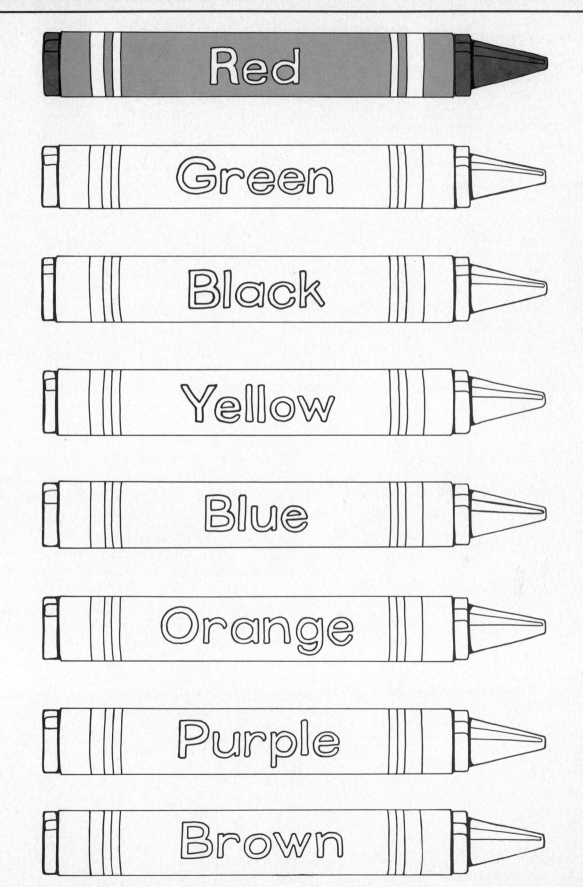

Color each crayon the correct color.

Color the picture.

Name ______________________________

Identify **circles, squares, triangles,** and **rectangles.** Color each kind of figure the same color.

Identify circles, squares, triangles, and rectangles. Color each kind of figure a different color.

Name ______________________________

Use the vocabulary **smaller, smallest** and **bigger, biggest.**

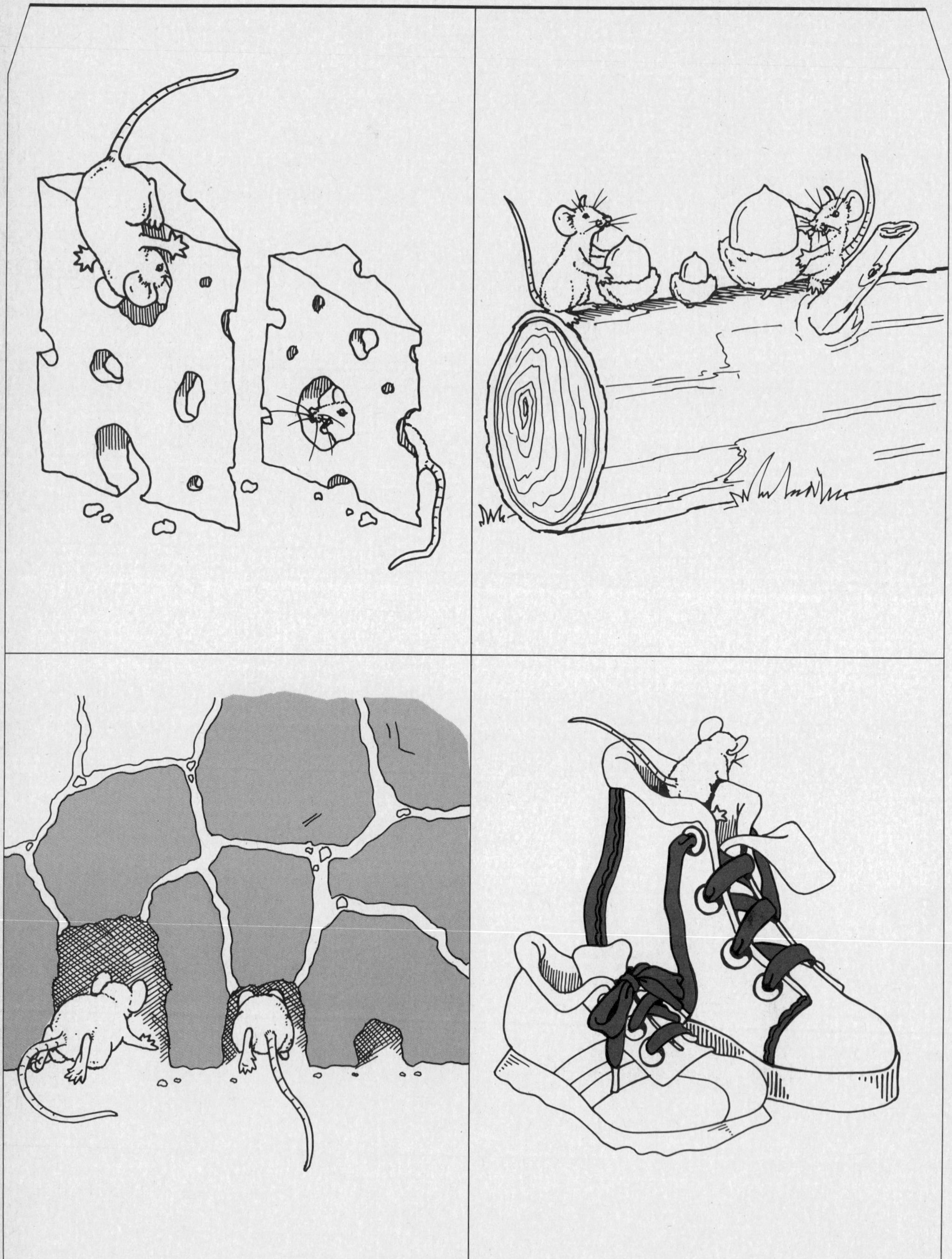

Use the vocabulary **smaller, smallest** and **larger, largest.**

Name ____

Use the vocabulary **shorter, shortest** and **taller, tallest.**

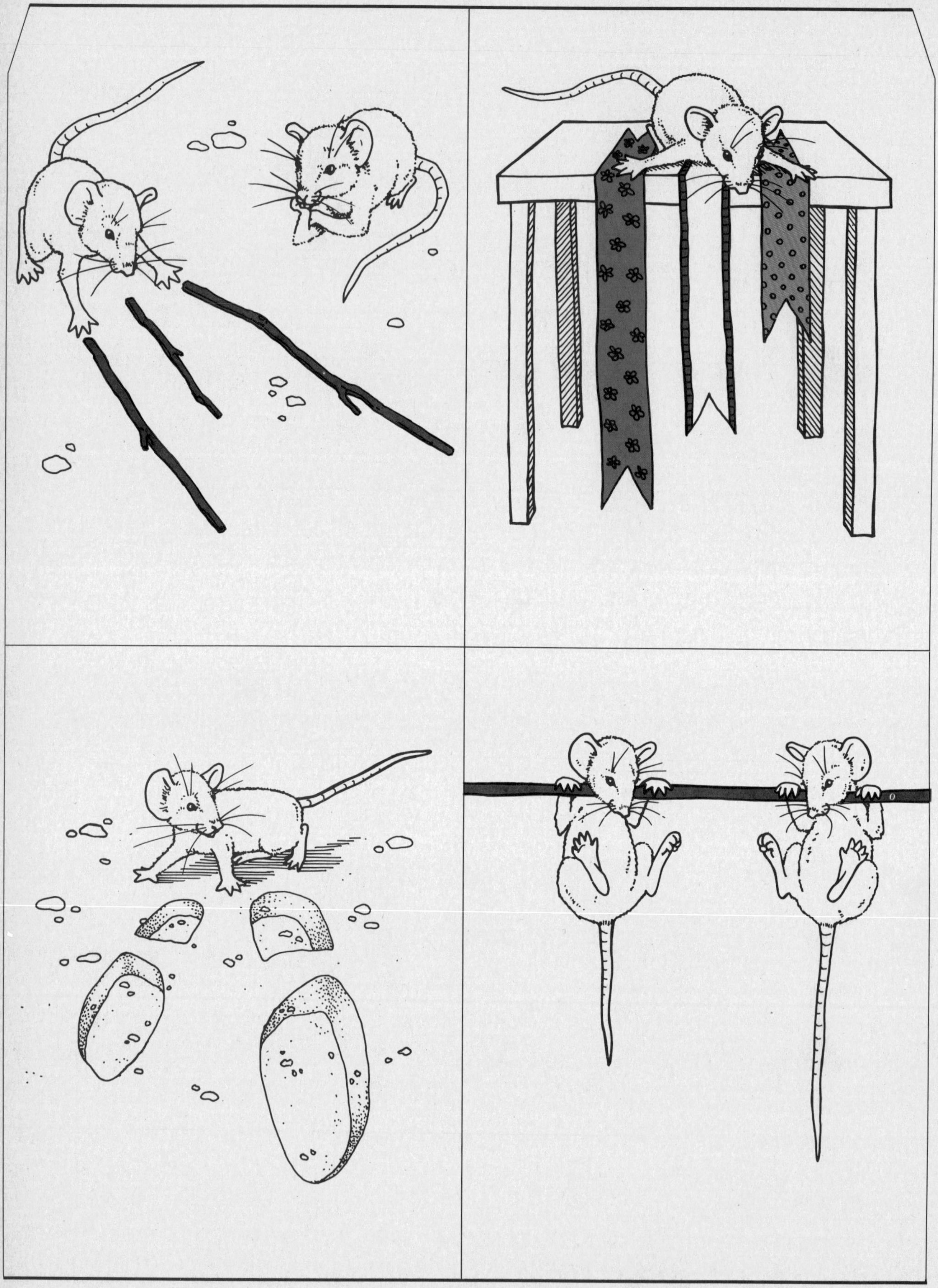

Use the vocabulary **shorter, shortest** and **longer, longest.**

Name ______________________________

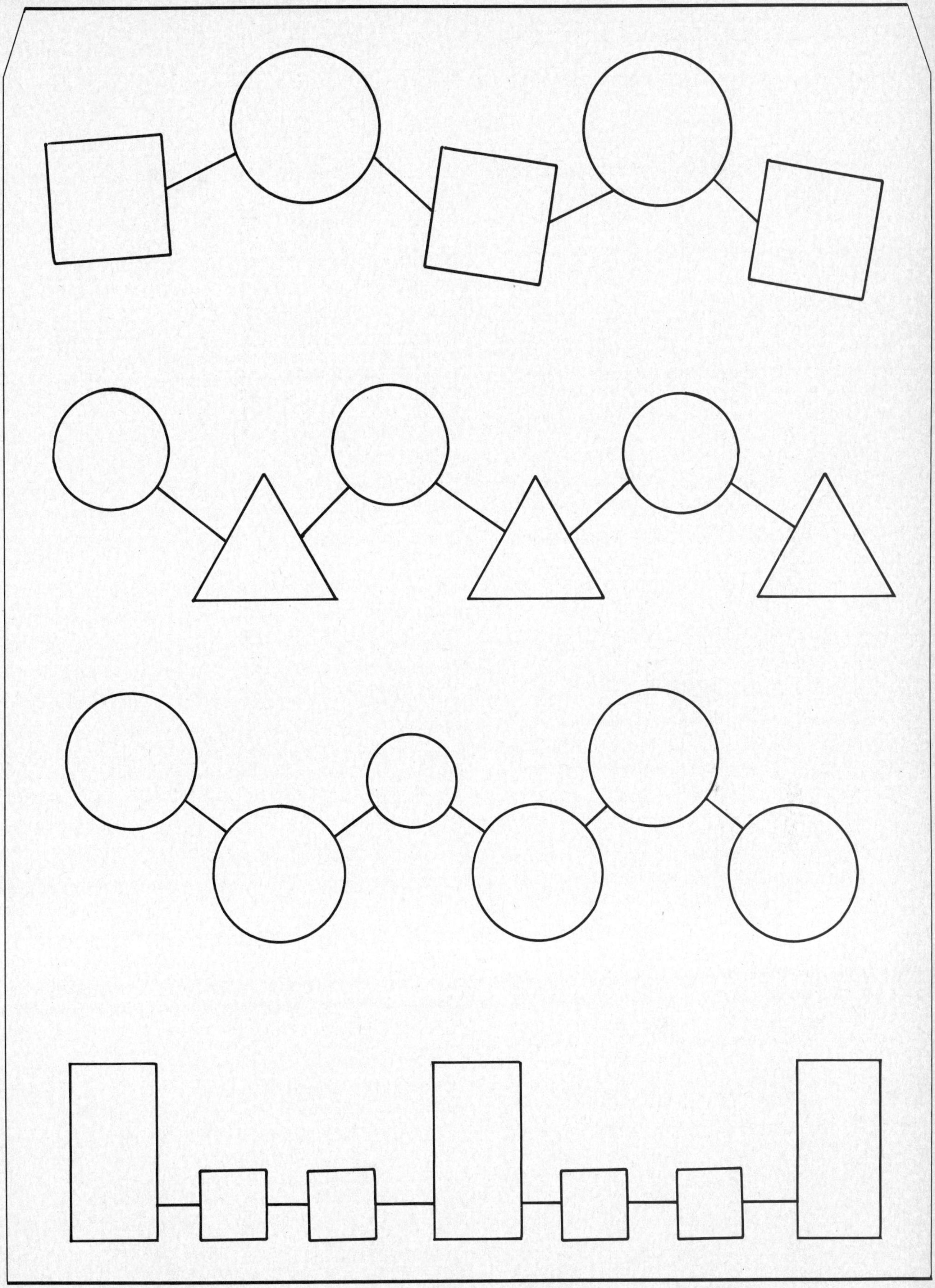

Use color to help identify the patterns.

Circle the figure that comes next in the pattern.

Name ______________________________

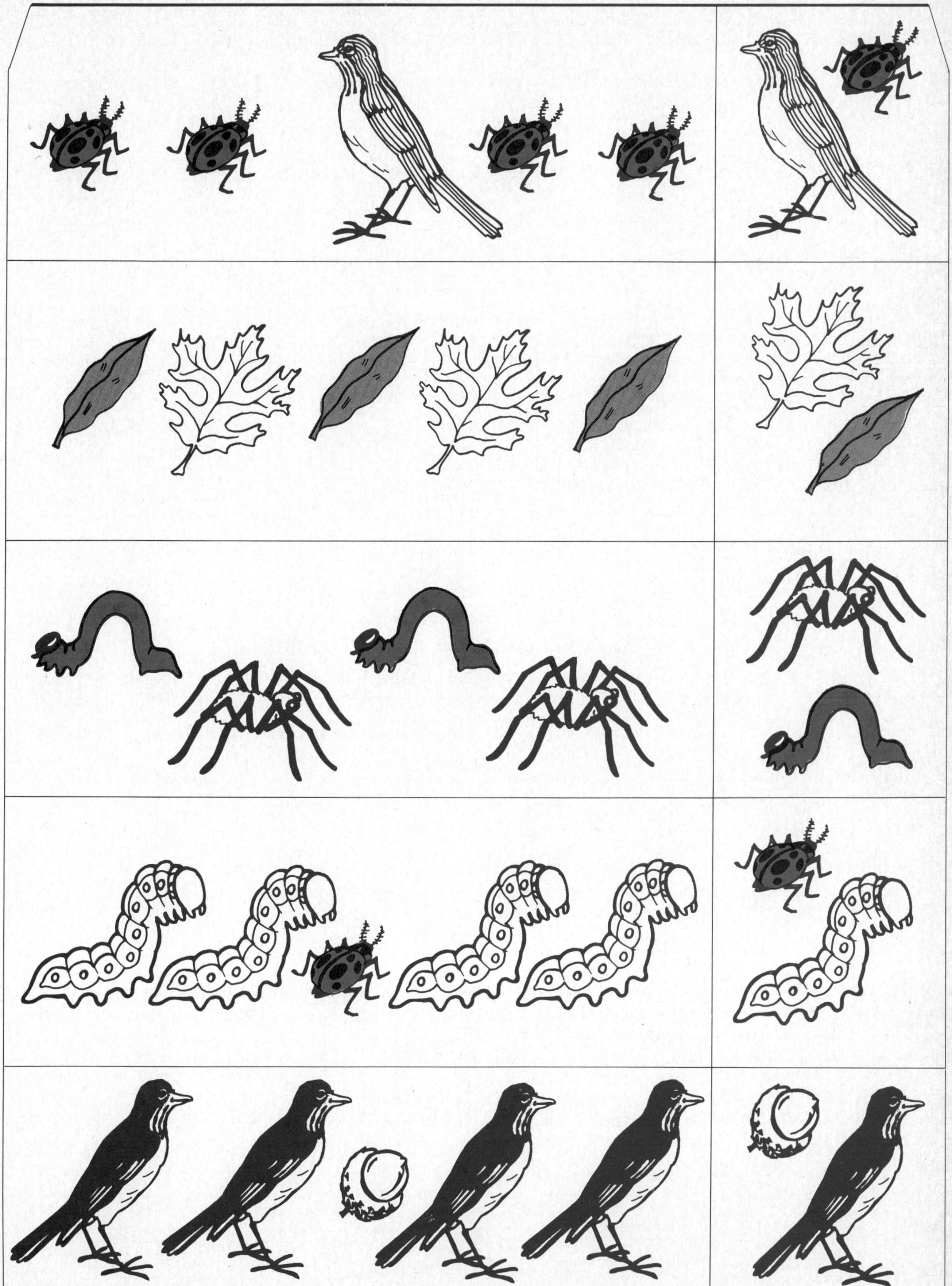

Circle the object that comes next in the pattern.

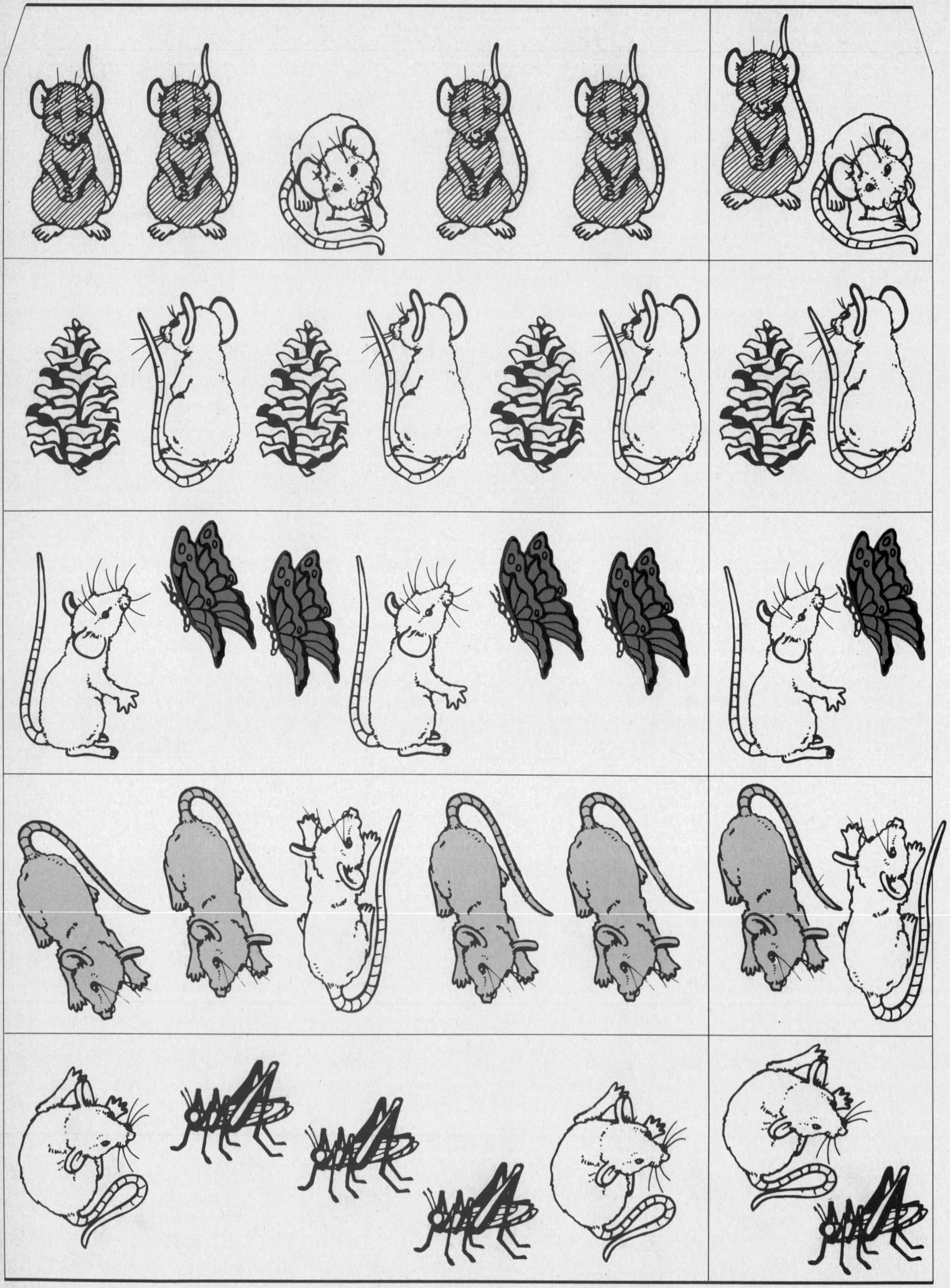

Circle the object that comes next in the pattern.

Name ______________________________

2 NUMBERS 1 THROUGH 5

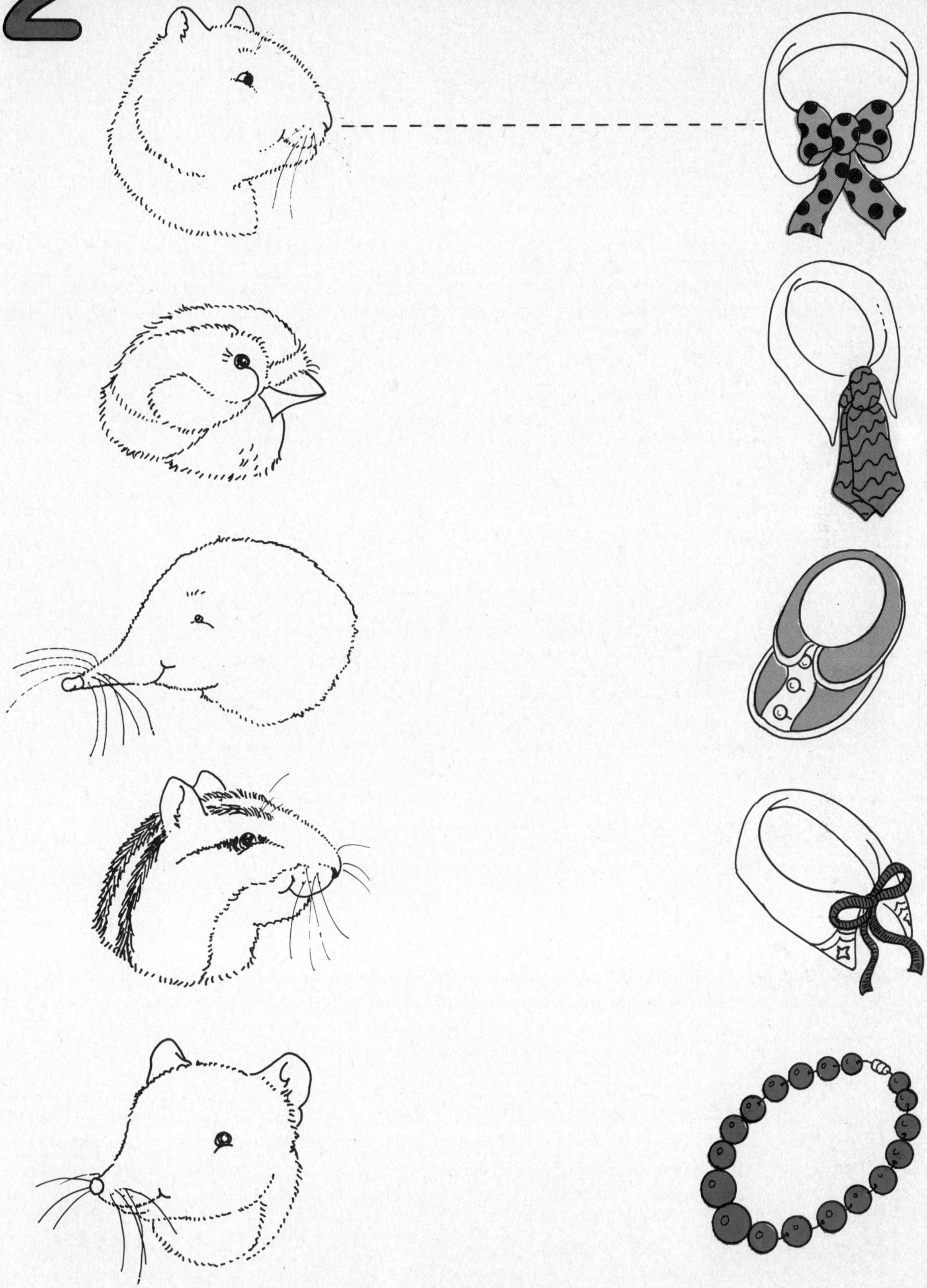

Draw a line from each animal to its collar to show one-to-one correspondence. Use the vocabulary **as many as.**

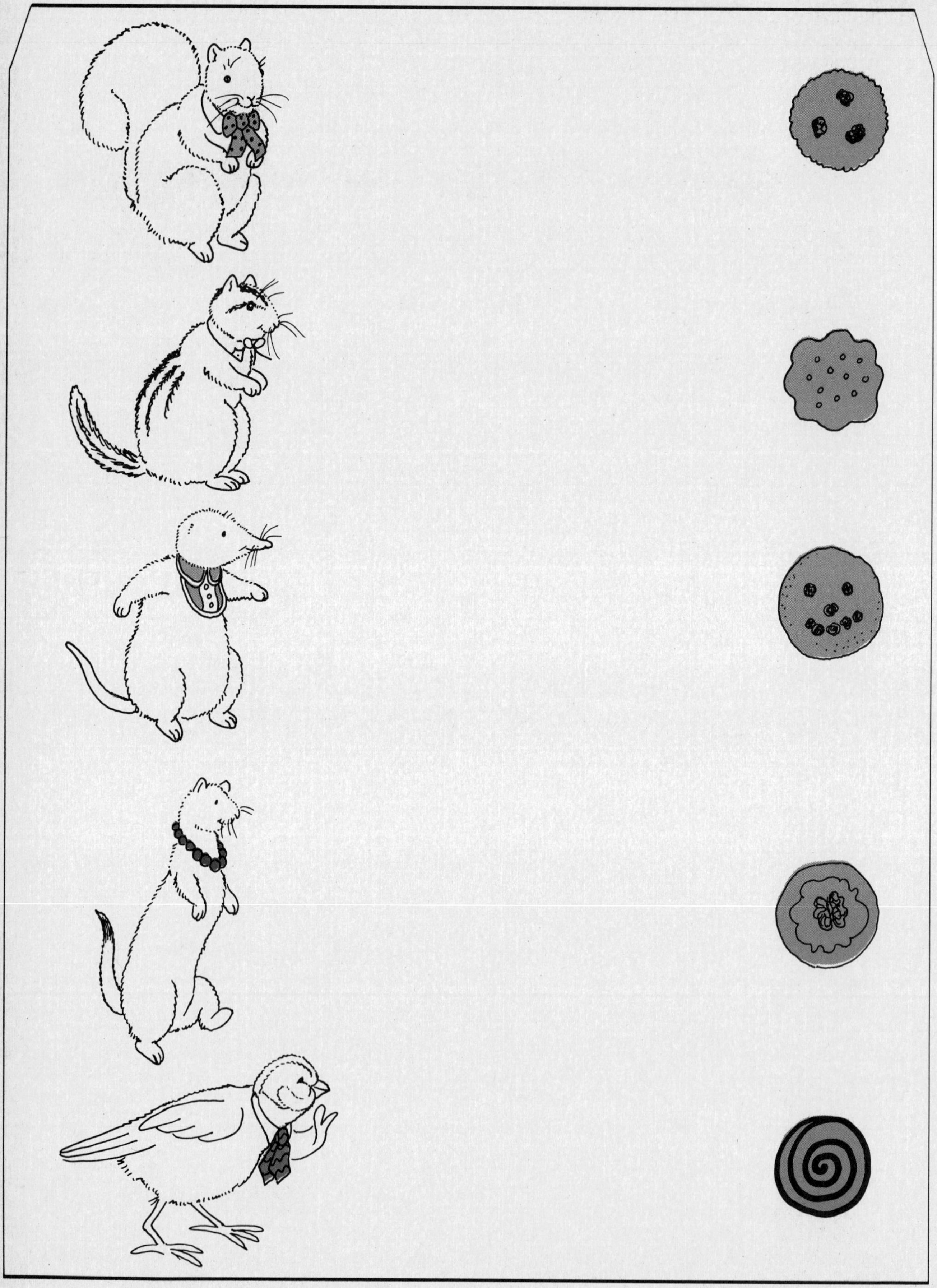

Draw a line from each animal to its treat to show one-to-one correspondence. Use the vocabulary **as many as.**

Name ______________________________

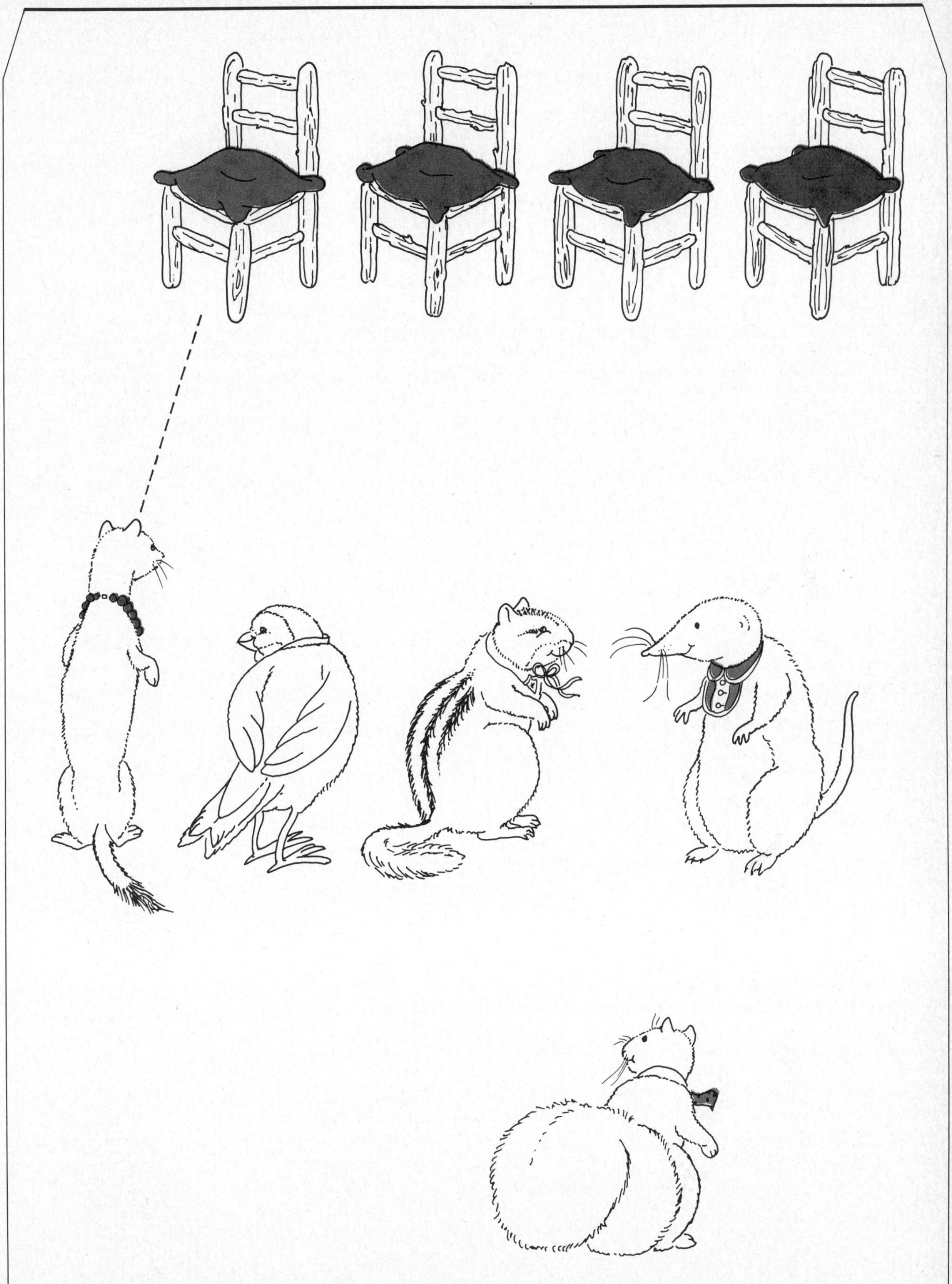

Draw a line from each animal to a chair to show one-to-one correspondence. Circle the set that has more.

Draw a line from each bird to a nest to show one-to-one correspondence. Circle the set that has less.

Name ______________________________

1

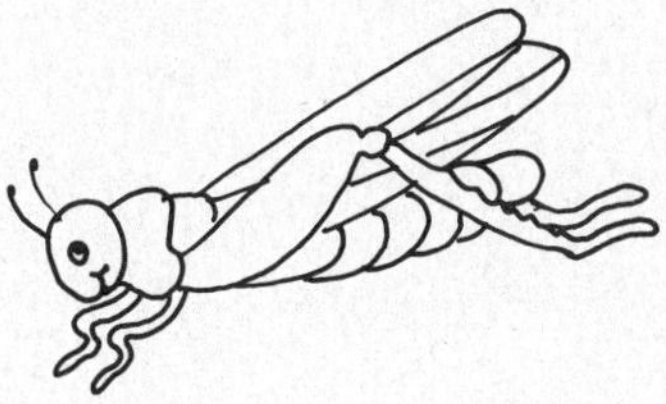

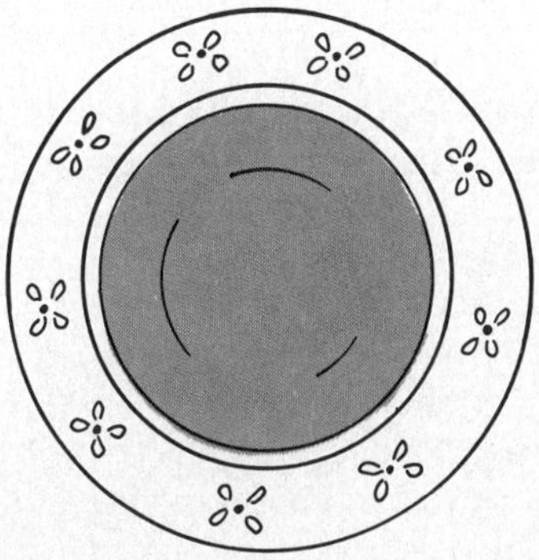

Circle each set of 1 object. Use the vocabulary **one.**

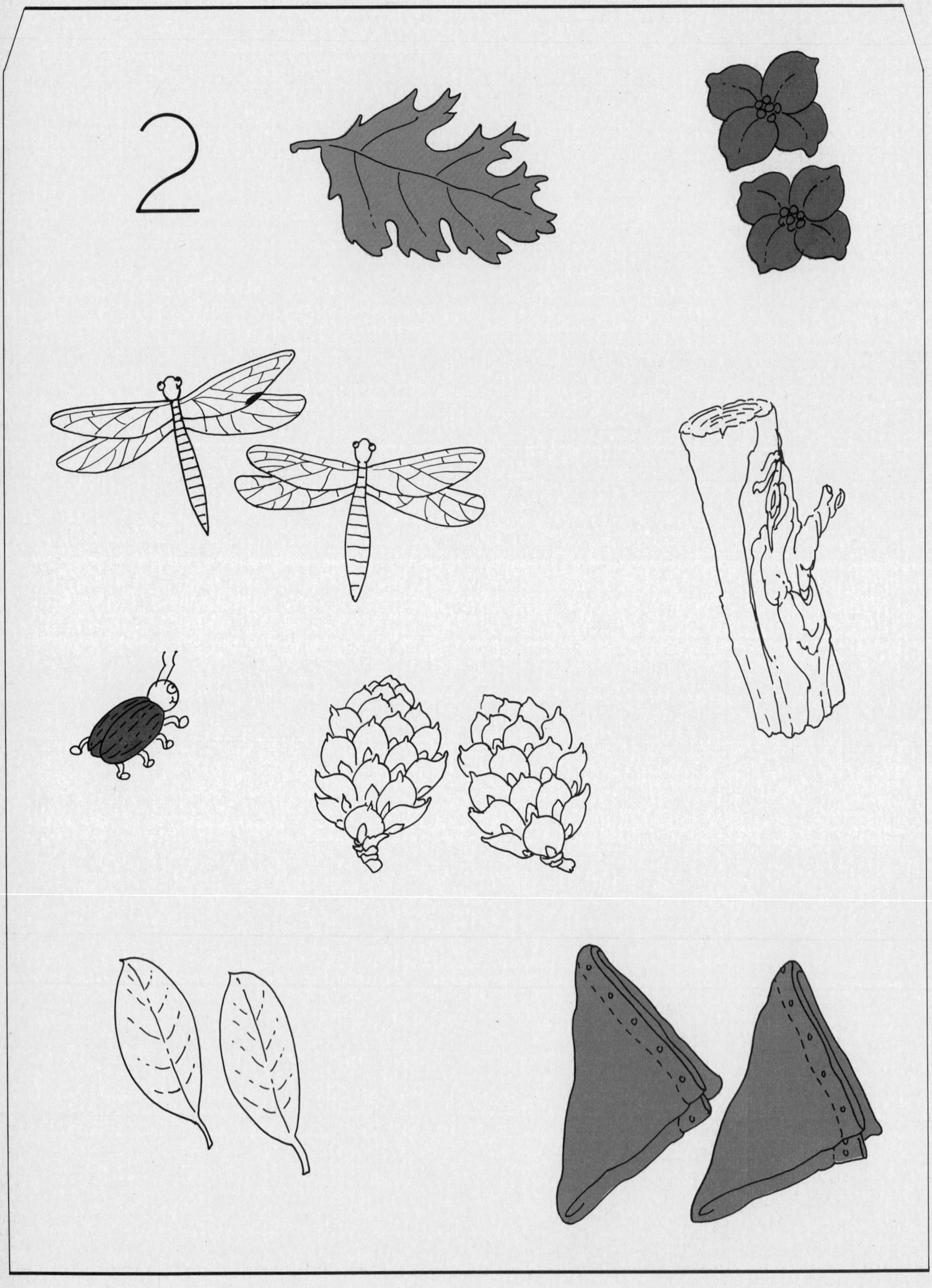

Circle each set of 2 objects. Use the vocabulary **two.**

Name _____

1   2

1   2

1   2

1   2

1   2

1   2

1   2

1   2

Circle the number that tells how many objects in each set.

1 2

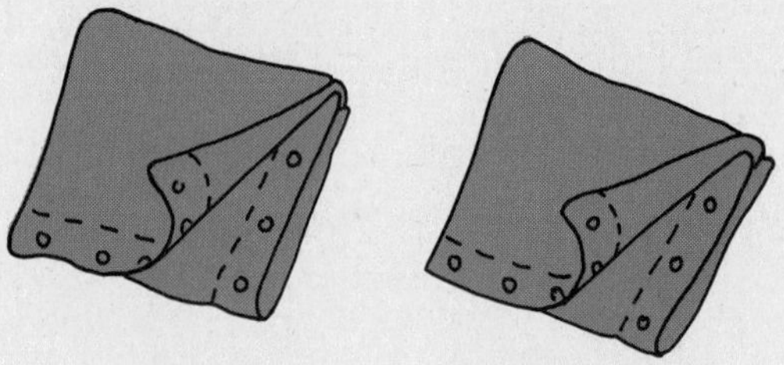

1 2

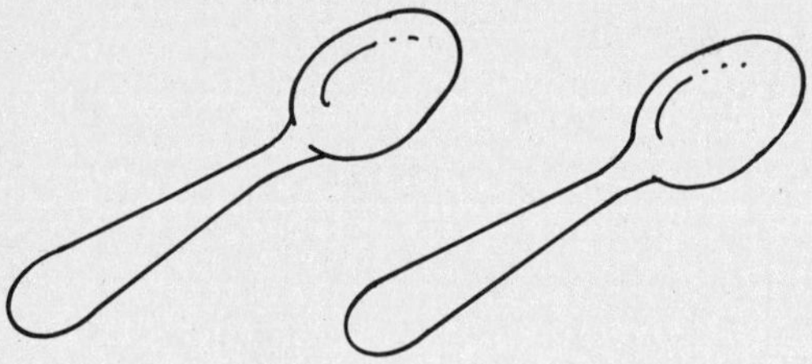

1 2

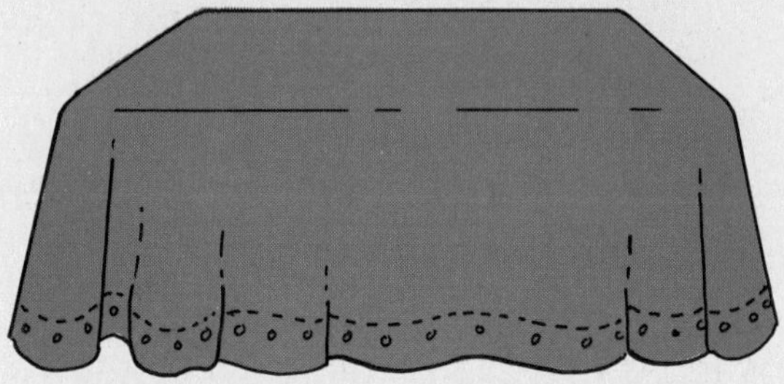

1 2

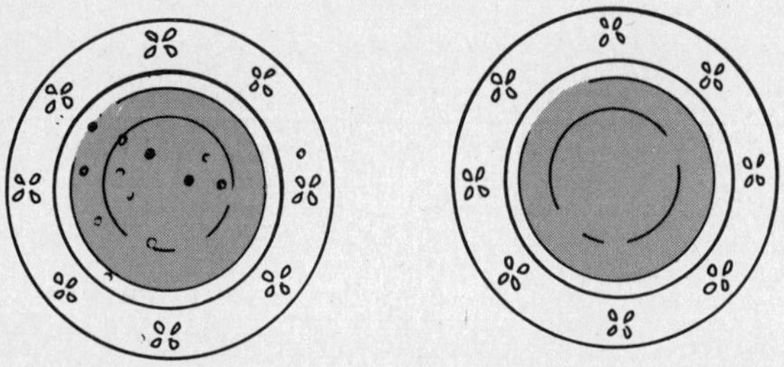

1 2

1 2

1 2

1 2

Circle the number that tells how many objects in each set.

Name ______________________________

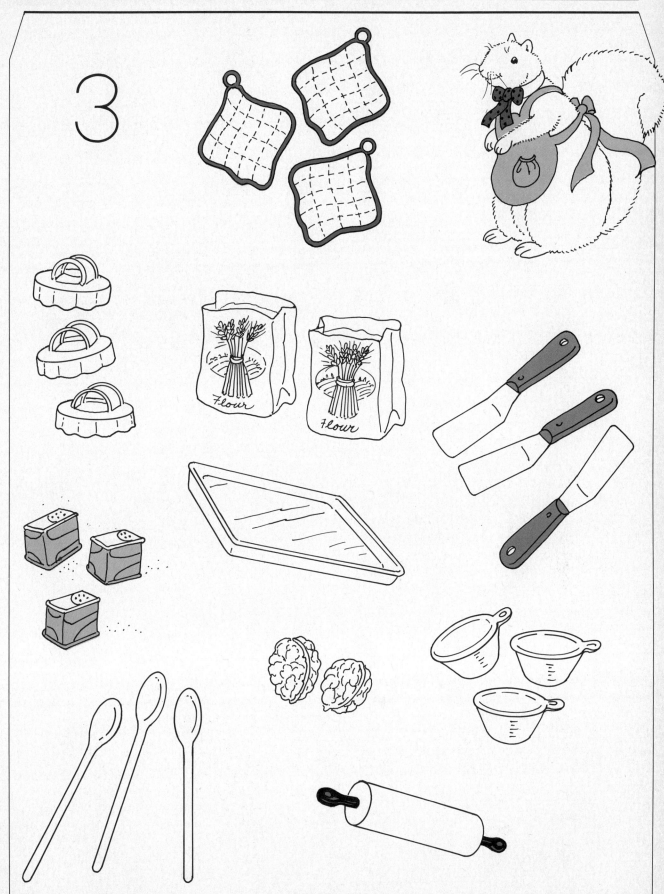

Circle each set of 3 objects. Use the vocabulary **three.**

1 2 3

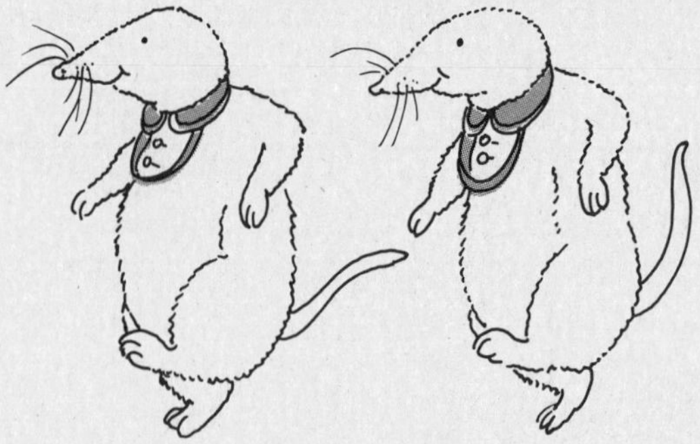

1 2 3

1 2 3

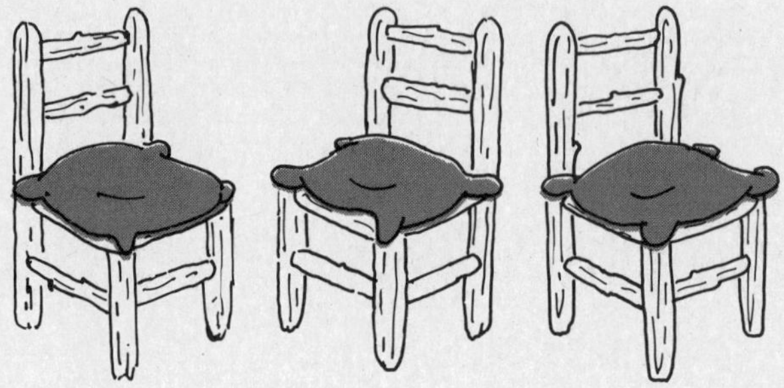

1 2 3

1 2 3

1 2 3

1 2 3

1 2 3

Circle the number that tells how many objects in each set.

Name ______________________________

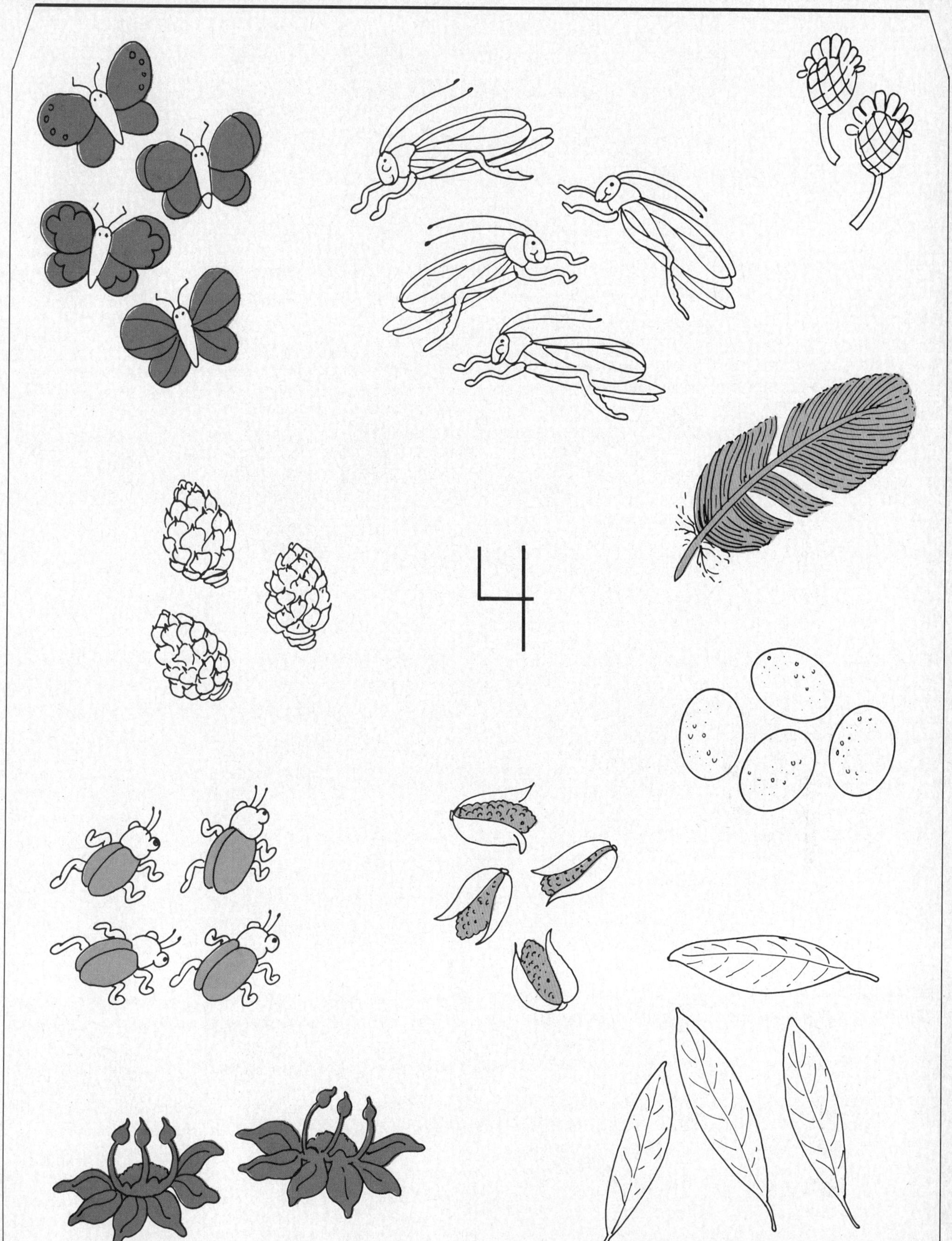

Circle each set of 4 objects. Use the vocabulary **four.**

1 2 3 4

1 2 3 4

1 2 3 4

1 2 3 4

1 2 3 4

1 2 3 4

1 2 3 4

1 2 3 4

Circle the number that tells how many objects in each set.

Name ____________________

Trace the path for writing 1 and 2.

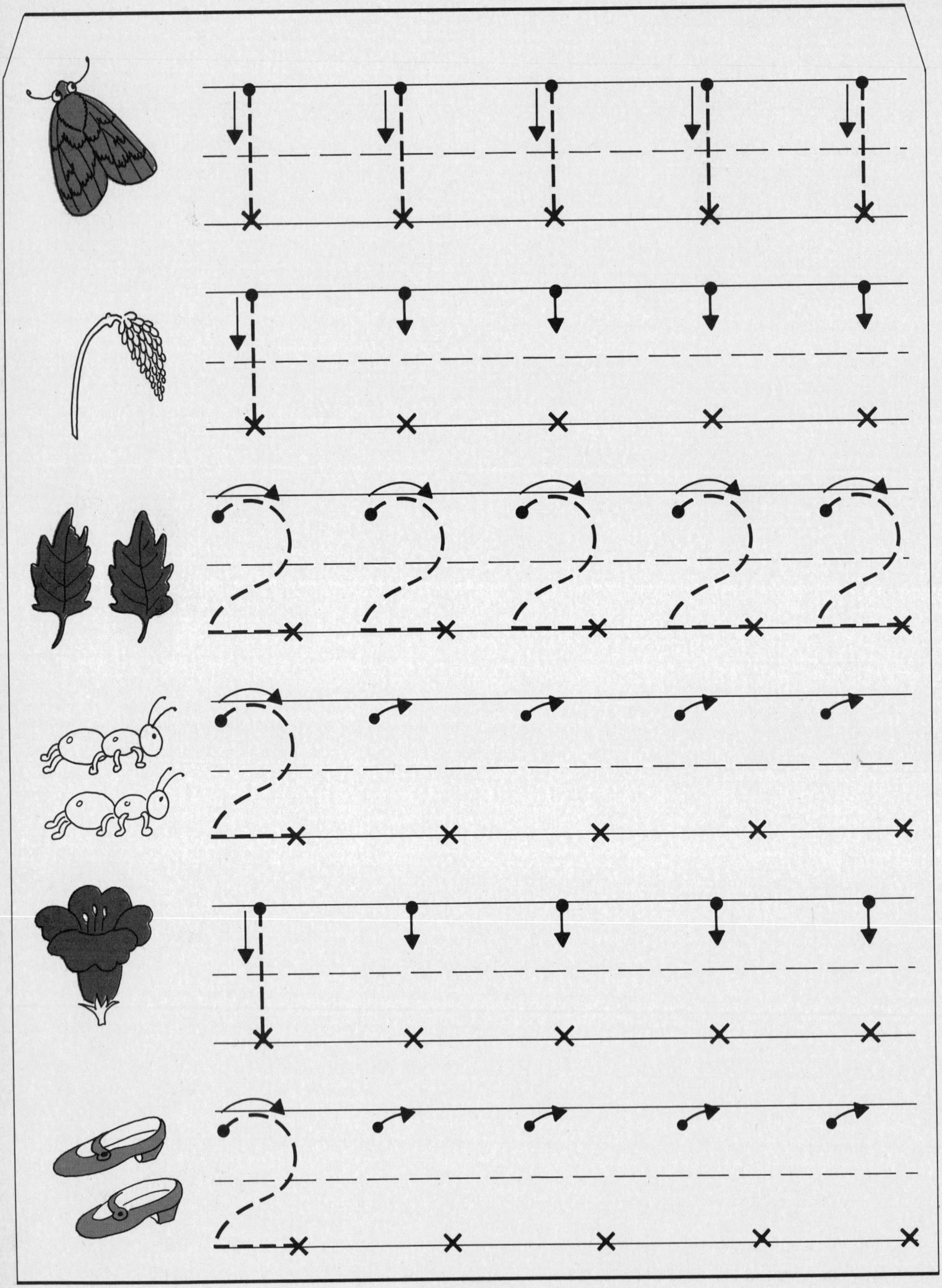

Write the numbers 1 and 2.

Name ______________________________

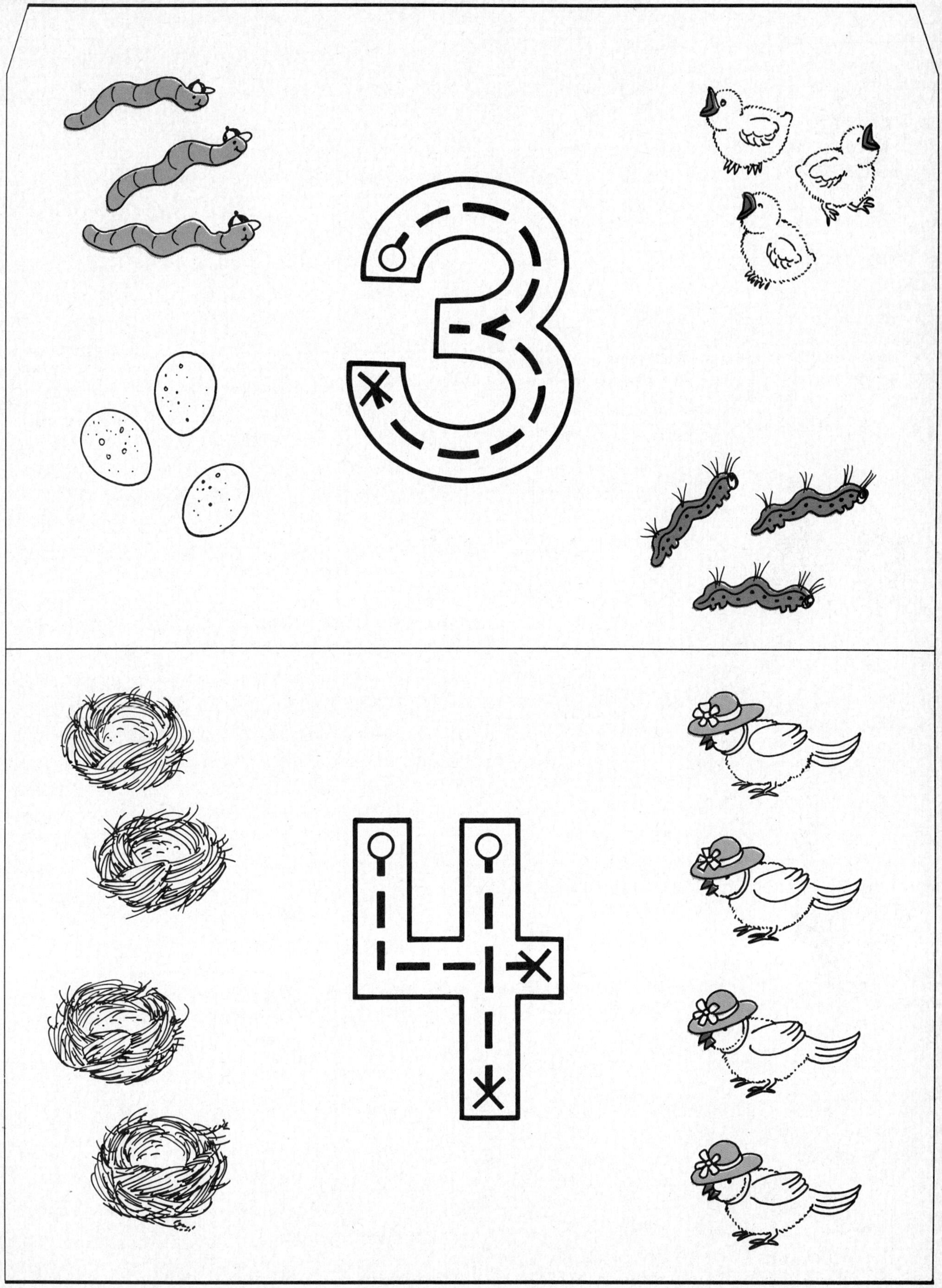

Trace the path for writing 3 and 4.

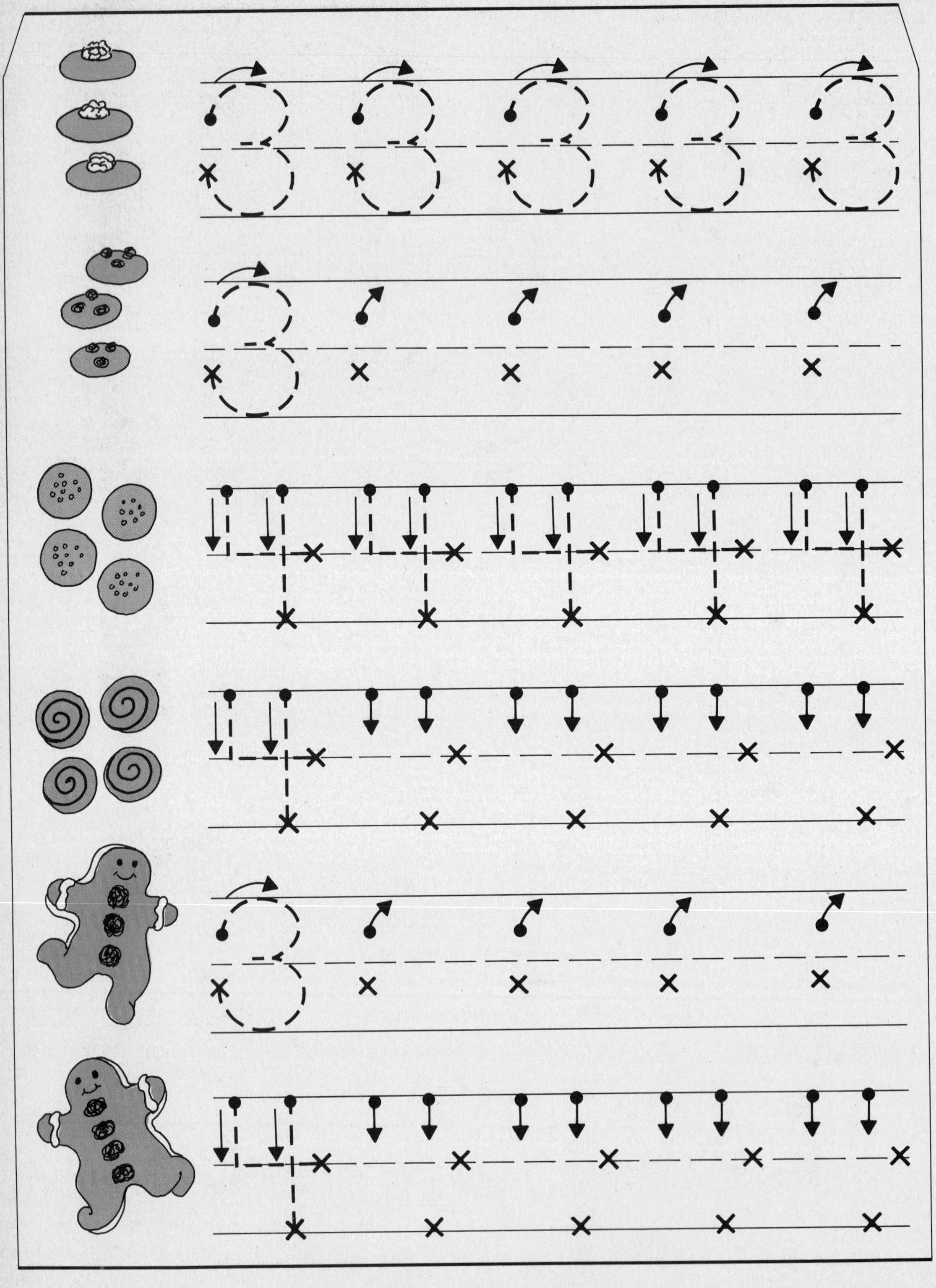

Write the numbers 3 and 4.

Name ____________________

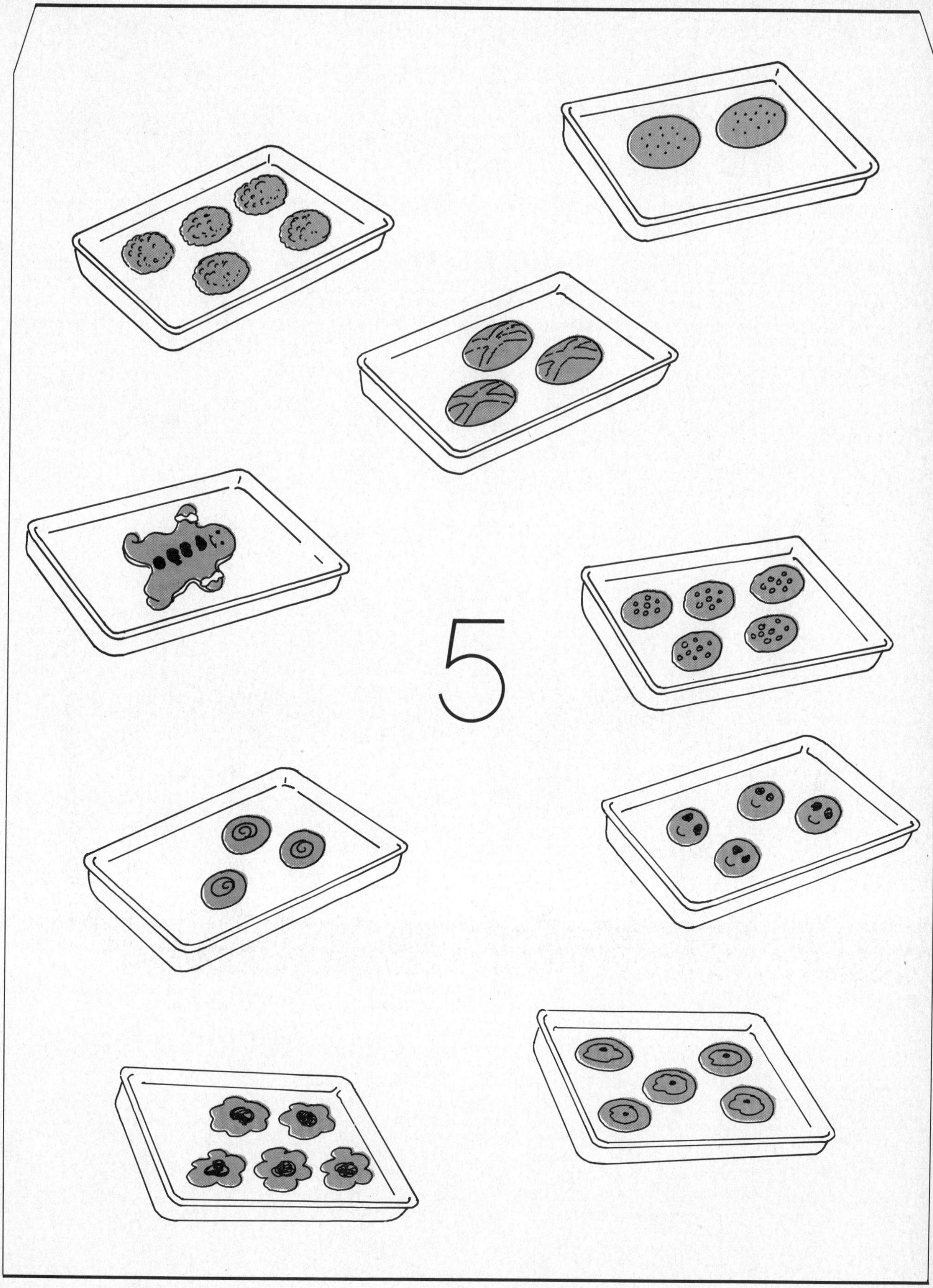

Circle each set of 5 objects. Use the vocabulary **five.**

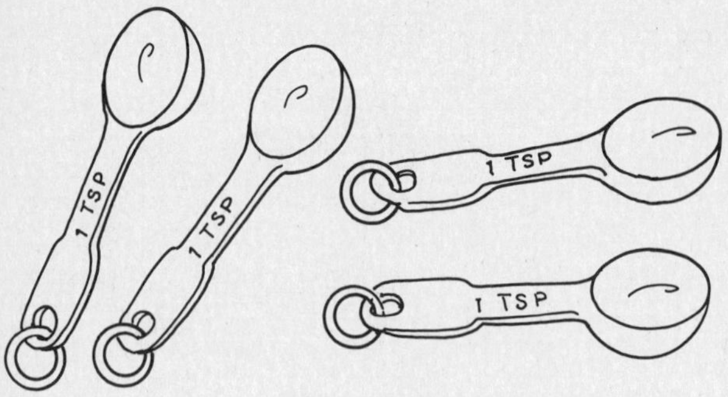

1 2 3 4

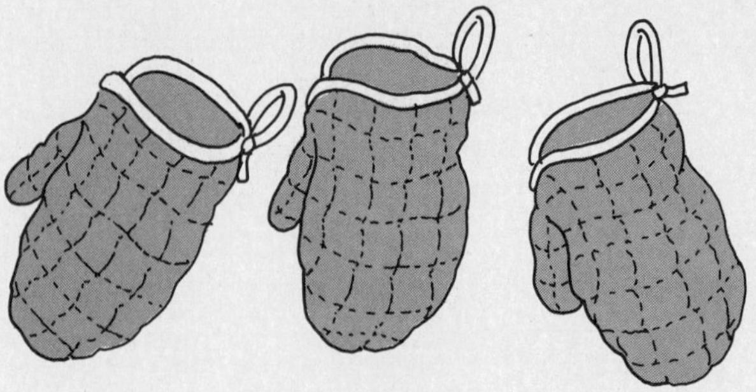

2 3 4 5

2 3 4 5

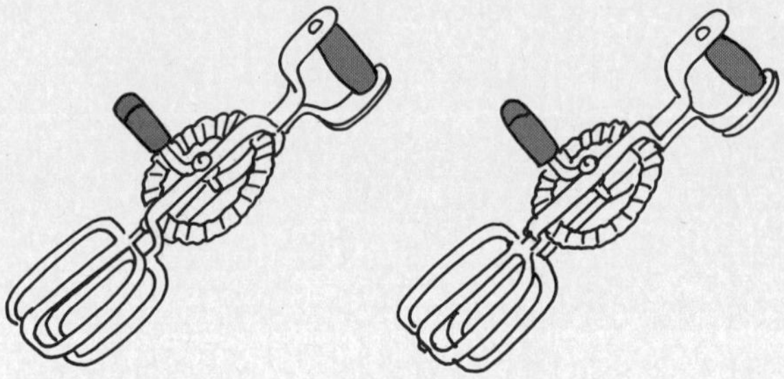

1 2 3 4

1 2 3 4

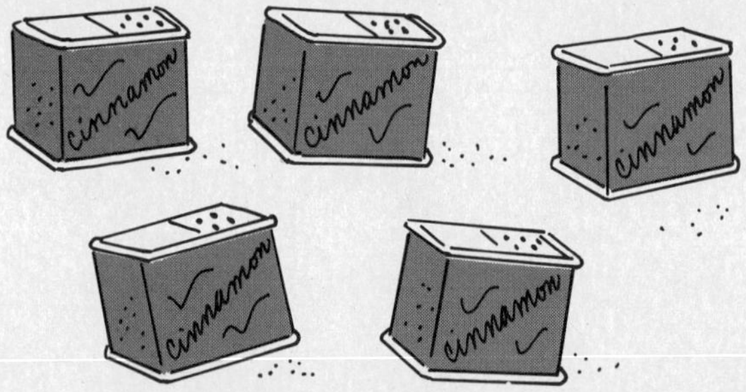

2 3 4 5

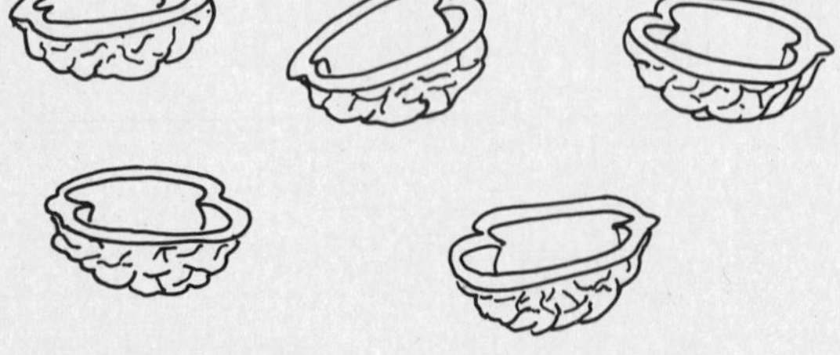

2 3 4 5

1 2 3 4

Circle the number that tells how many objects in each set.

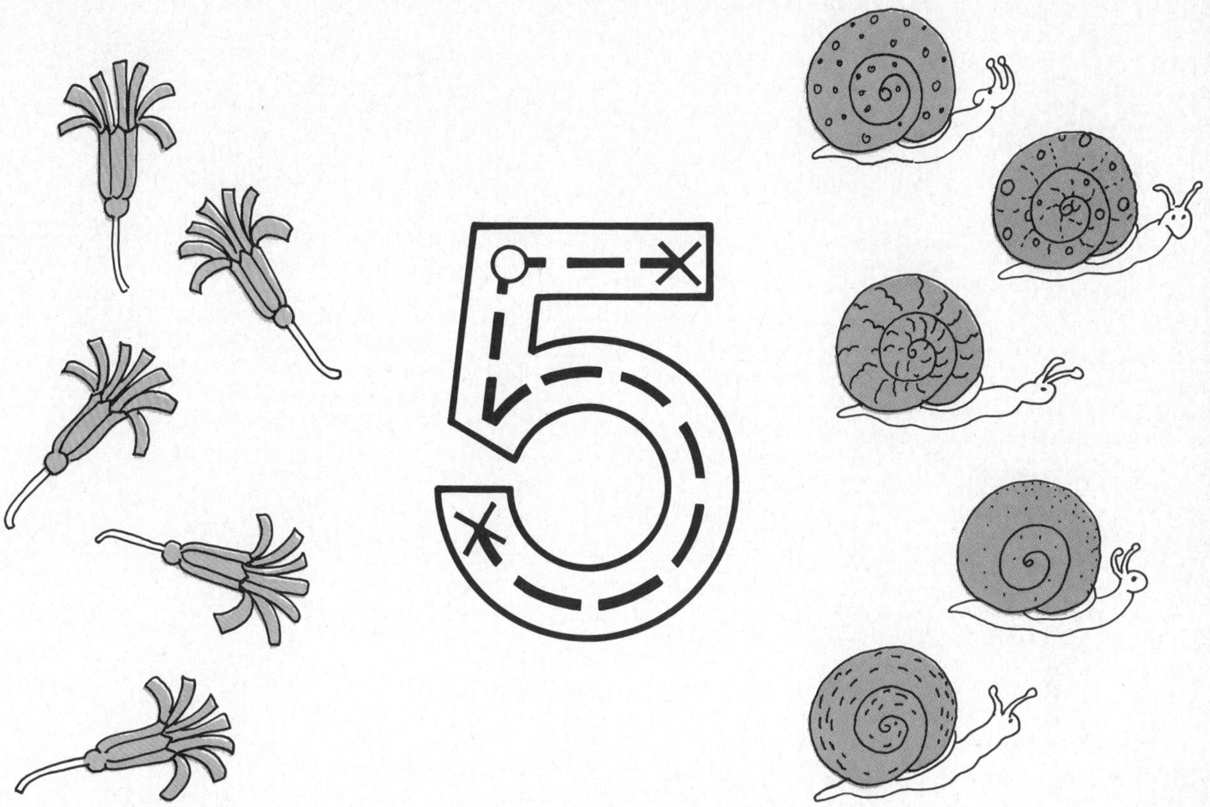

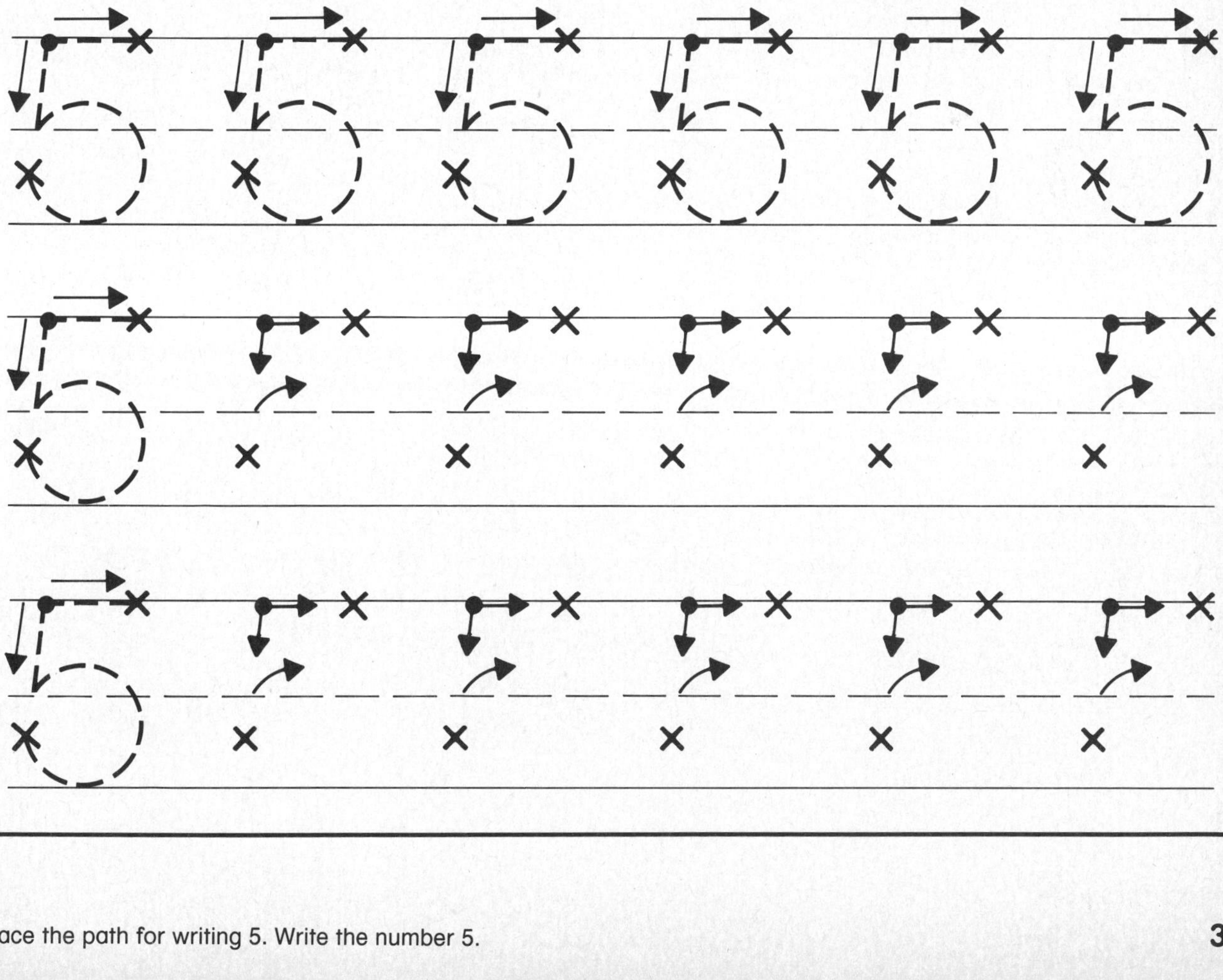

Trace the path for writing 5. Write the number 5.

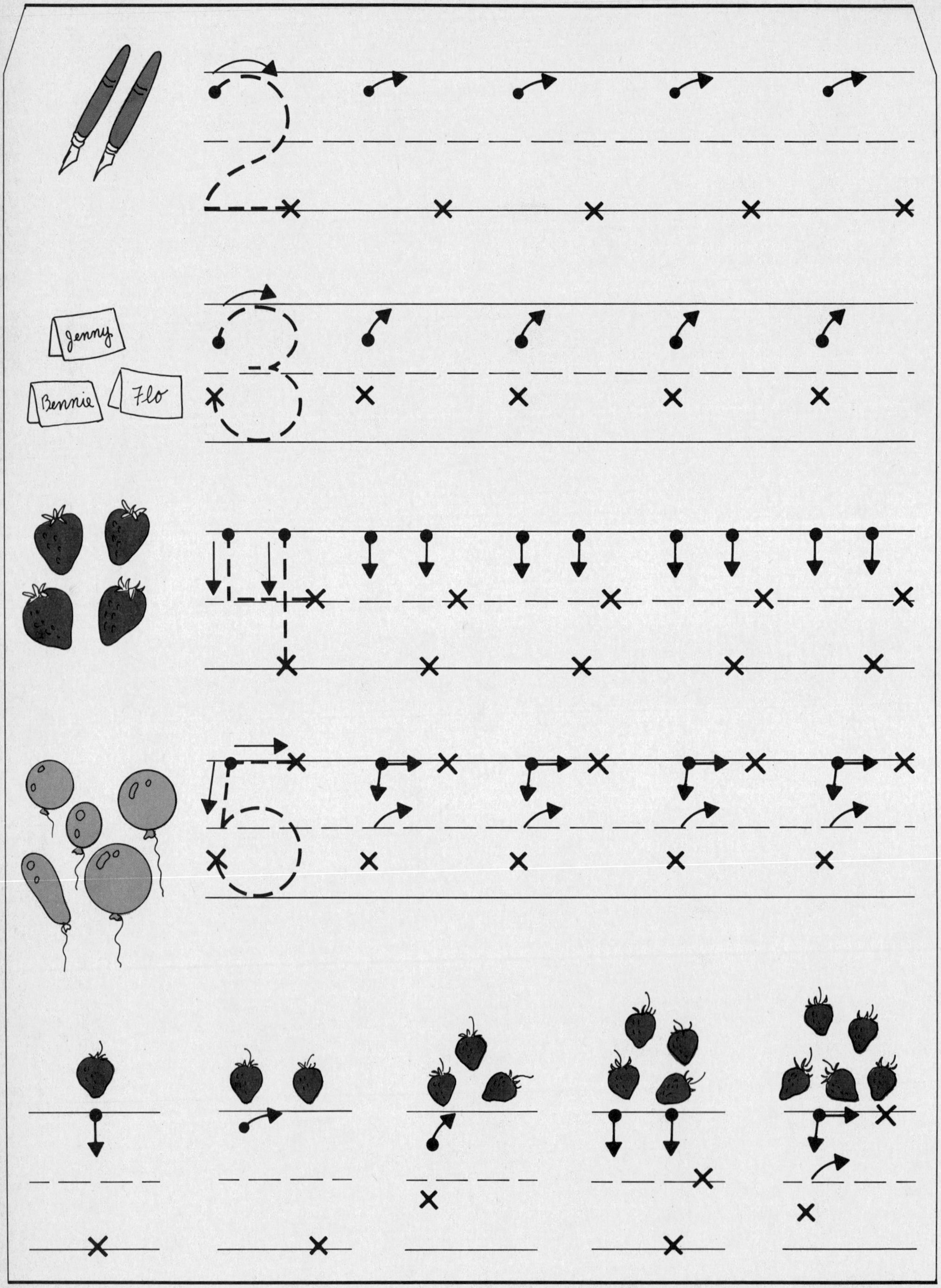

Write the numbers 1 through 5.

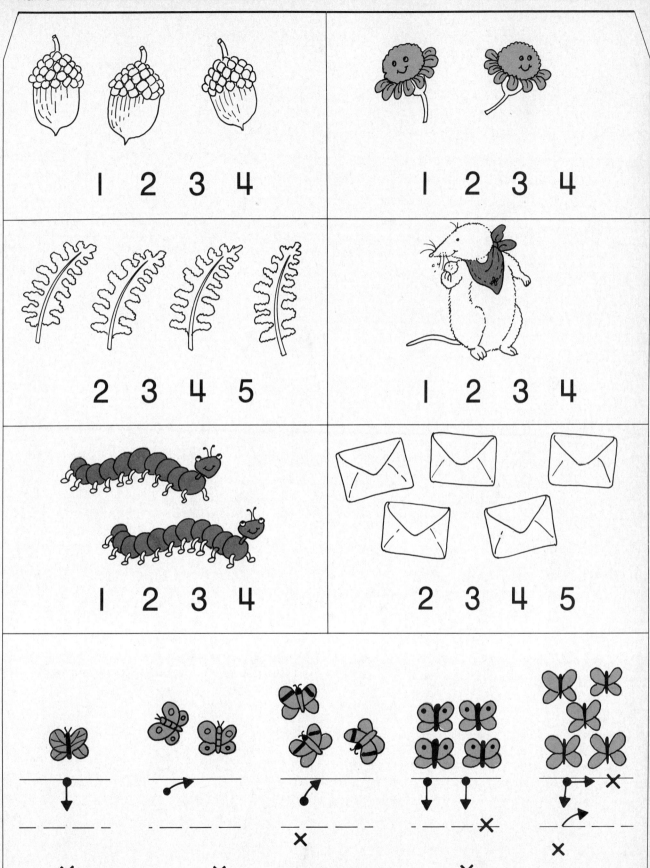

Name ______________________________

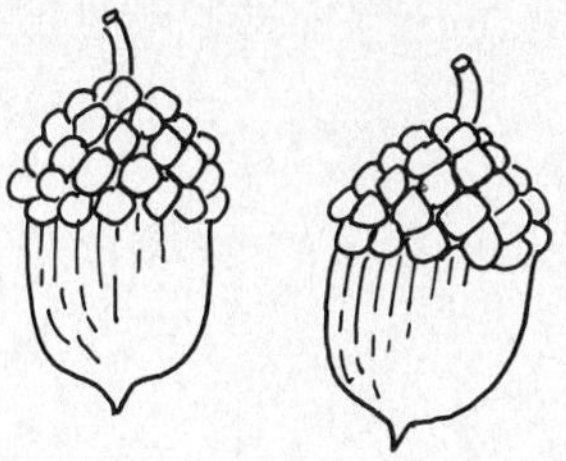

1 2 3 4

1 2 3 4

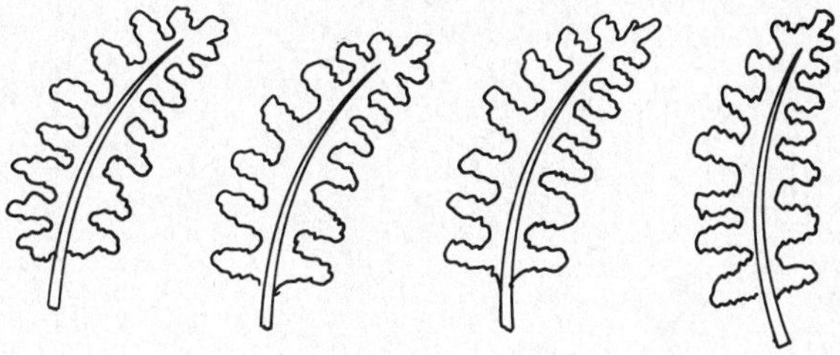

2 3 4 5

1 2 3 4

1 2 3 4

2 3 4 5

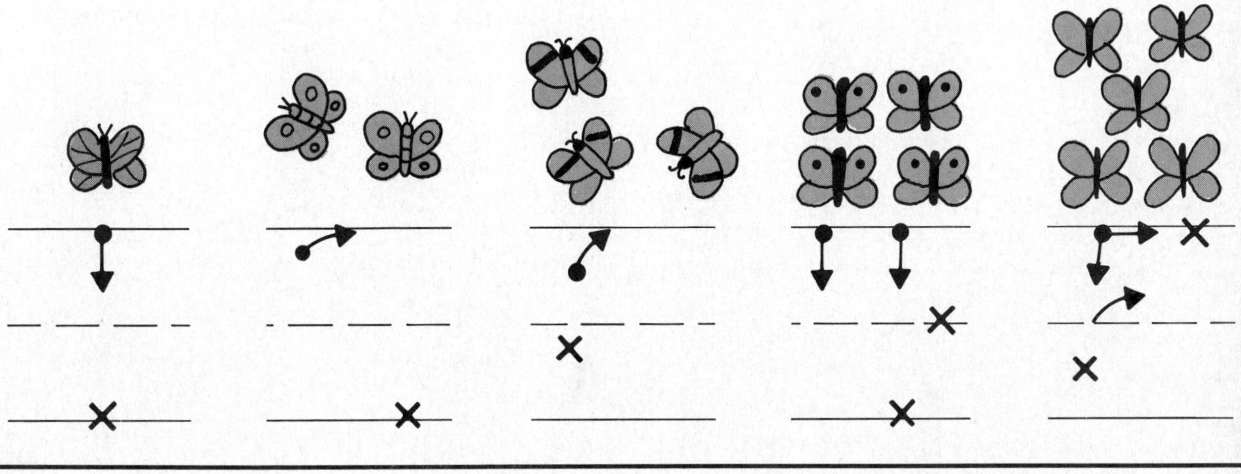

Chapter Checkup Circle the number that tells how many objects in each set. Write the numbers 1 through 5.

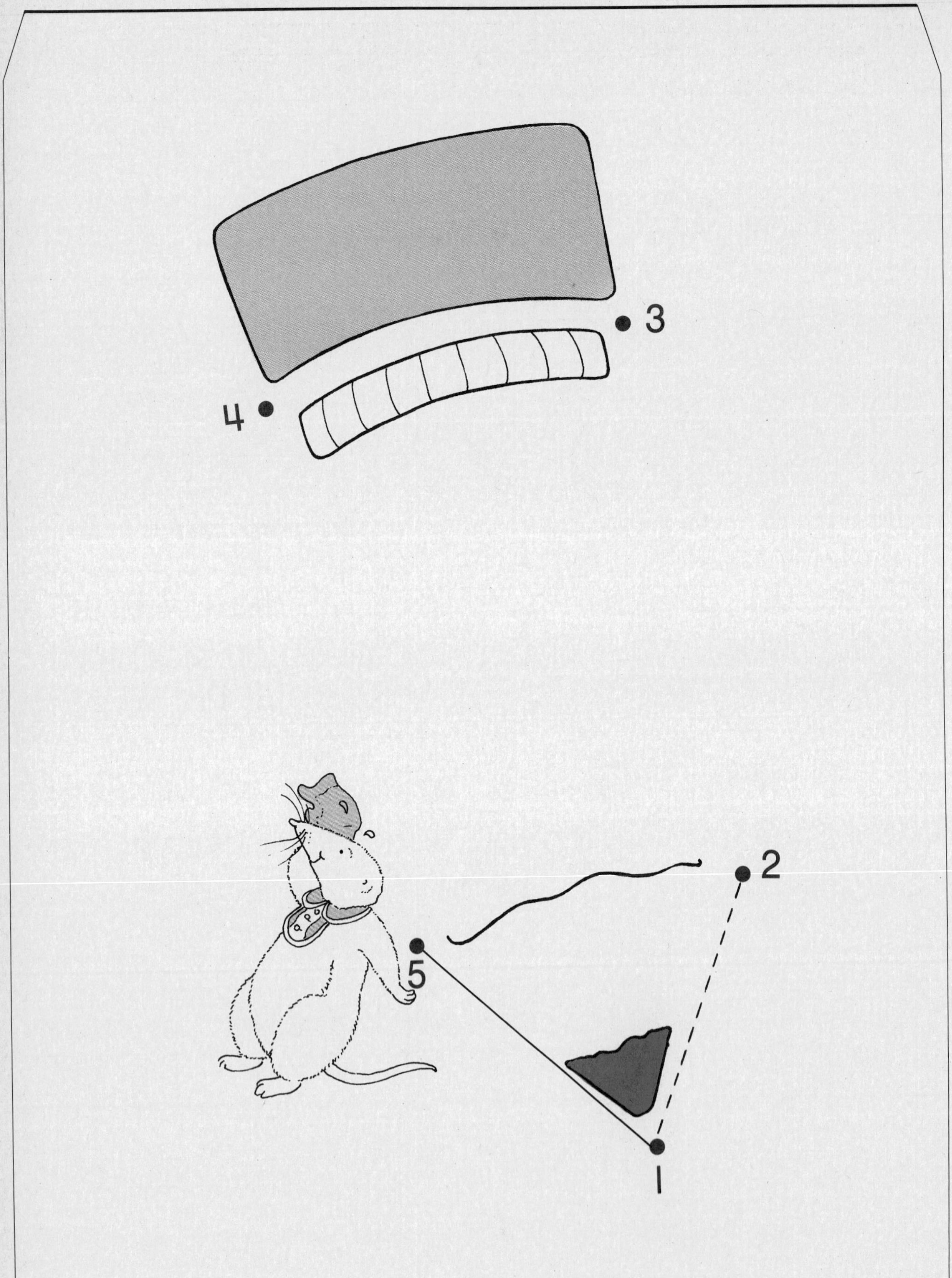

Field Trip Connect the dots in order from I through 5.

Name ______________________________

3 NUMBERS 6 THROUGH 9 AND 0

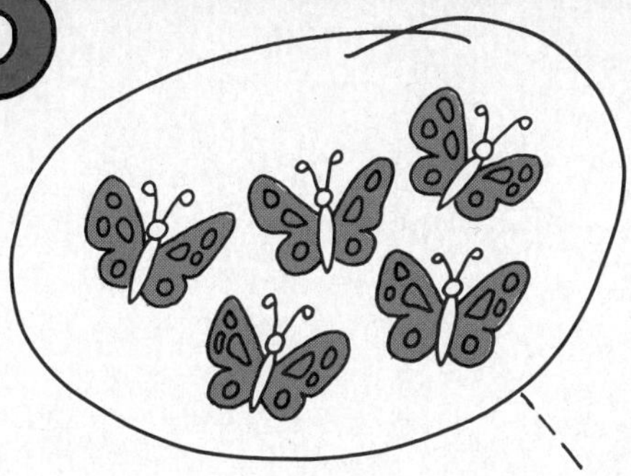

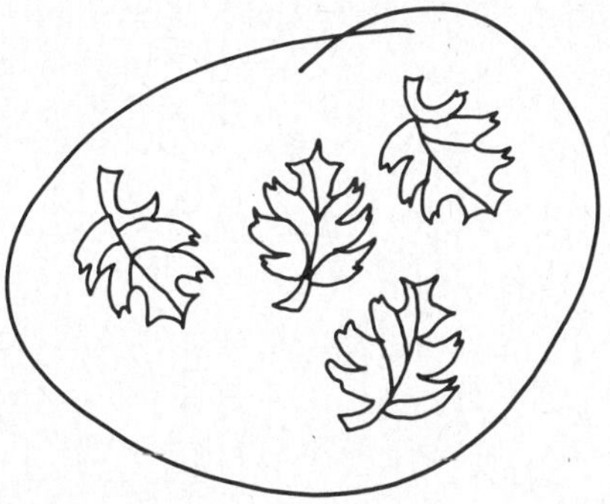

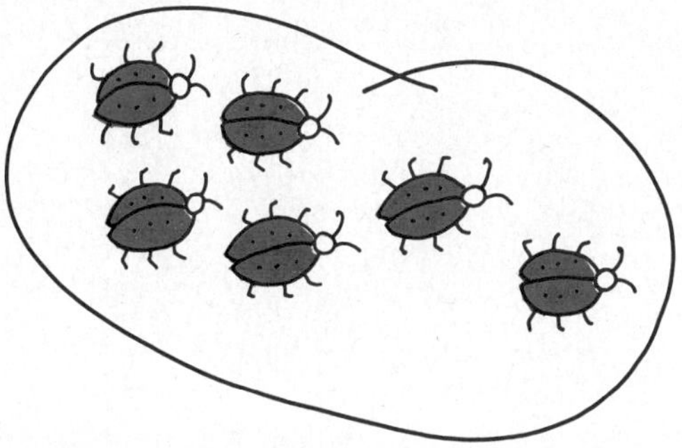

4
6
1
3
5
2

Draw a line from the set to the number of objects in that set.

 3 4 5 6	 2 3 4 5
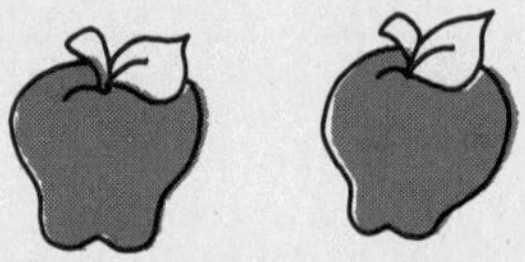 1 2 3 4	 3 4 5 6
 1 2 3 4	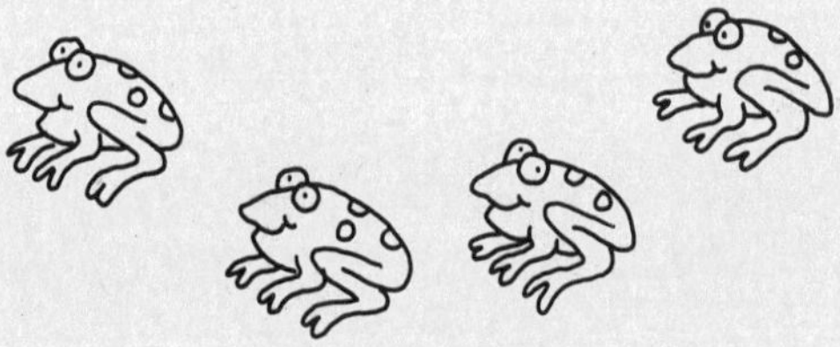 1 2 3 4
 3 4 5 6	 4 5 6 7
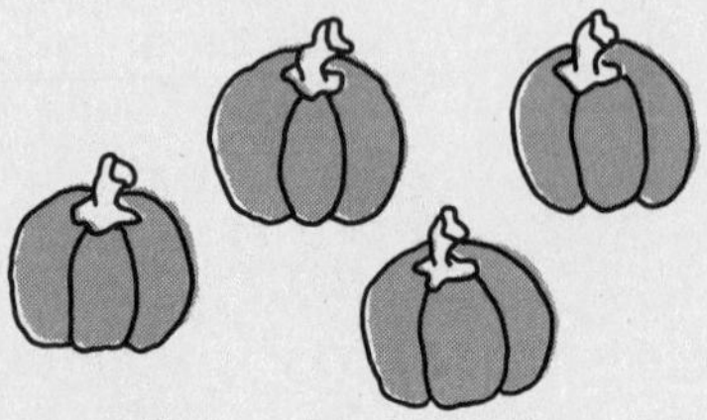 2 3 4 5	 3 4 5 6

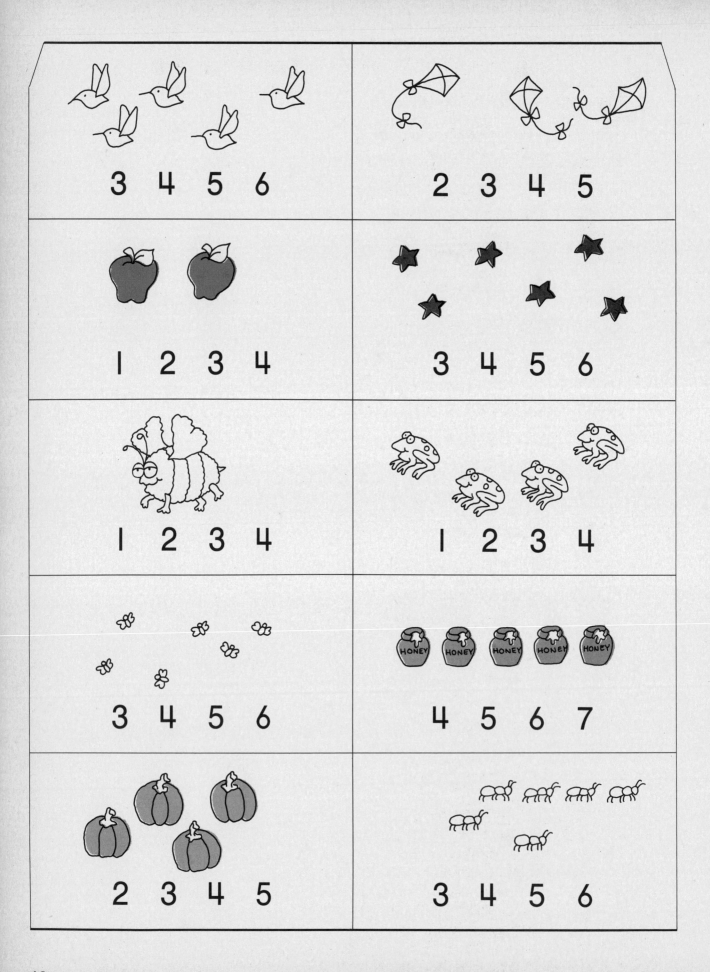

Circle the number that tells how many objects in each set.

Name ____________________

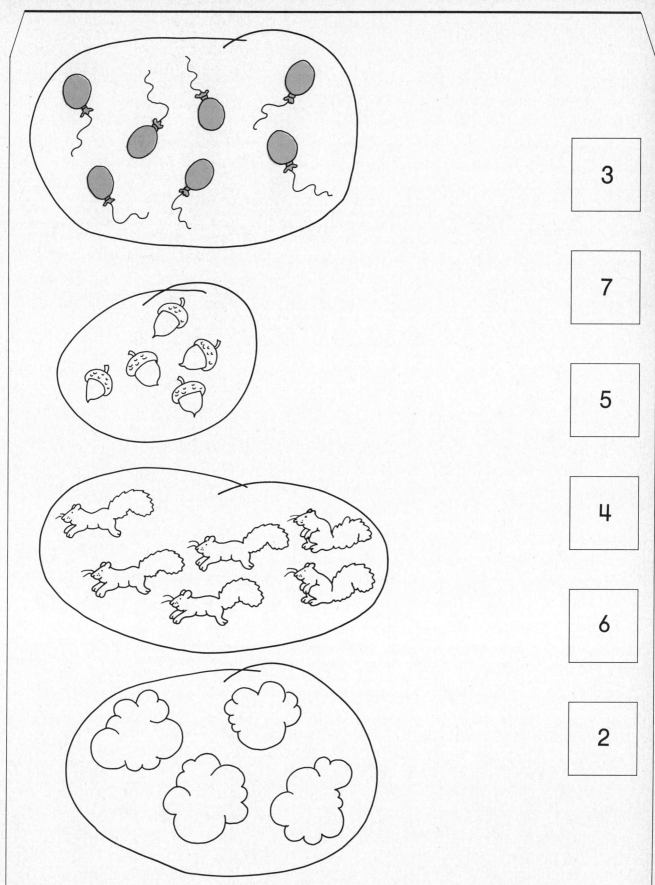

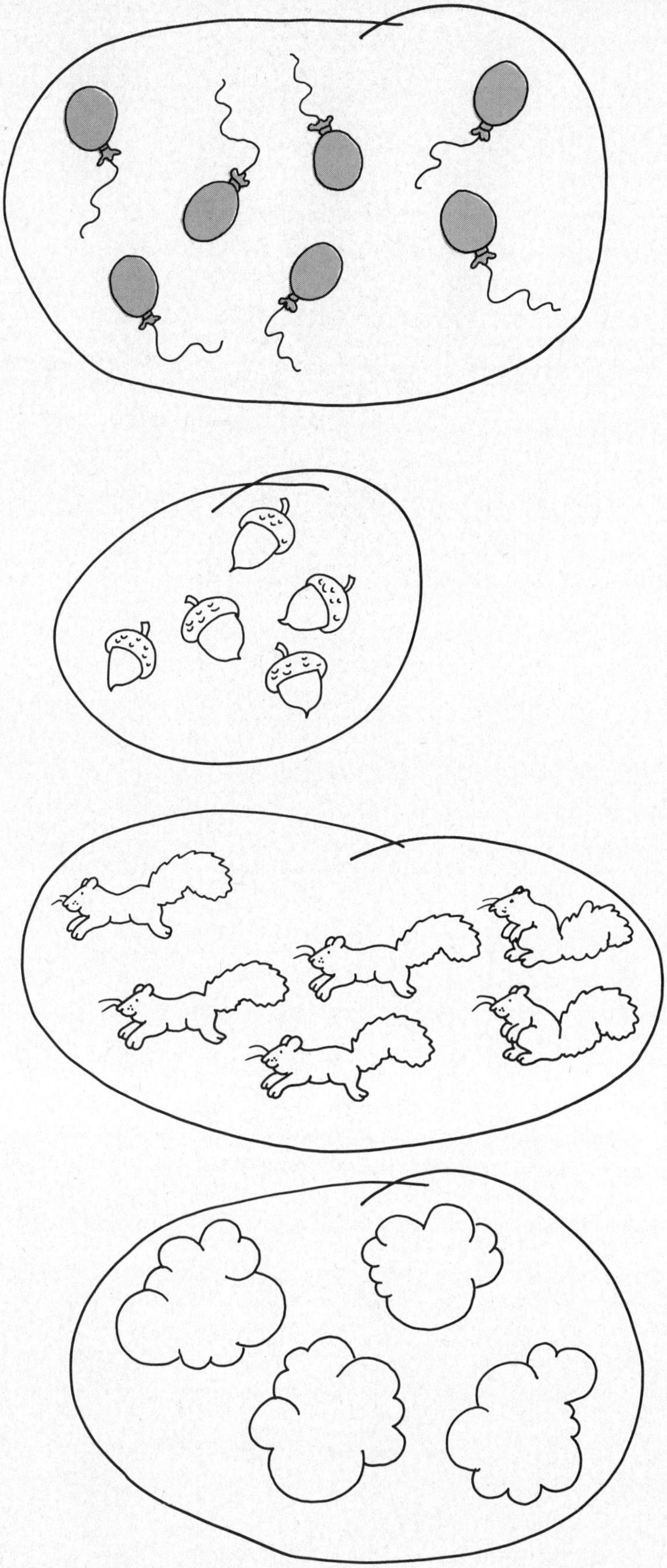

3

7

5

4

6

2

Draw a line from the set to the number of objects in that set.

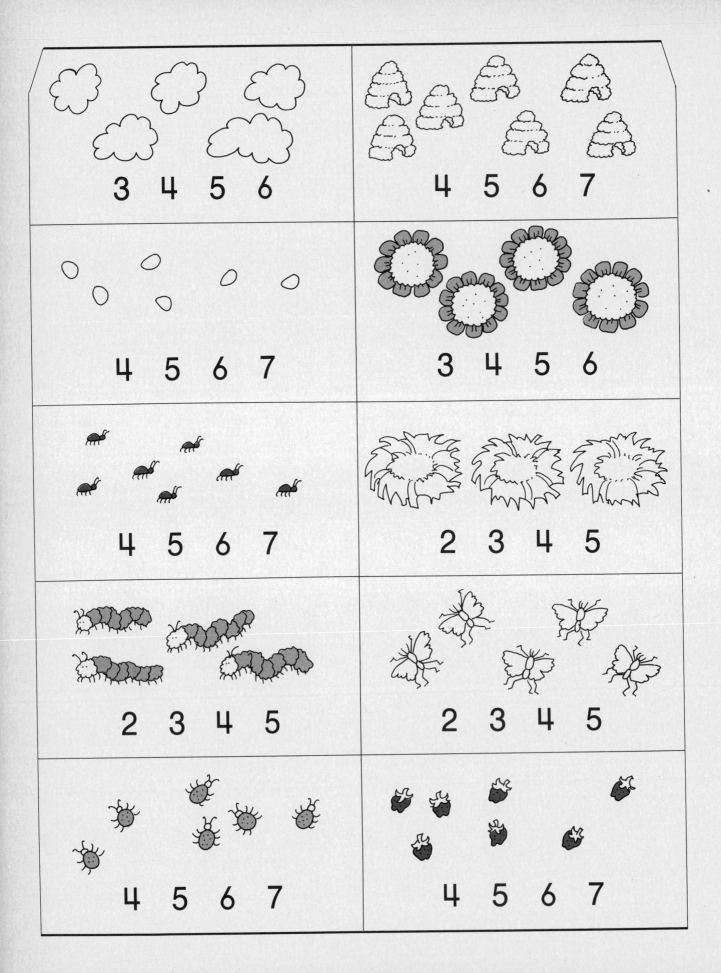

3 4 5 6

4 5 6 7

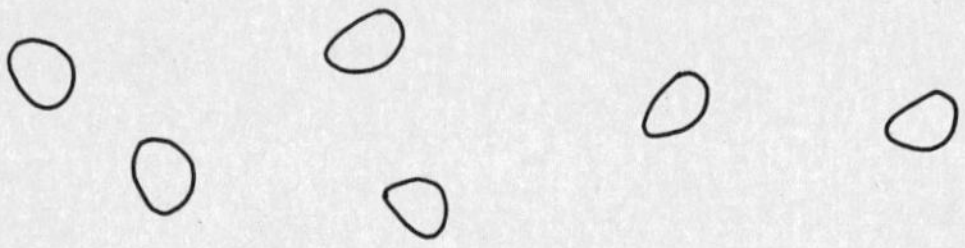

4 5 6 7

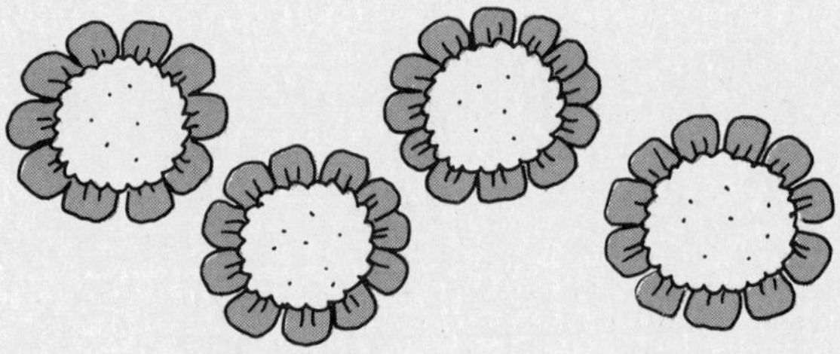

3 4 5 6

4 5 6 7

2 3 4 5

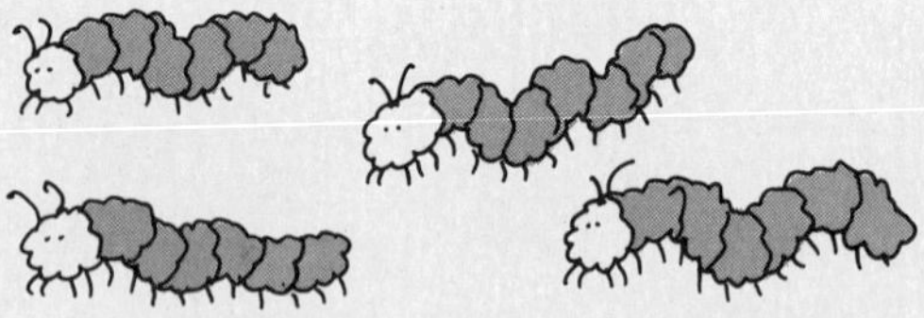

2 3 4 5

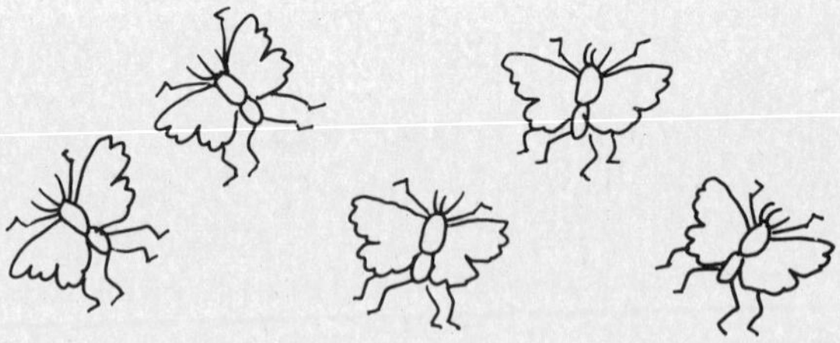

2 3 4 5

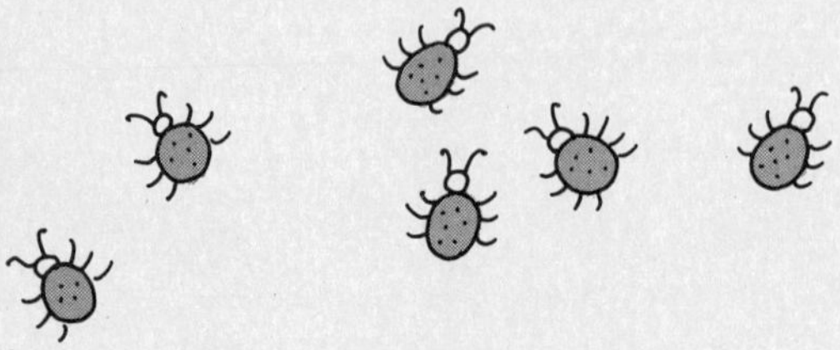

4 5 6 7

4 5 6 7

Circle the number that tells how many objects in each set.

Name _____

3   4   5   6

4   5   6   7

2   3   4   5

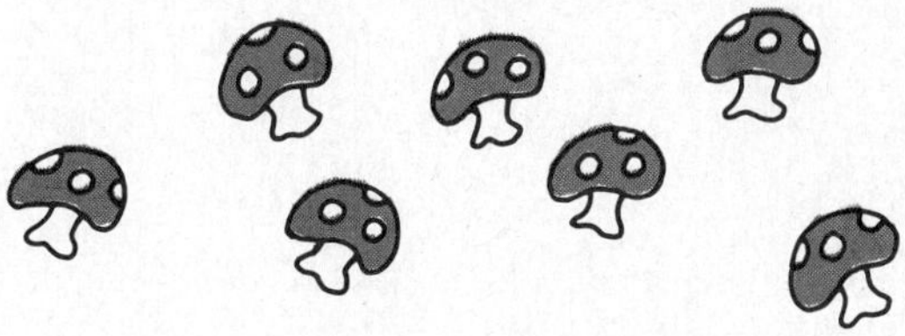

4   5   6   7

1   2   3   4

4   5   6   7

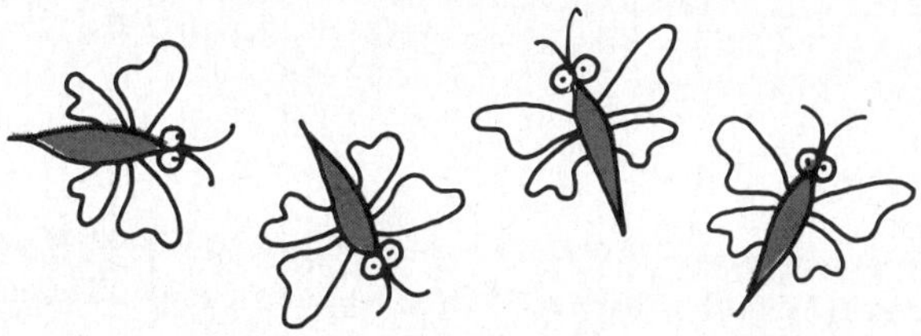

3   4   5   6

4   5   6   7

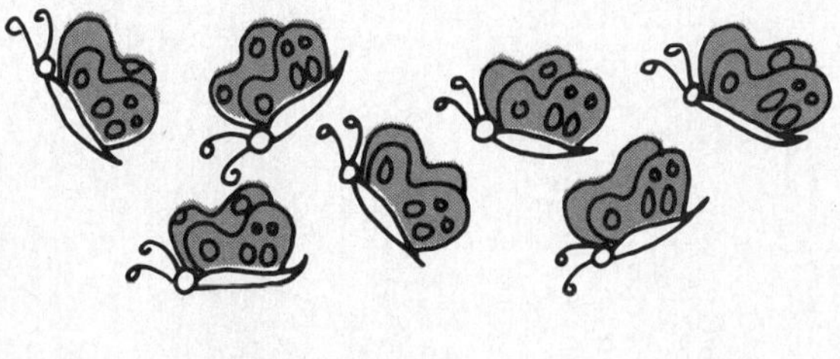

4   5   6   7

4   5   6   7

Circle the number that tells how many objects in each set.

Connect the dots in order from 1 through 7.

Name ________________________________

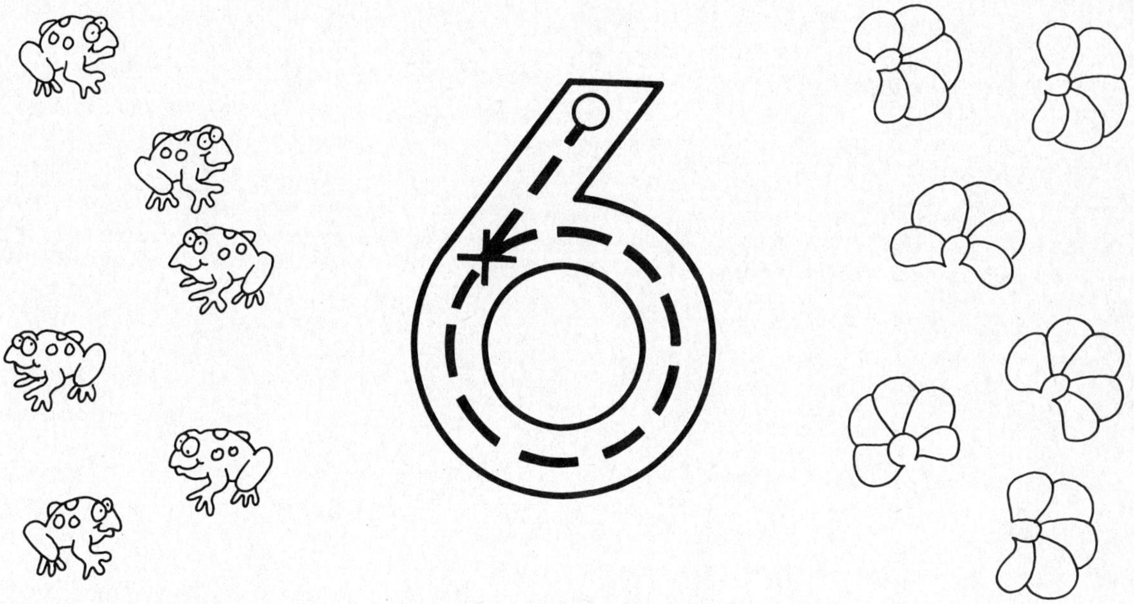

Trace the path for writing 6 and 7.

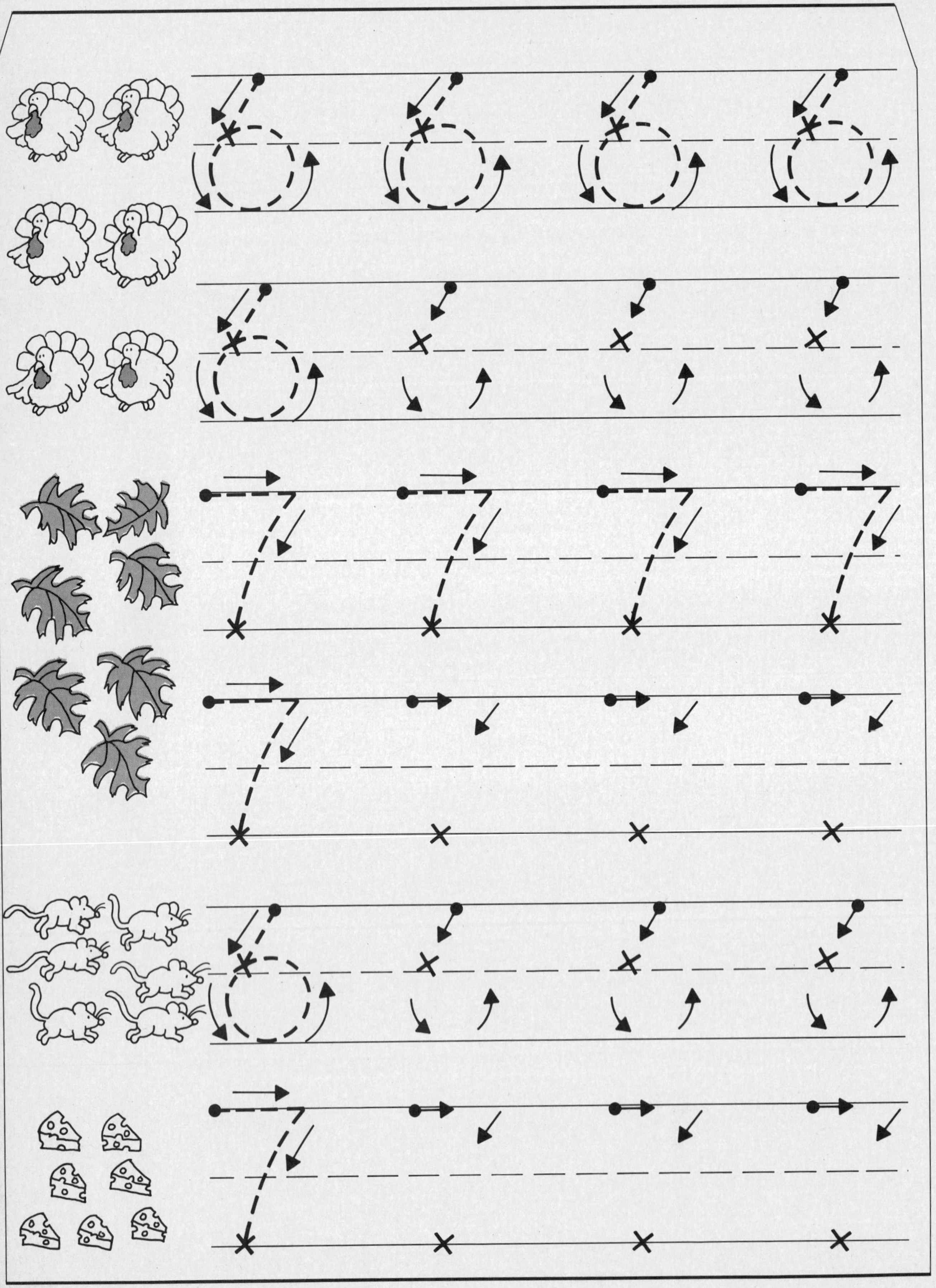

Write the numbers 6 and 7.

Draw a line from the set to the number of objects in that set.

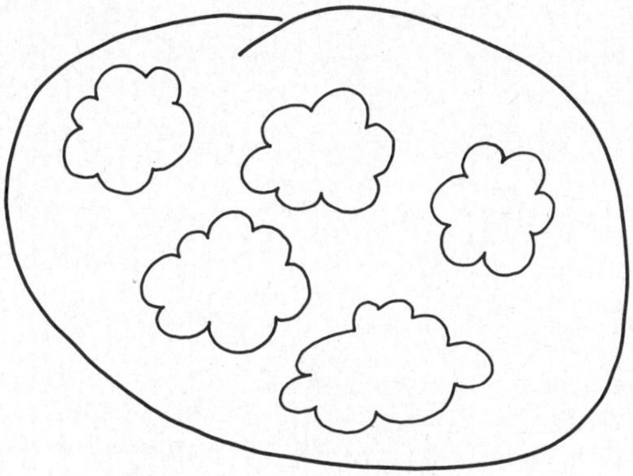

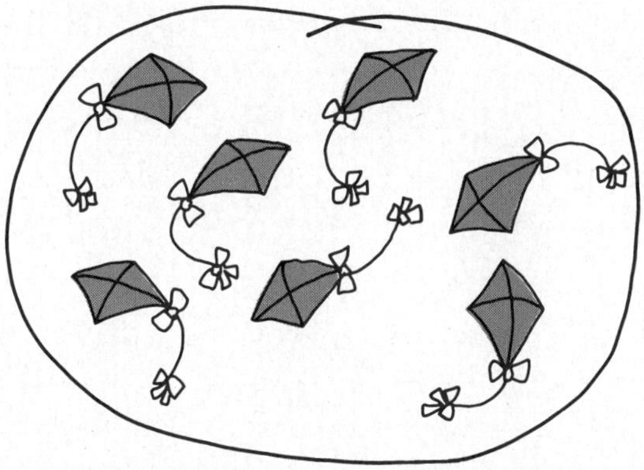

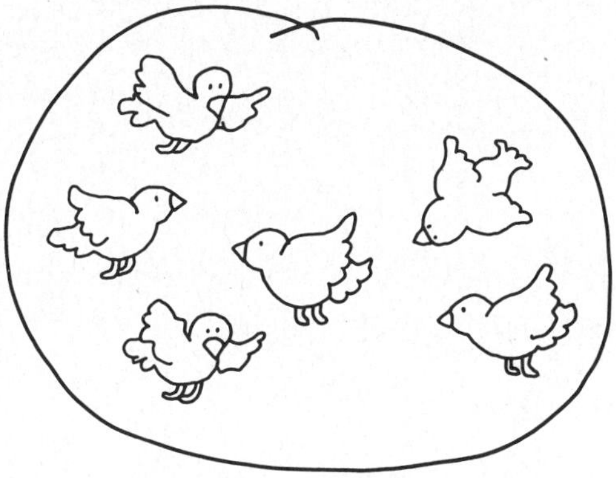

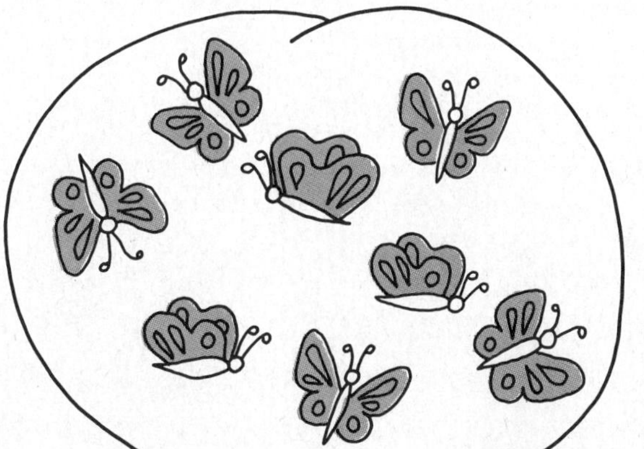

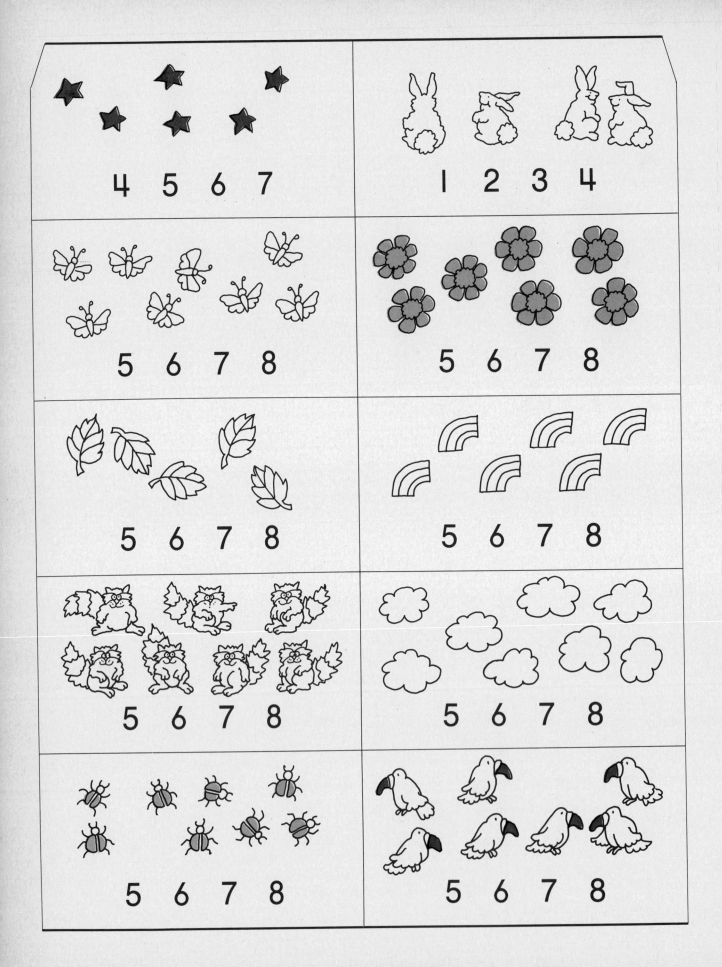

4 5 6 7

1 2 3 4

5 6 7 8

5 6 7 8

5 6 7 8

5 6 7 8

5 6 7 8

5 6 7 8

5 6 7 8

5 6 7 8

Circle the number that tells how many objects in each set.

Name ______________________________

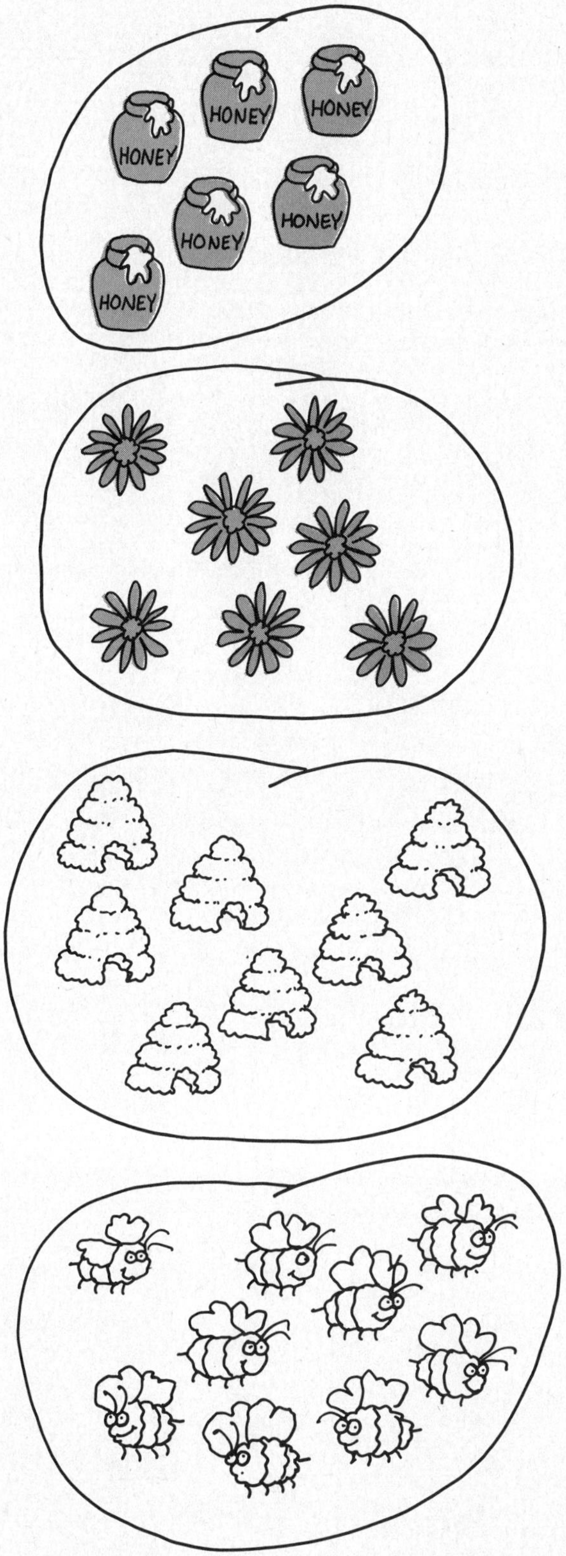

5

9

7

6

8

4

Draw a line from the set to the number of objects in that set.

6 7 8 9

6 7 8 9

6 7 8 9

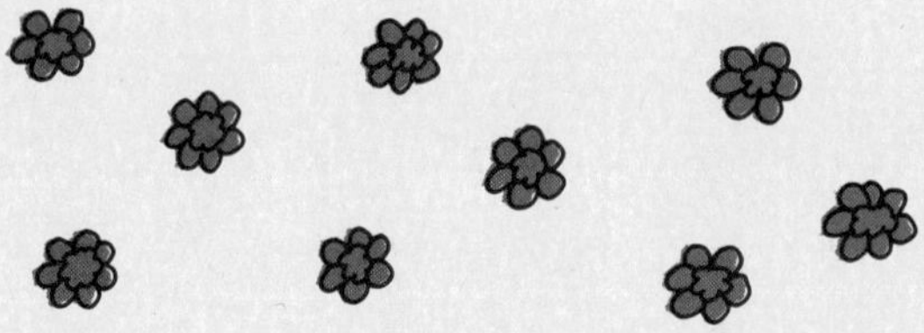

6 7 8 9

6 7 8 9

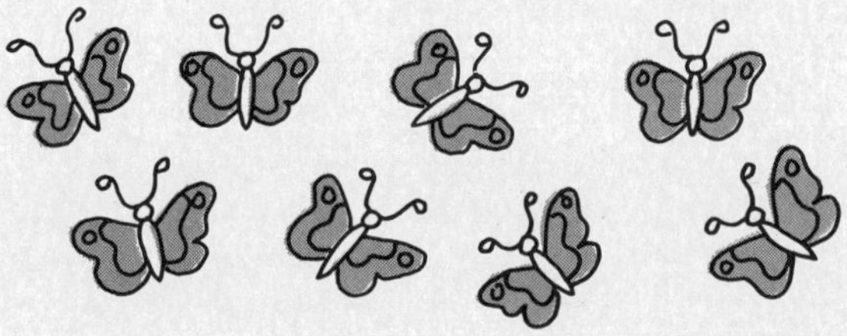

6 7 8 9

6 7 8 9

6 7 8 9

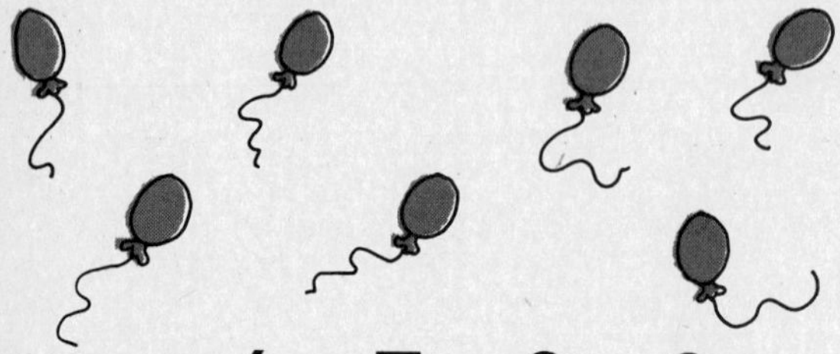

6 7 8 9

6 7 8 9

Circle the number that tells how many objects in each set.

Name ______________________________

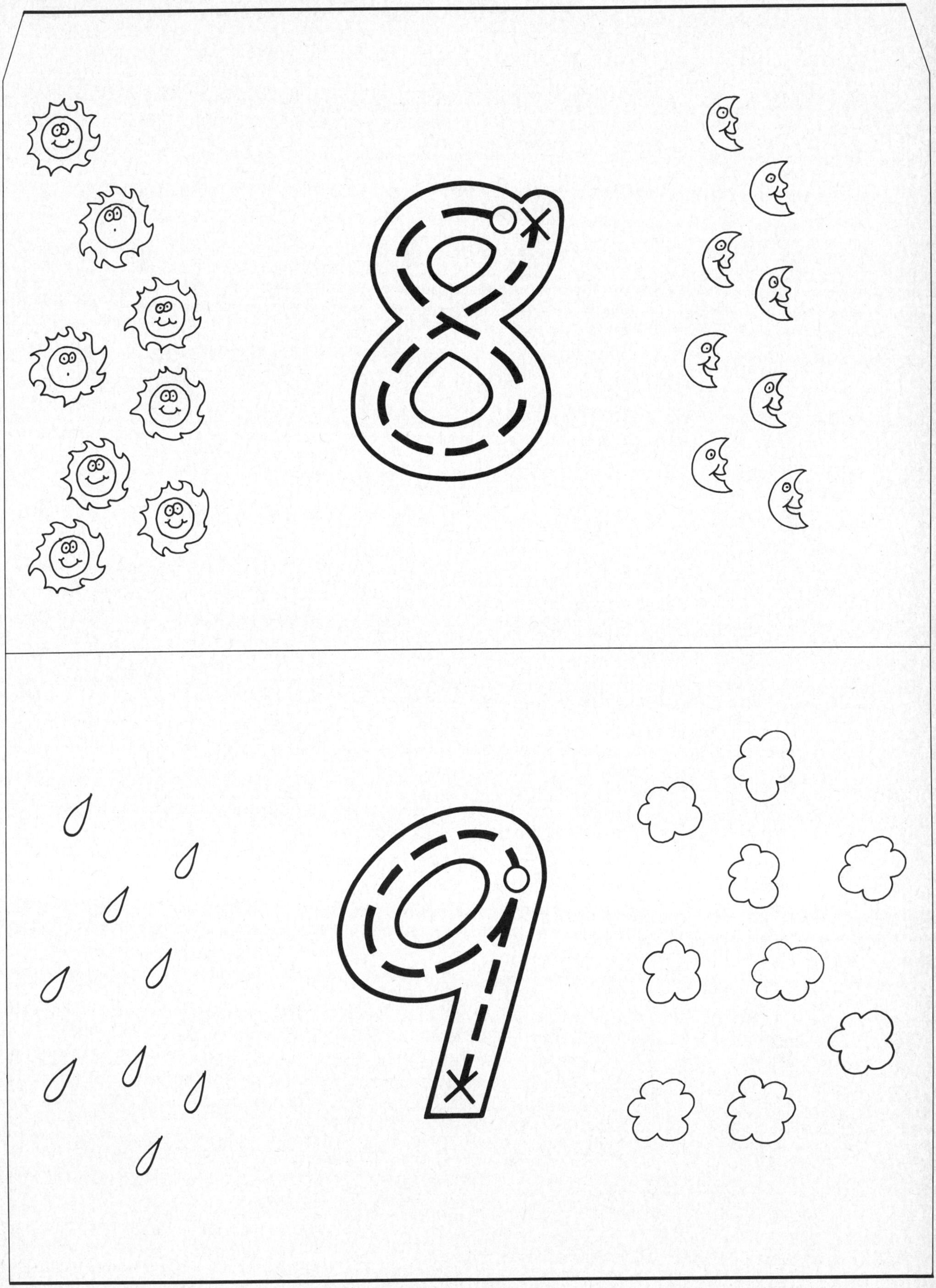

Trace the path for writing 8 and 9.

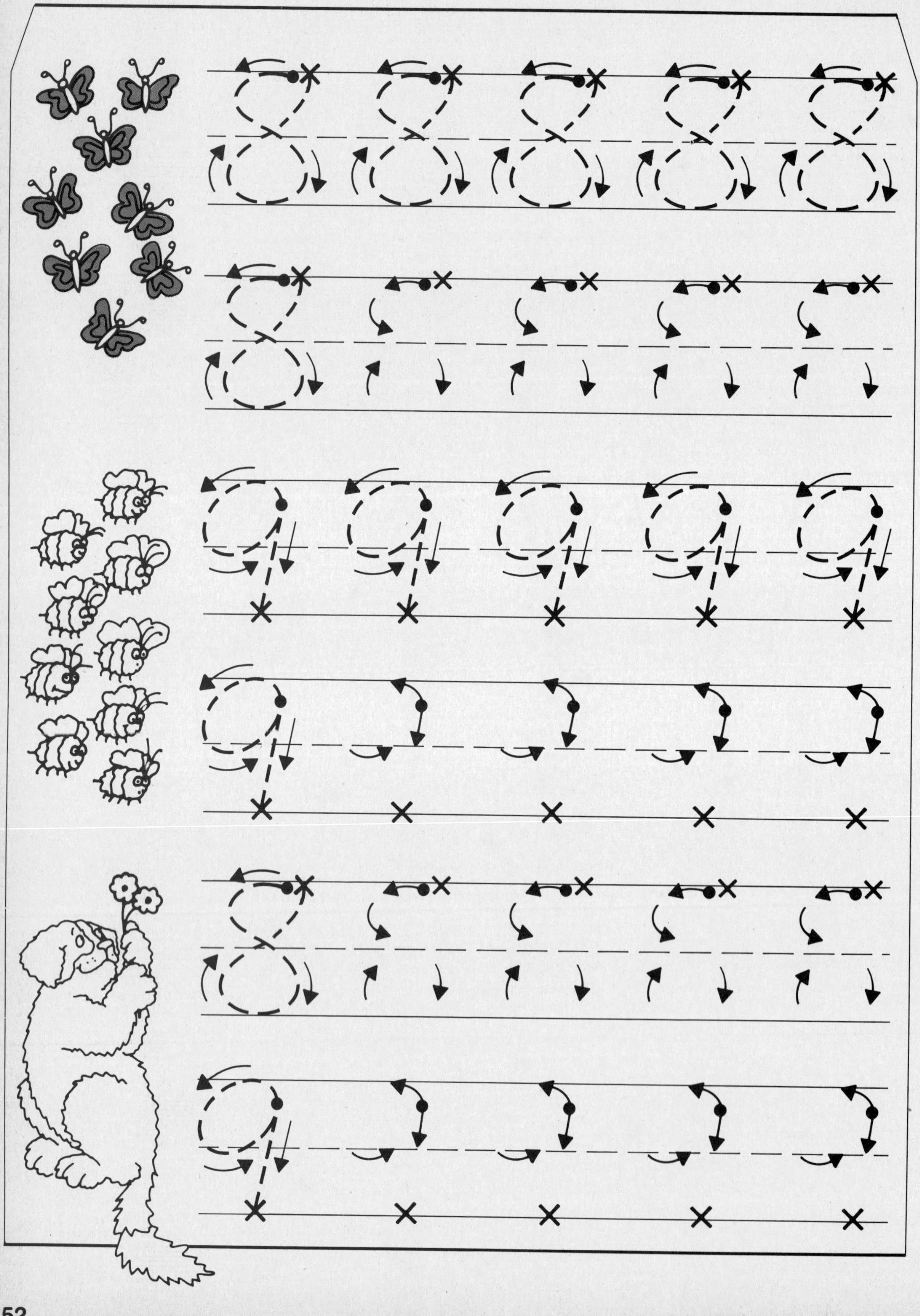

Write the numbers 8 and 9.

Name ____________________

0

Circle each set of 0 objects.

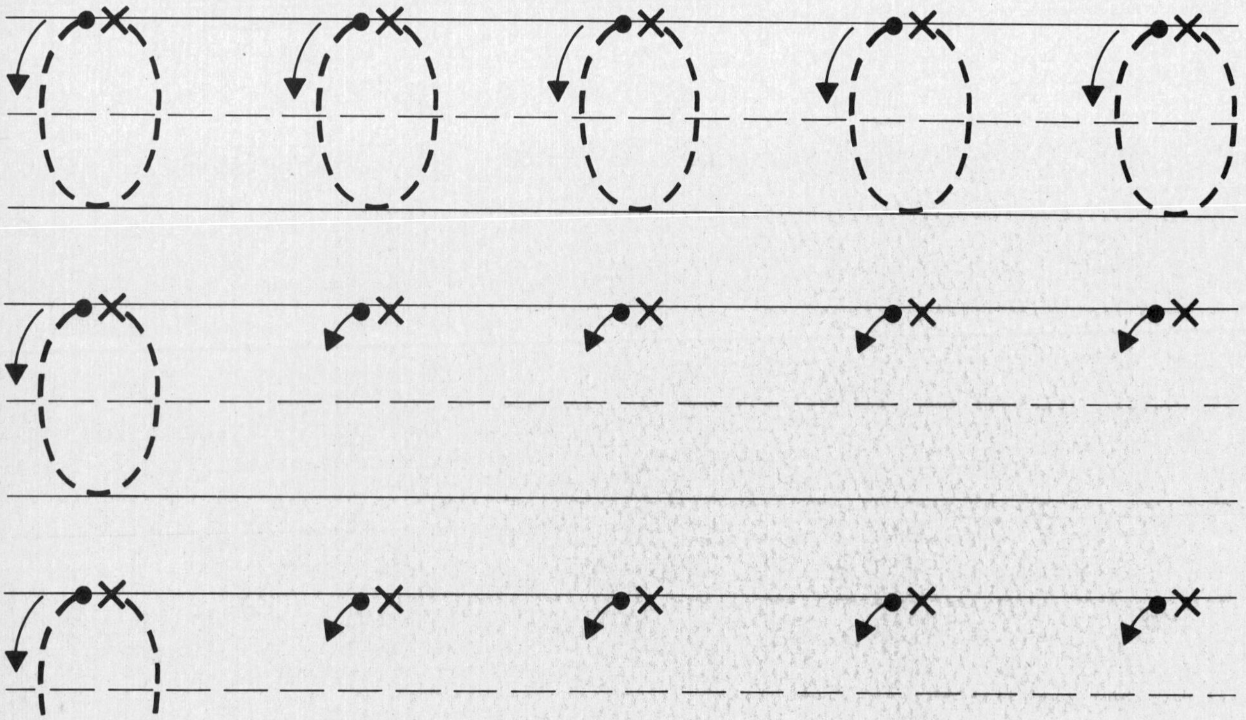

Trace the path for writing 0. Write the number 0.

Name _____

6 7 8 9   0 1 2 3

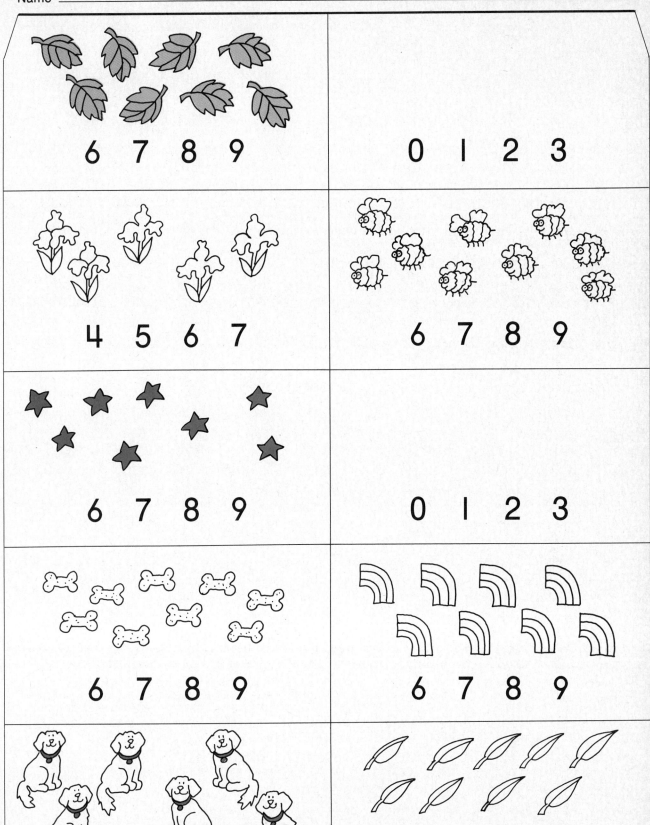

4 5 6 7   6 7 8 9

6 7 8 9   0 1 2 3

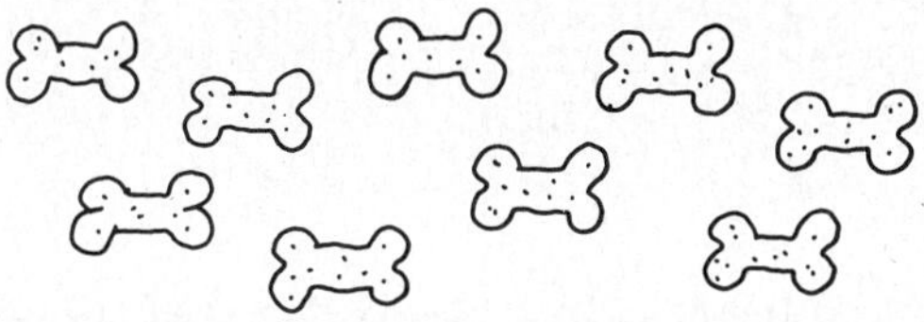

6 7 8 9   6 7 8 9

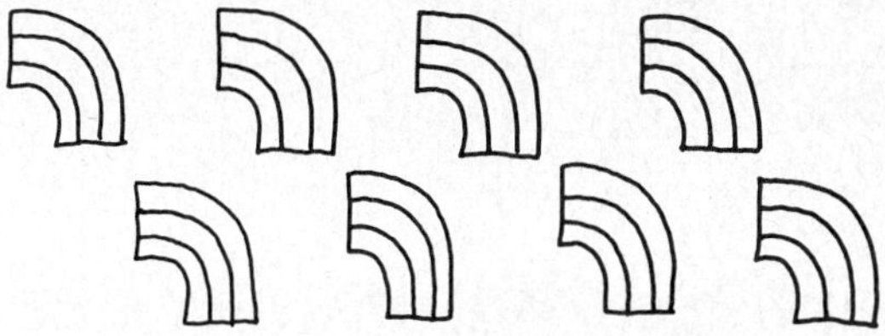

6 7 8 9   6 7 8 9

Circle the number that tells how many objects in each set.

Write the numbers 8, 9 and 0.

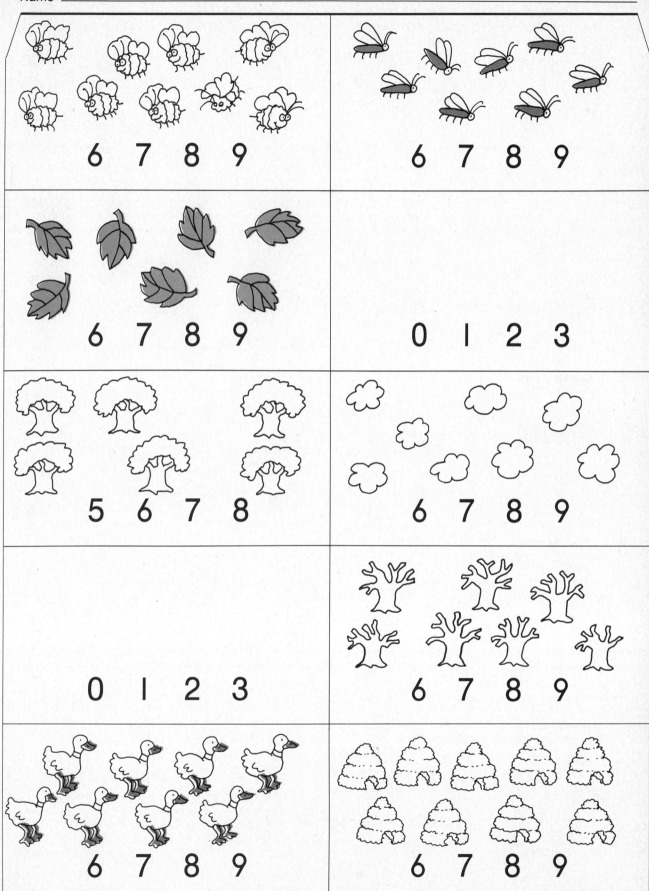

6 7 8 9

6 7 8 9

6 7 8 9

0 1 2 3

5 6 7 8

6 7 8 9

0 1 2 3

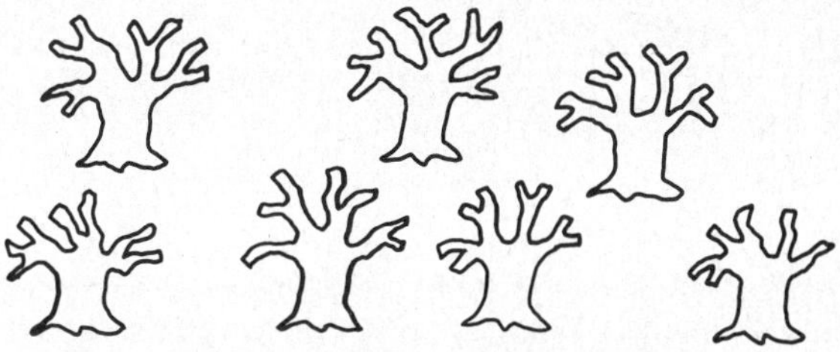

6 7 8 9

6 7 8 9

6 7 8 9

Circle the number that tells how many objects in each set.

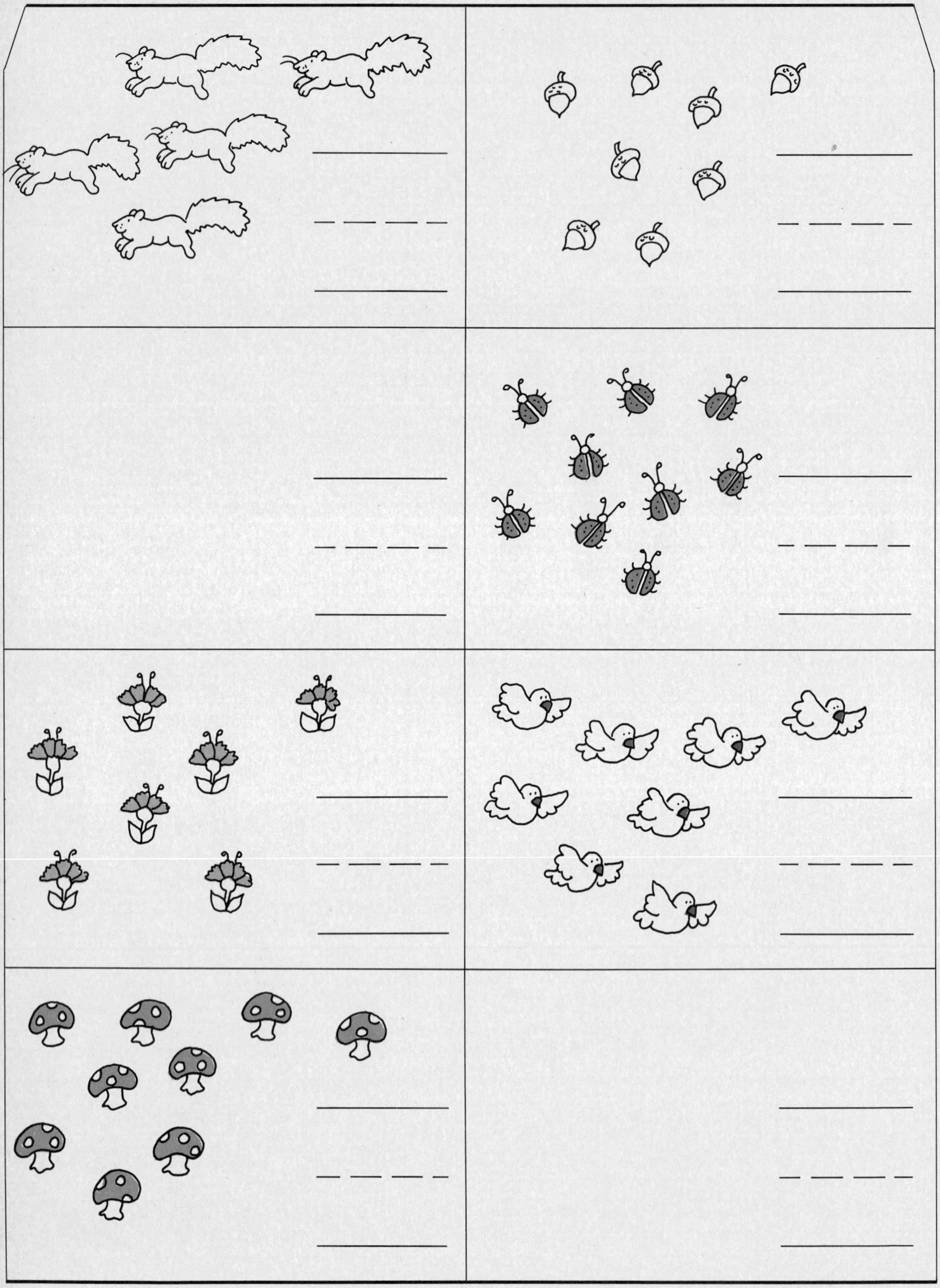

Count the objects in each set and write the number.

Name ______________________________

3 4 5 6

3 4 5 6

6 7 8 9

6 7 8 9

6 7 8 9

0 1 2 3

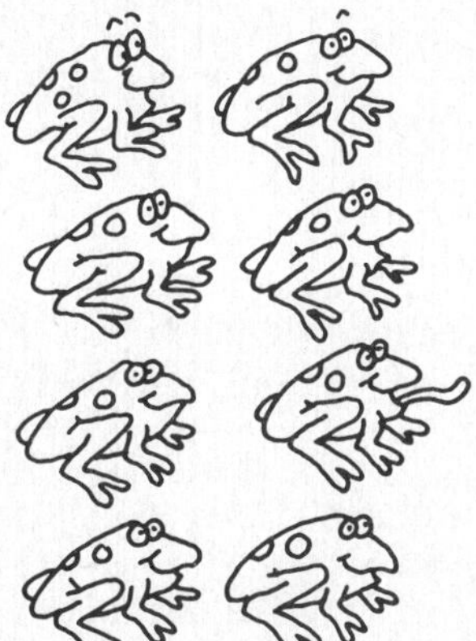

Chapter Checkup Circle the number that tells how many objects in each set. Count the objects in each set and write the number.

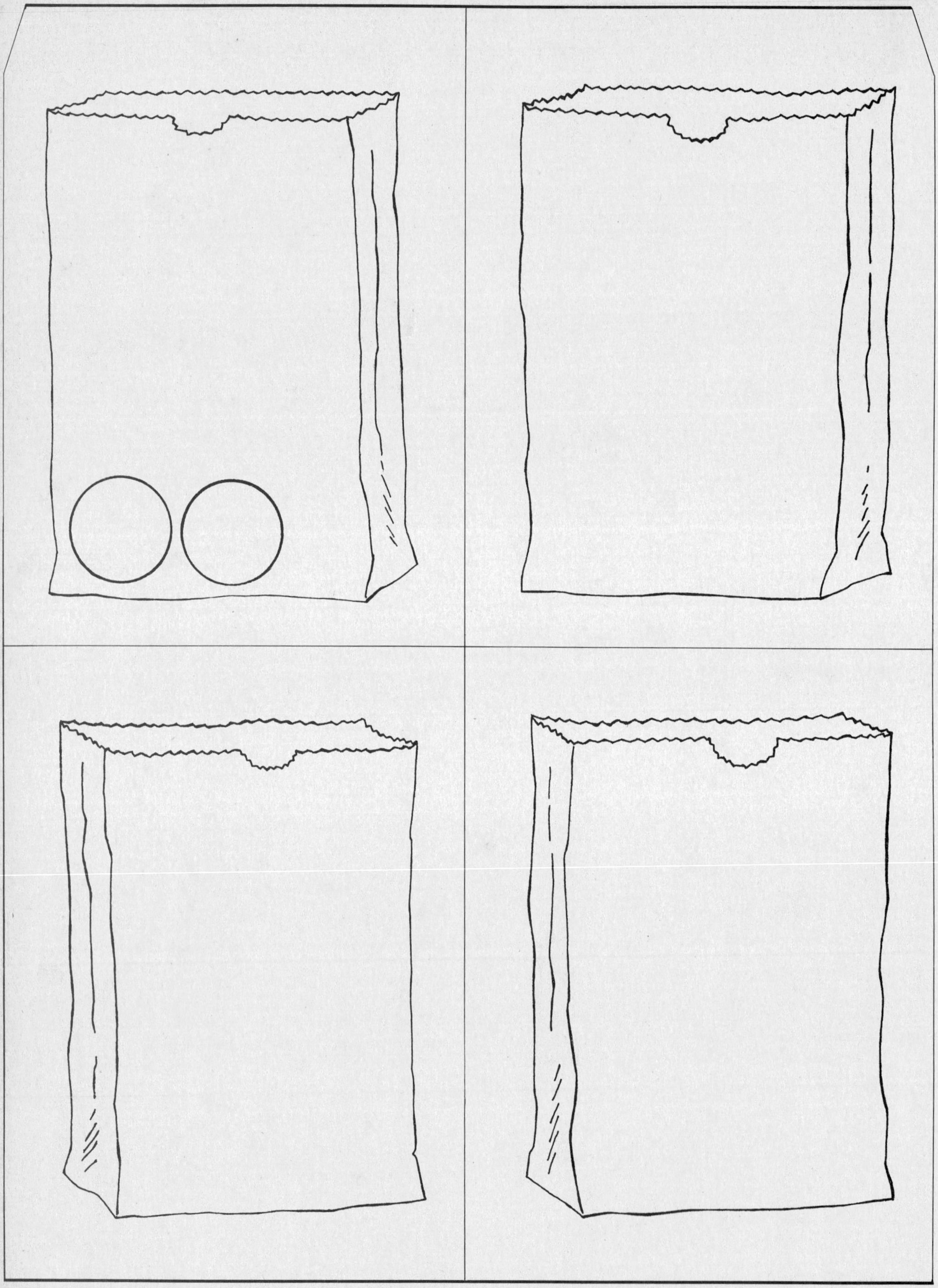

Field Trip Draw 6 rolls in the first sack, 7 in the second, 8 in the third, and 9 in the fourth.

Name ______________________________

4 NUMBERS 0 THROUGH 12

5 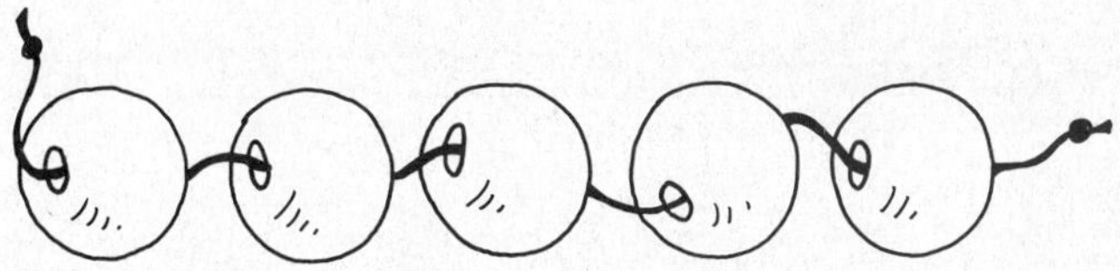

6 

9 

7 

8 

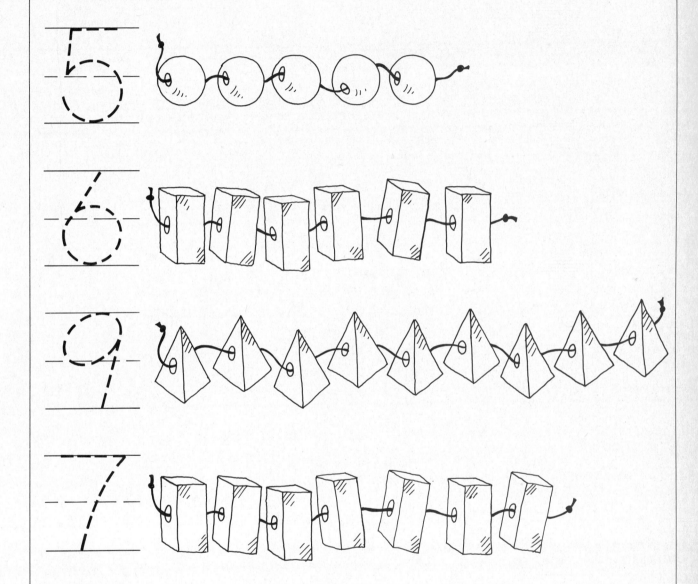

Trace each number. Color that many shapes.

Count the objects in each set and write the number.

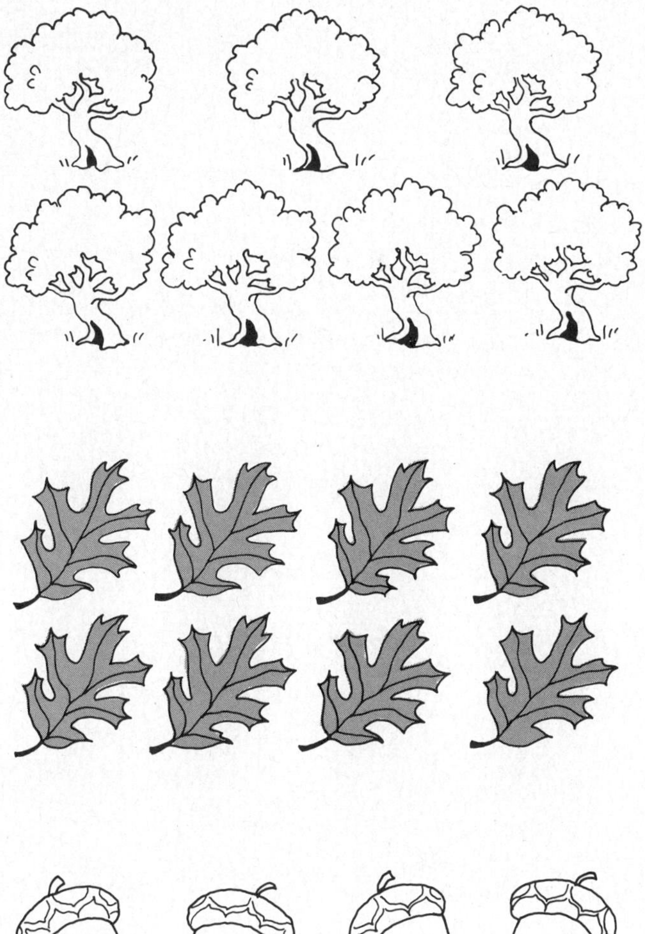

6

8

10

9

7

5

4

Draw a line from the set to the number of objects in that set.

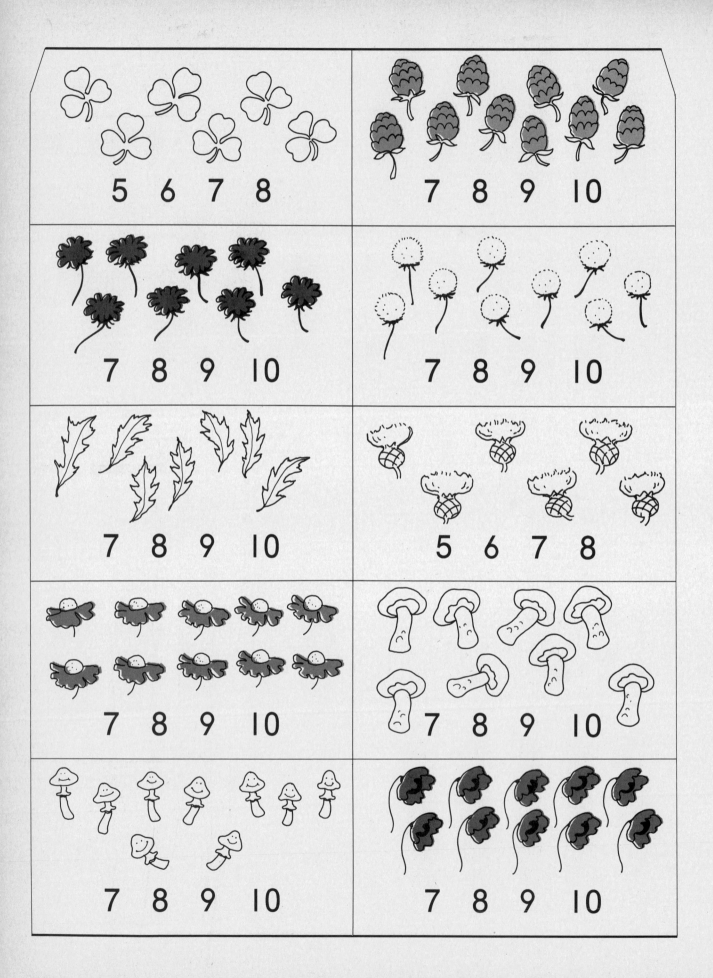

5 6 7 8

7 8 9 10

7 8 9 10

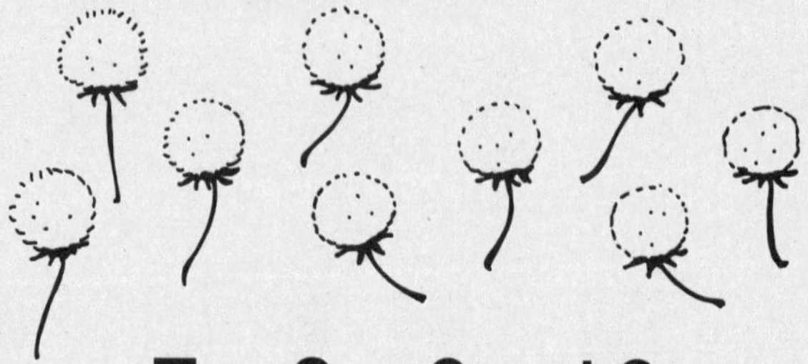

7 8 9 10

7 8 9 10

5 6 7 8

7 8 9 10

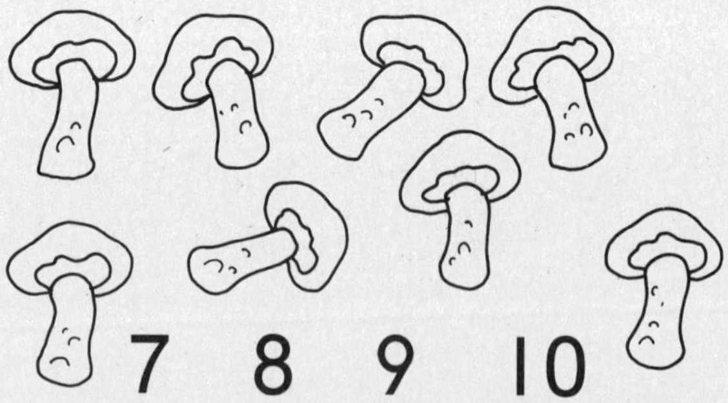

7 8 9 10

7 8 9 10

7 8 9 10

Circle the number that tells how many objects in each set.

Name ______________________________

11

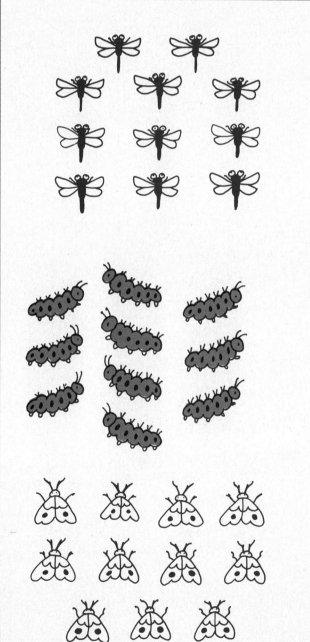

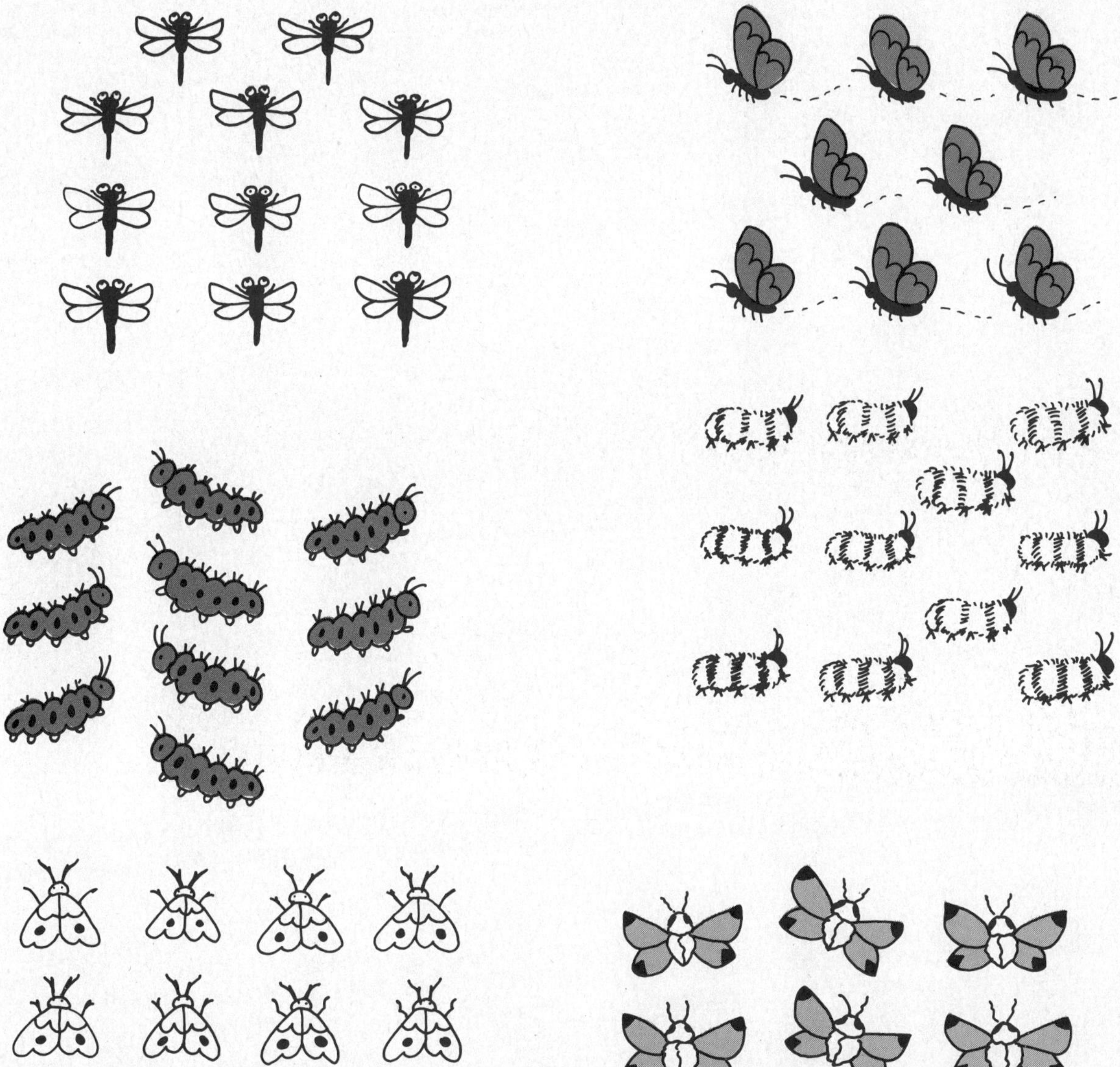

Count the objects in each set. Circle the sets of 11 objects.

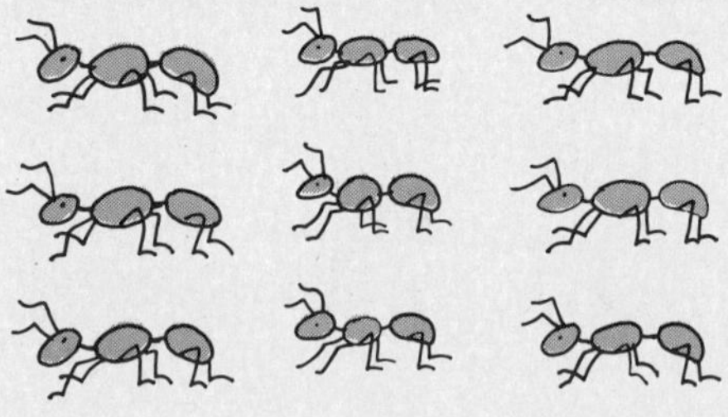

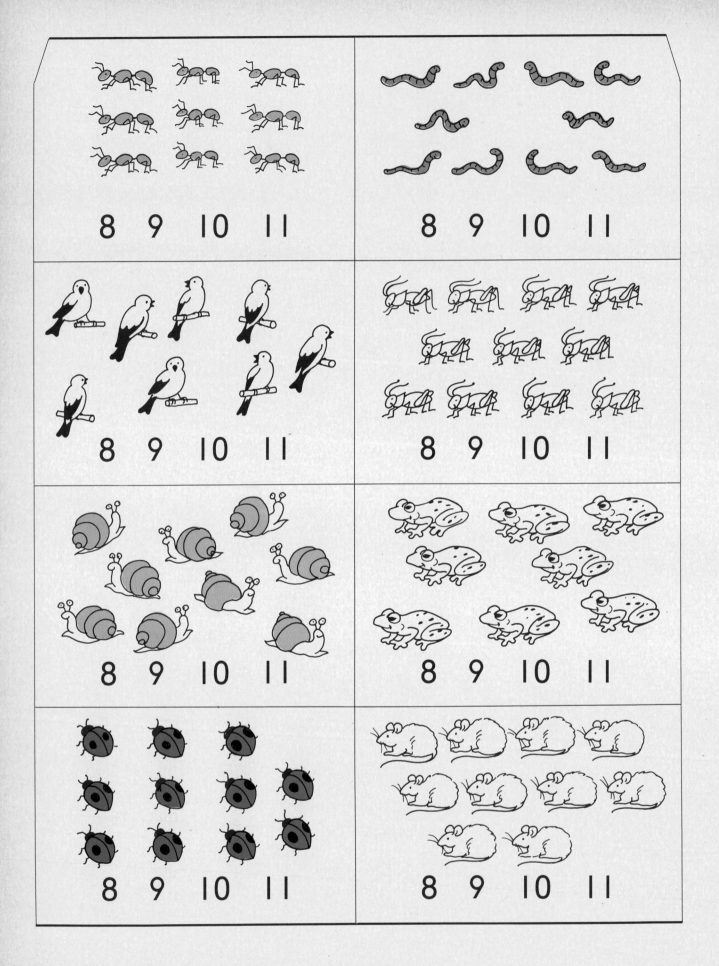

8 9 10 11

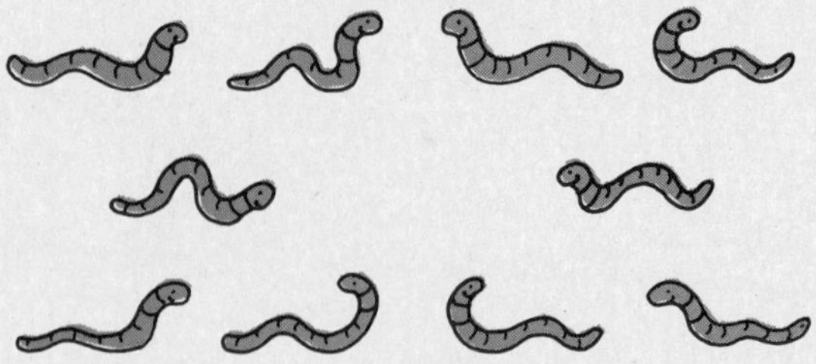

8 9 10 11

8 9 10 11

8 9 10 11

8 9 10 11

8 9 10 11

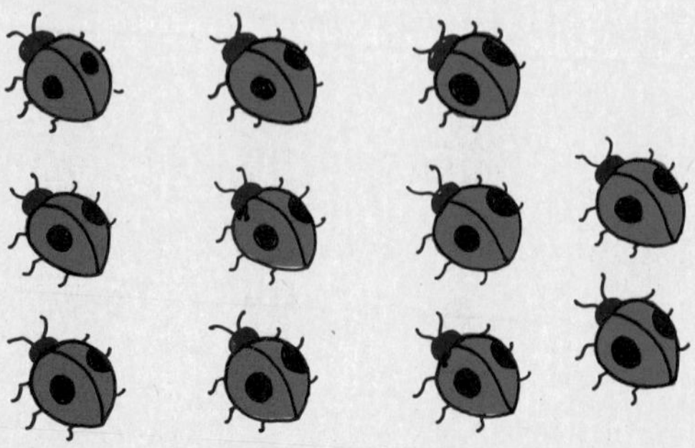

8 9 10 11

8 9 10 11

Circle the number that tells how many objects in each set.

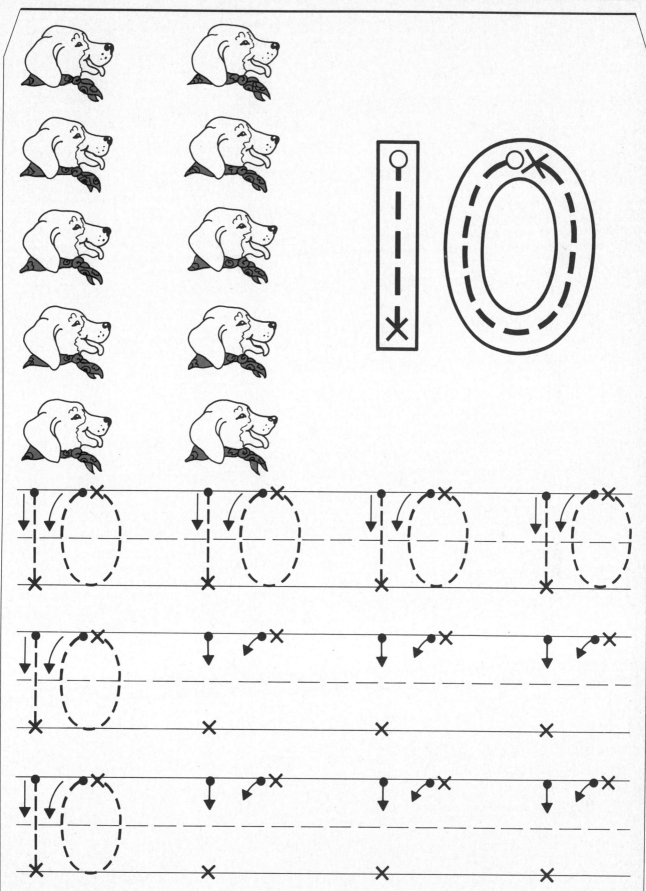

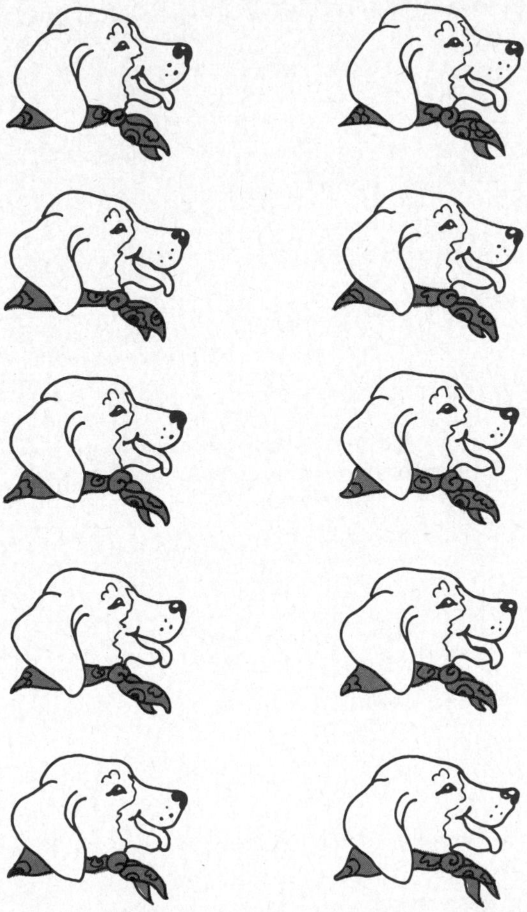

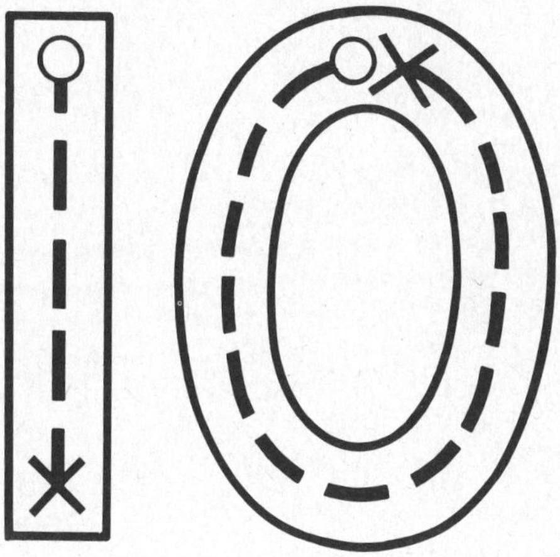

Trace the path for writing 10. Write the number 10.

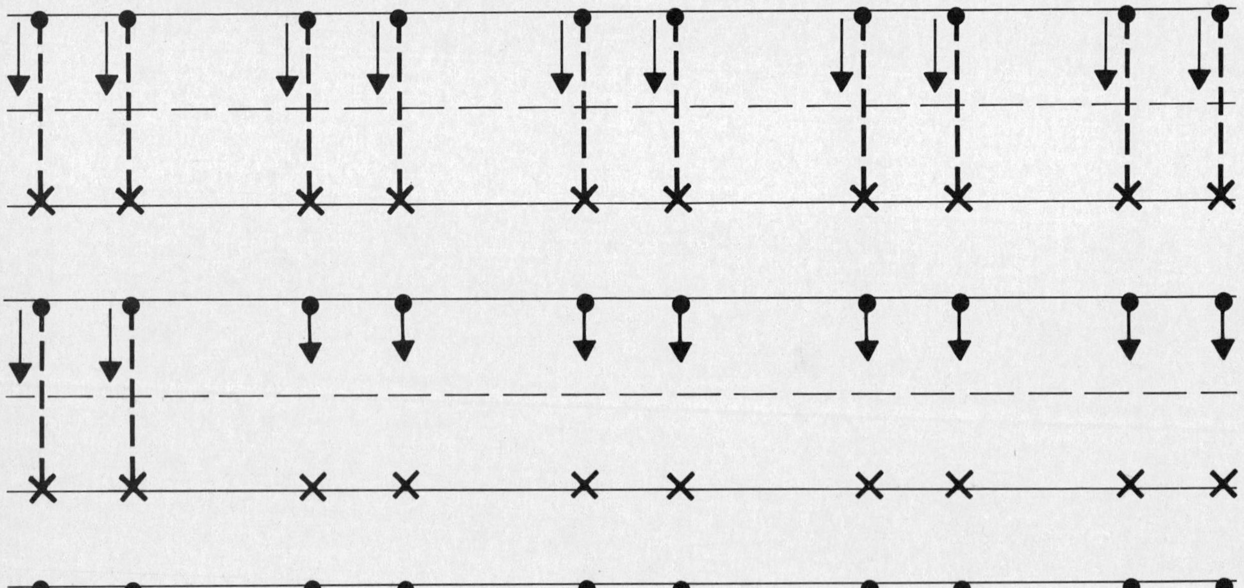

Trace the path for writing 11. Write the number 11.

Name ________________________________

12

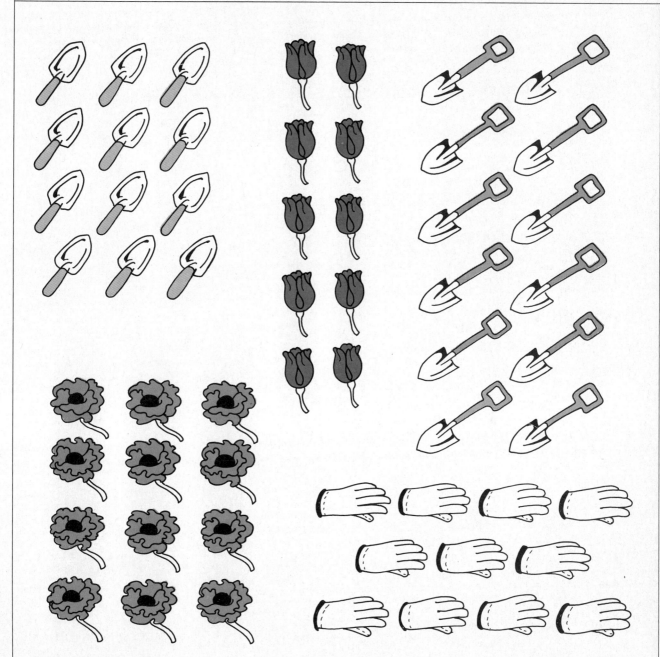

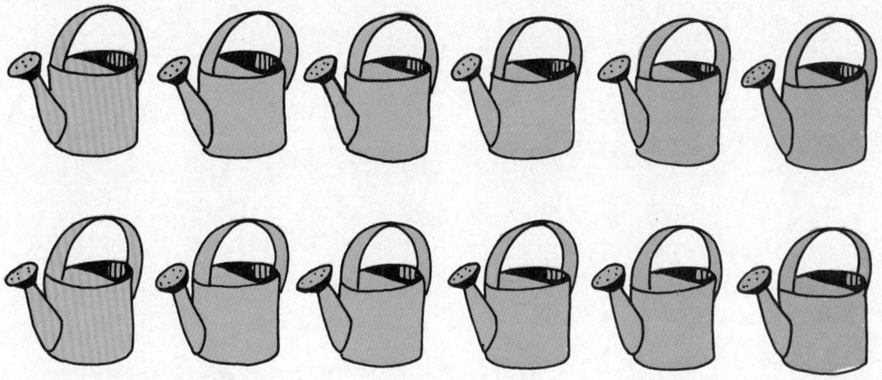

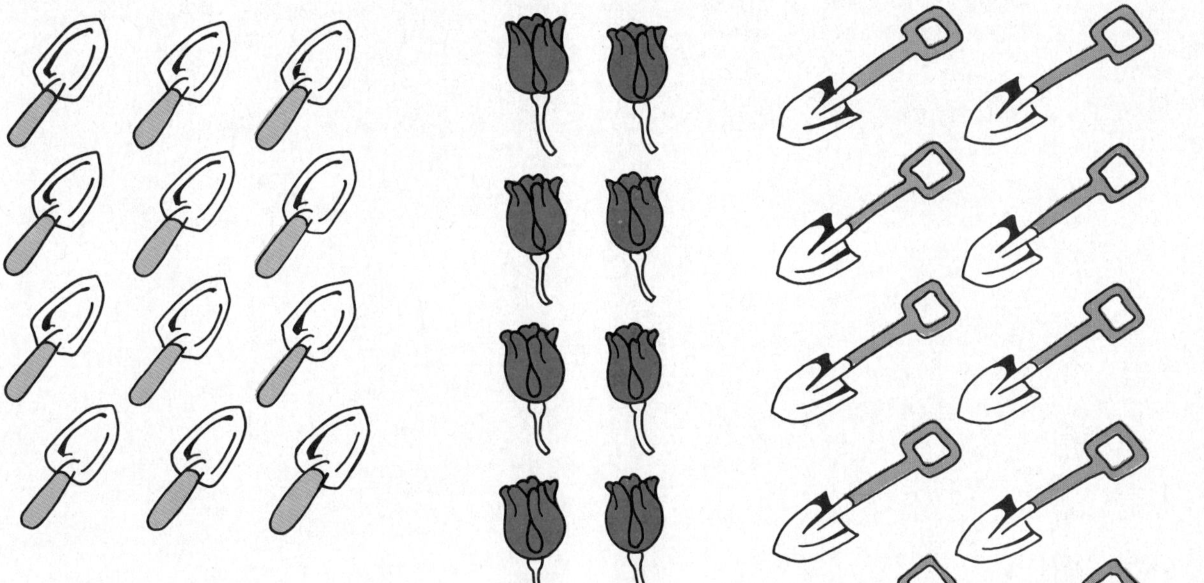

Count the objects in each set. Circle the sets of 12 objects.

9 10 11 12

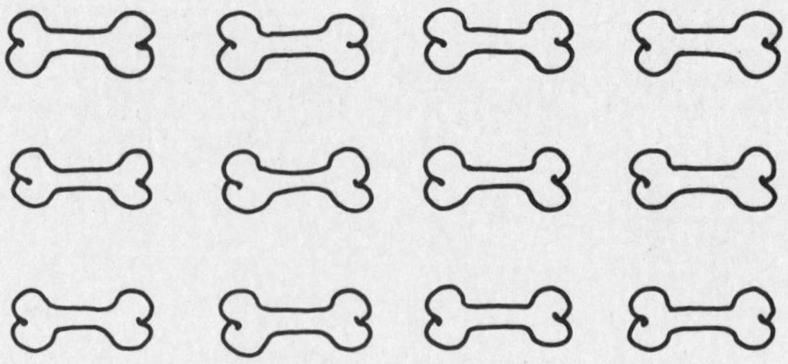

9 10 11 12

9 10 11 12

9 10 11 12

9 10 11 12

9 10 11 12

9 10 11 12

9 10 11 12

Circle the number that tells how many objects in each set.

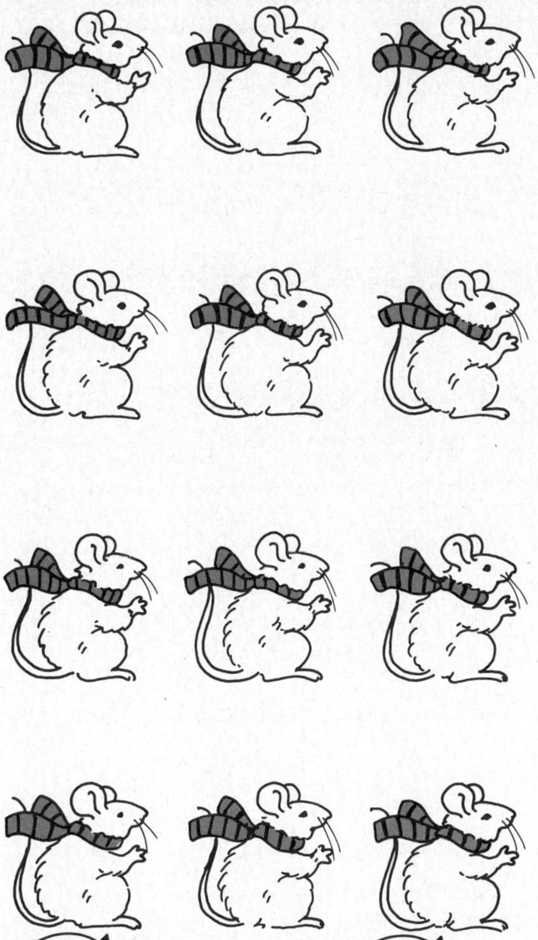

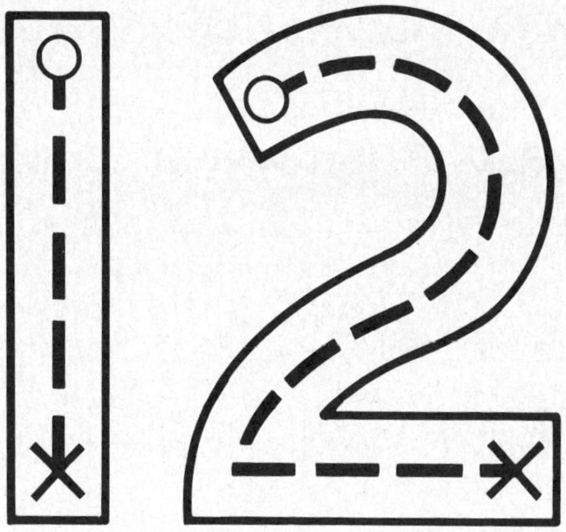

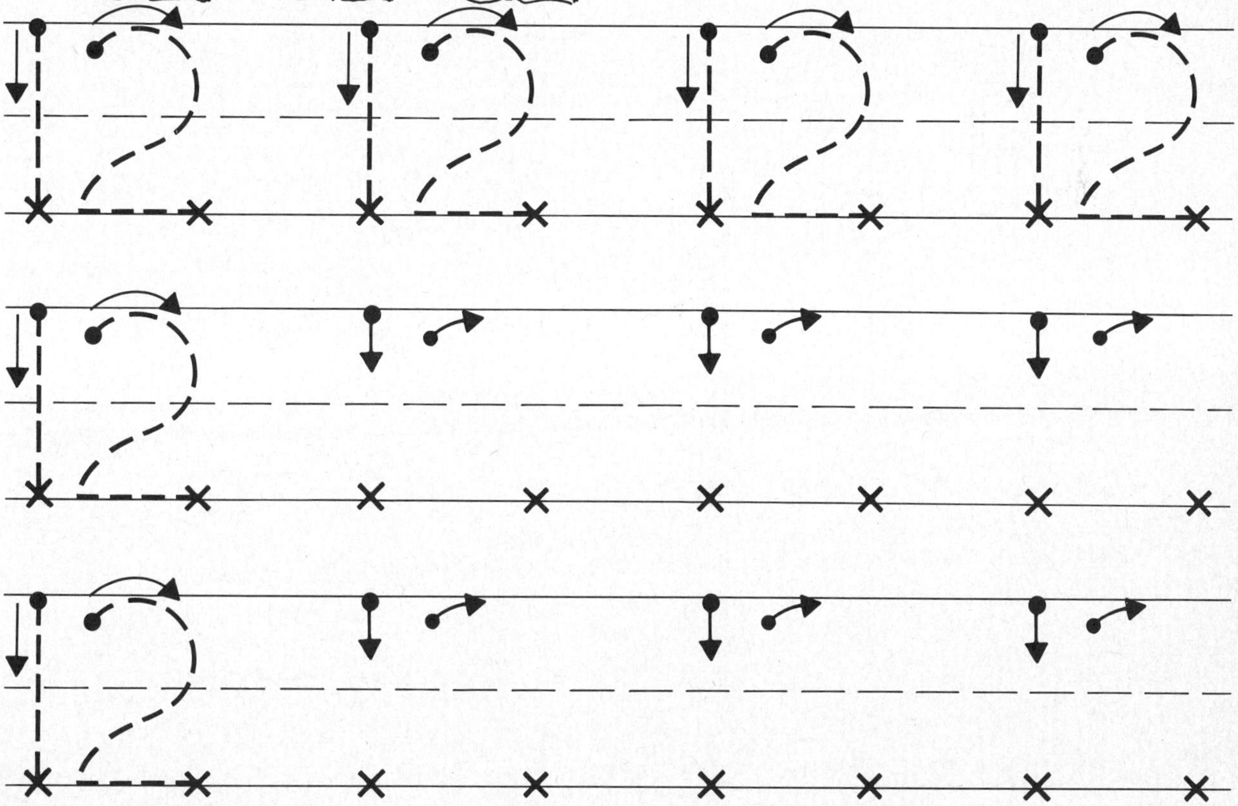

Trace the path for writing 12. Write the number 12.

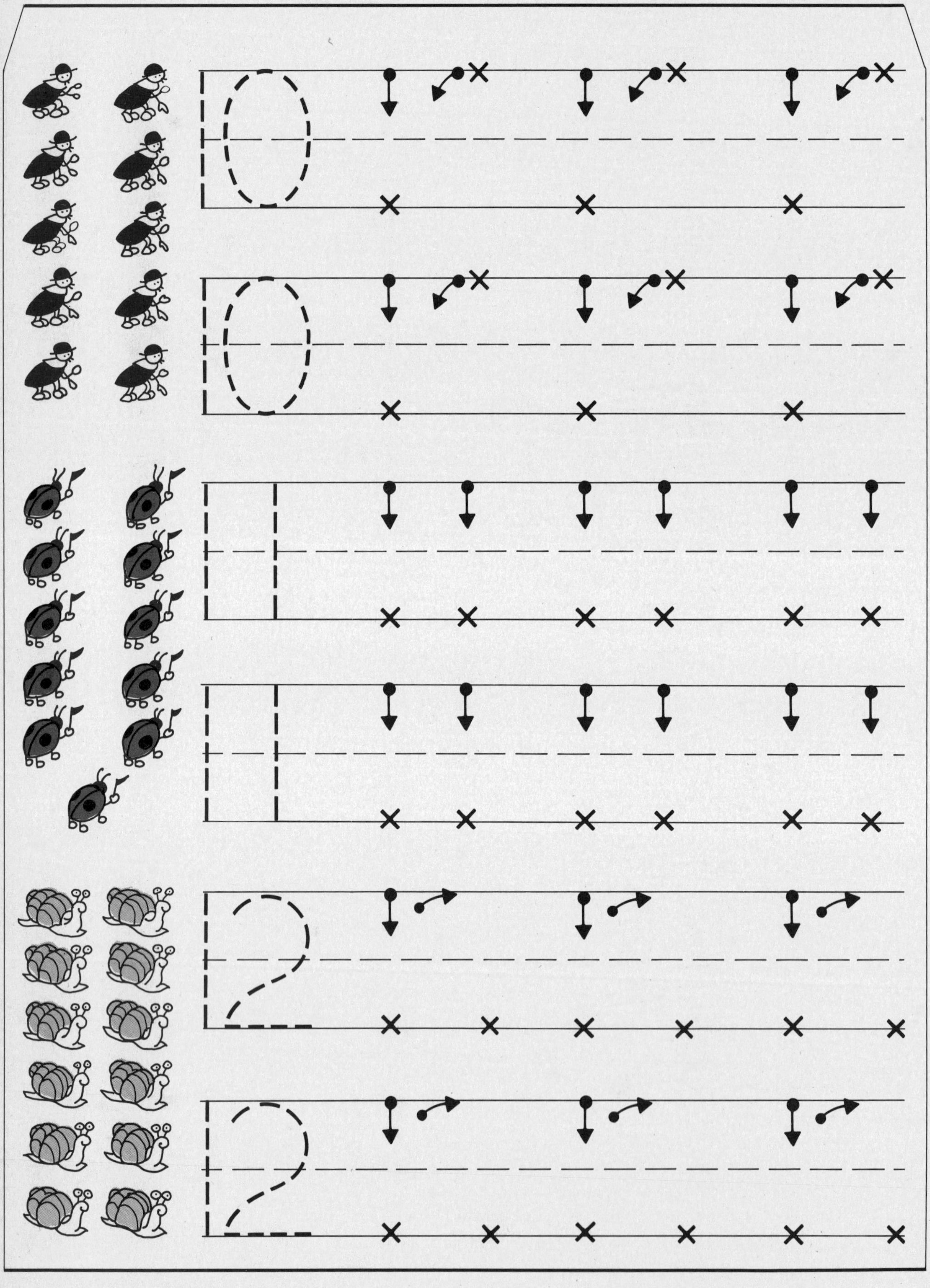

Write the numbers 10, 11 and 12.

Name ____________________

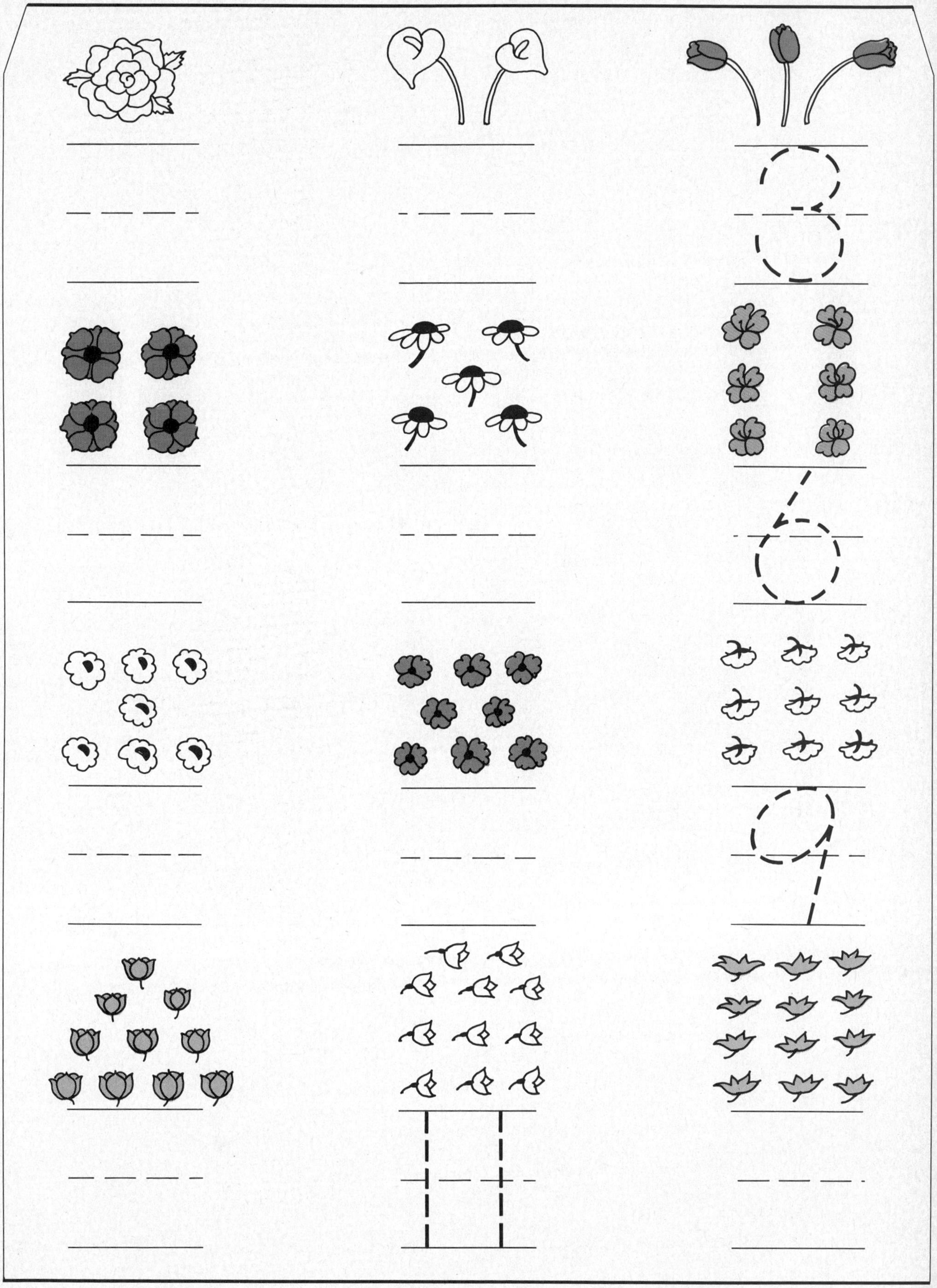

Write the numbers 1 through 12 in order.

Connect the dots in order from 0 through 12.

Name ____________________

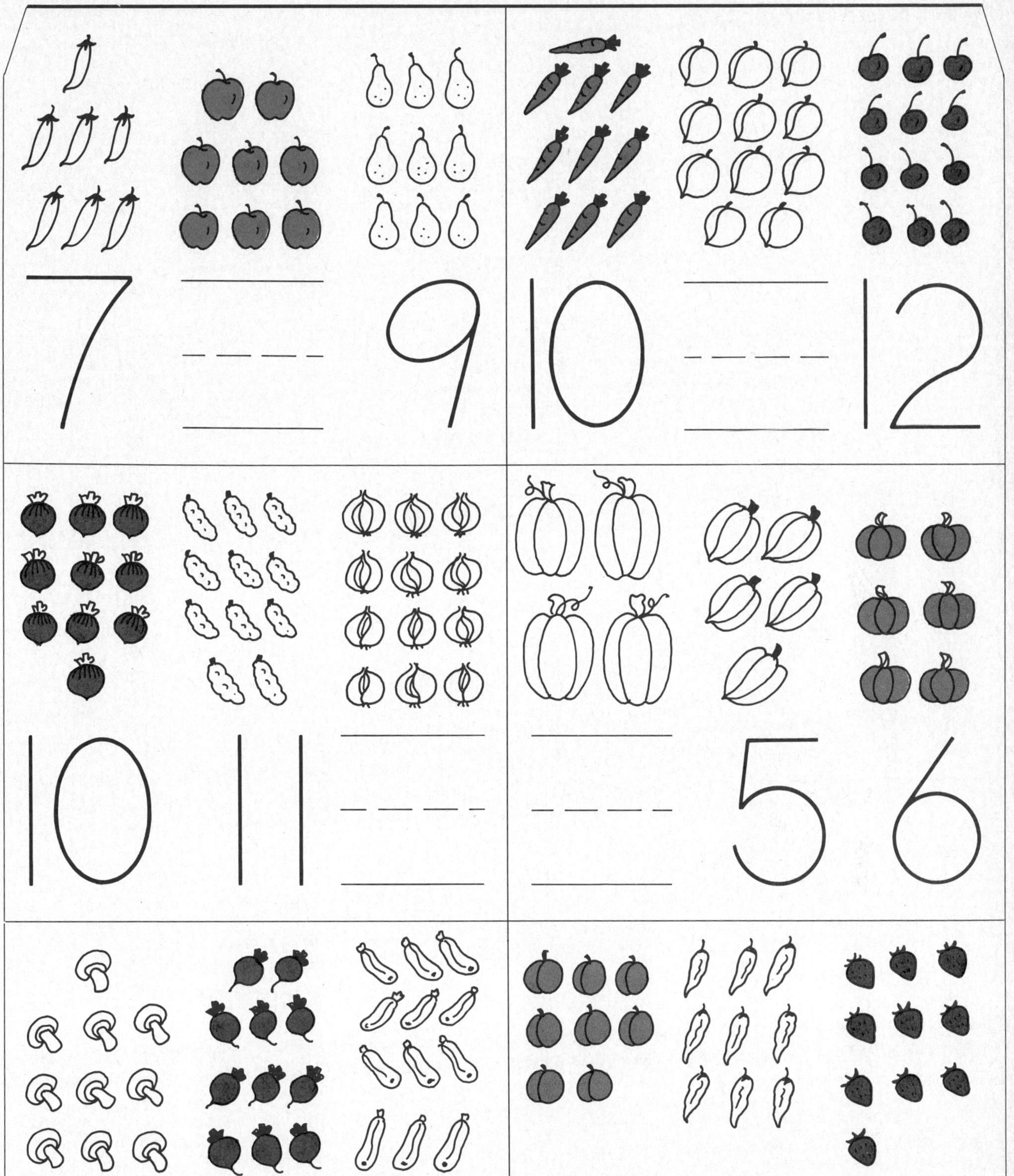

Write the missing number before, after or between the given numbers.

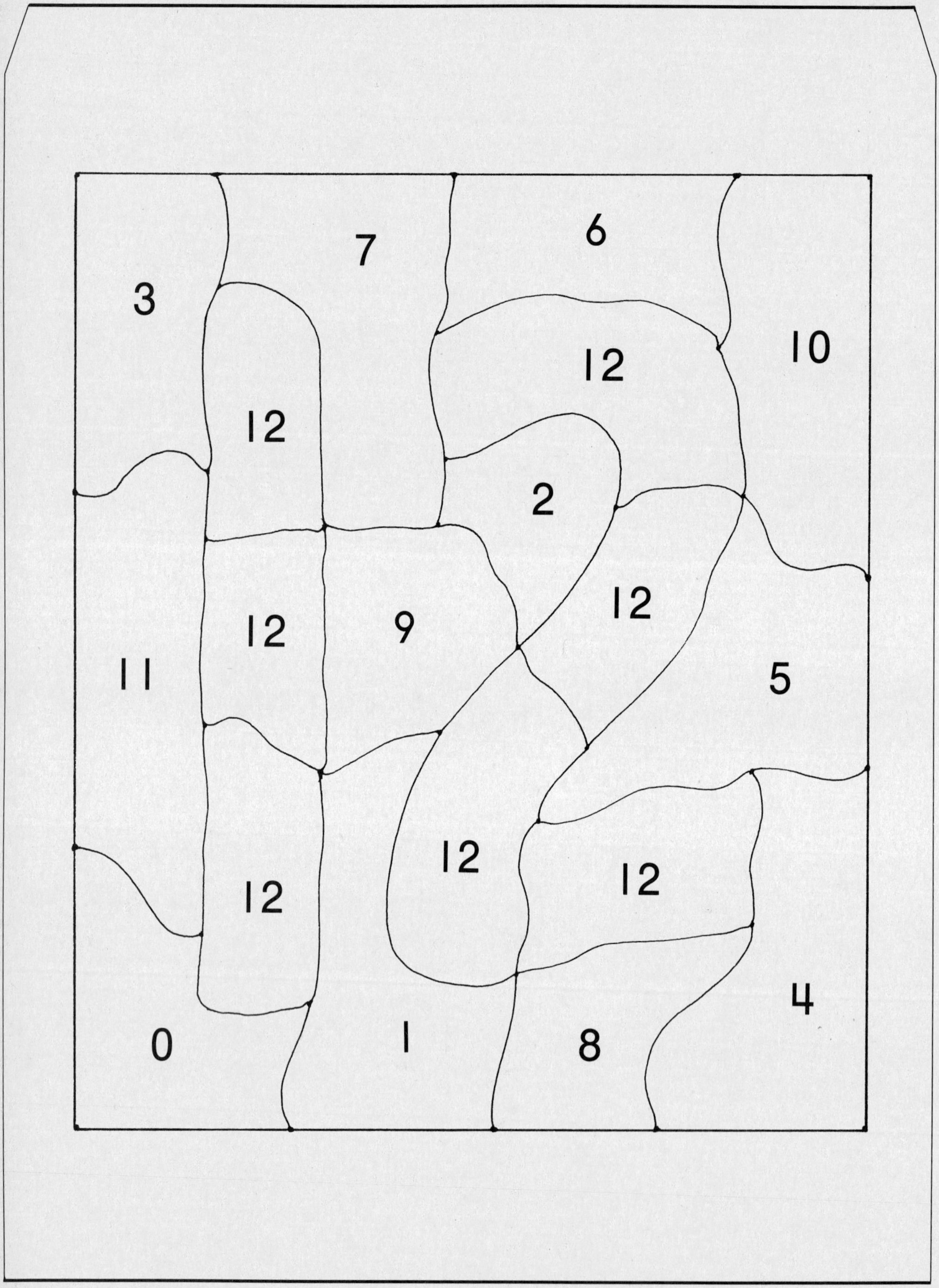

Color all the spaces with the number 12 in them. What do you see?

Name ________________________________

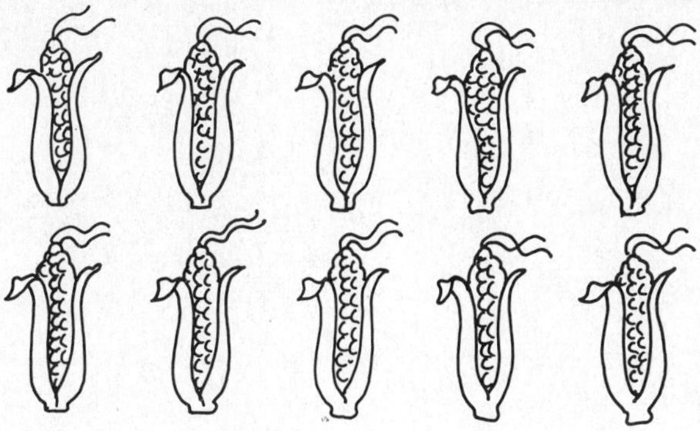

9 10 11 12

9 10 11 12

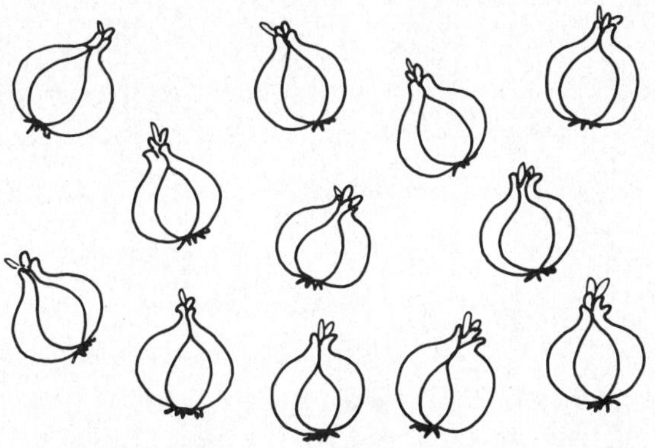

9 10 11 12

9 10 11 12

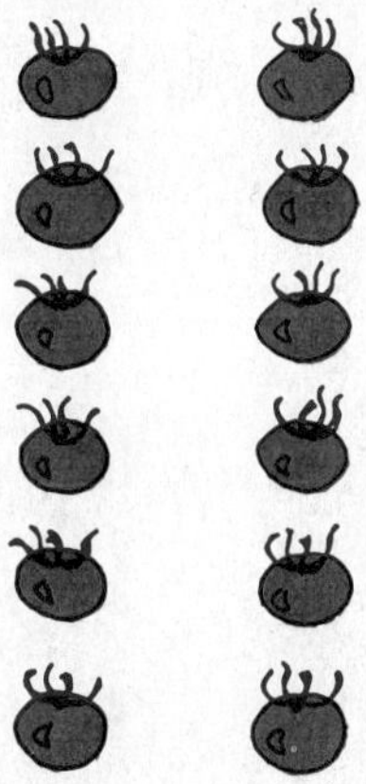

Chapter Checkup Circle the number that tells how many in each set.
Count the objects in each set and write the number.

Field Trip Tally the number of each kind of animal in the picture and then write the number.

Name ______________________________

5 TIME AND MONEY

Circle the event that happens first.

Circle the event that happens first.
Put a check on the one that happens second.

Name ________________________________

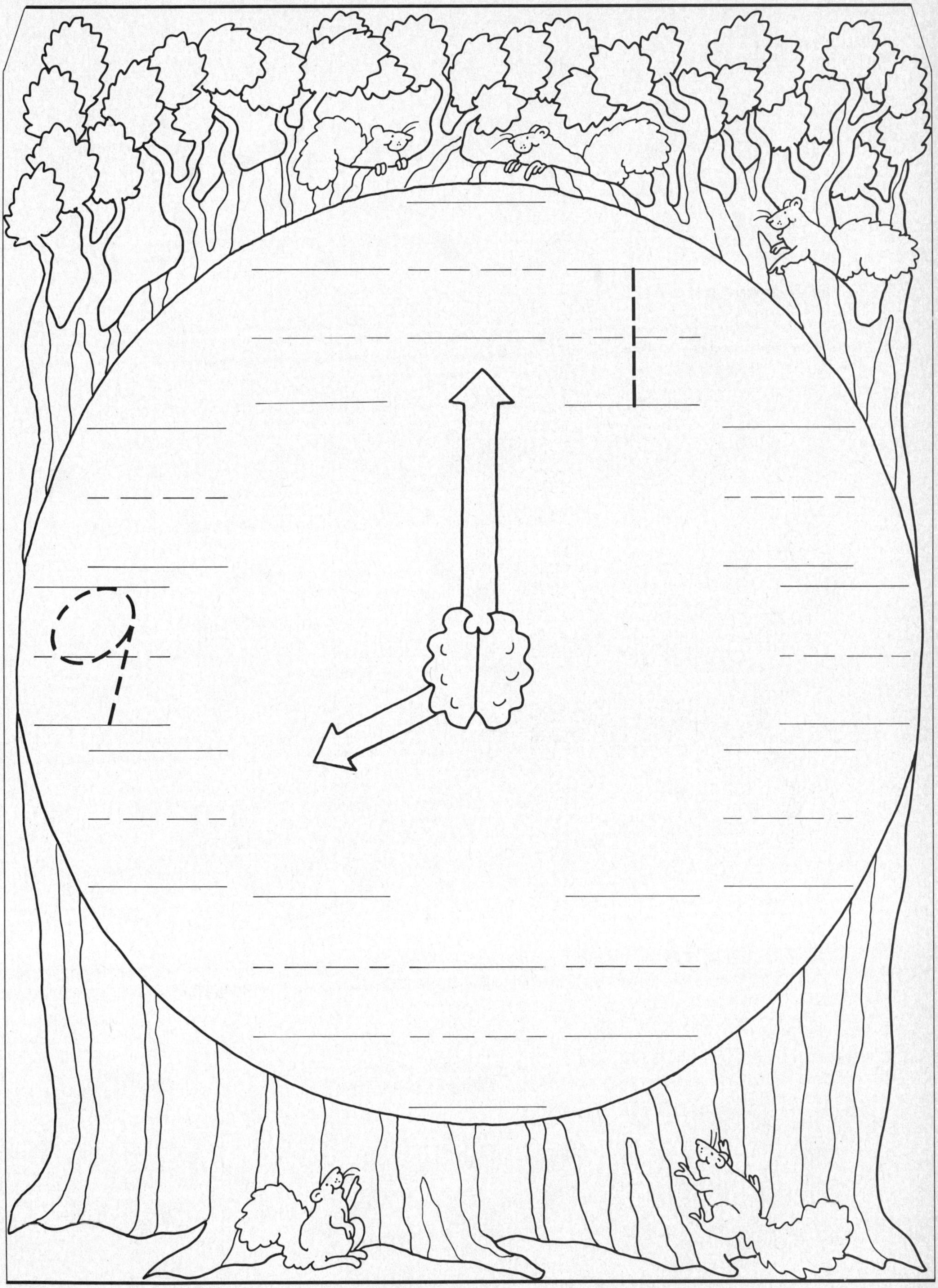

Write the numbers on the clock face.
Color the minute hand red and the hour hand blue.

4:00

8:00

12:00

7:00

Circle the clock that shows the correct time for the picture.

Name ____________________

Circle the digital clock that matches the clock face.

Draw a line from each clock face to the matching digital clock.

Name ______________________________

2 ¢

____ ¢

____ ¢

____ ¢

____ ¢

____ ¢

____ ¢

Count the pennies and write how much money.

____

_ _ _ _ ¢

____

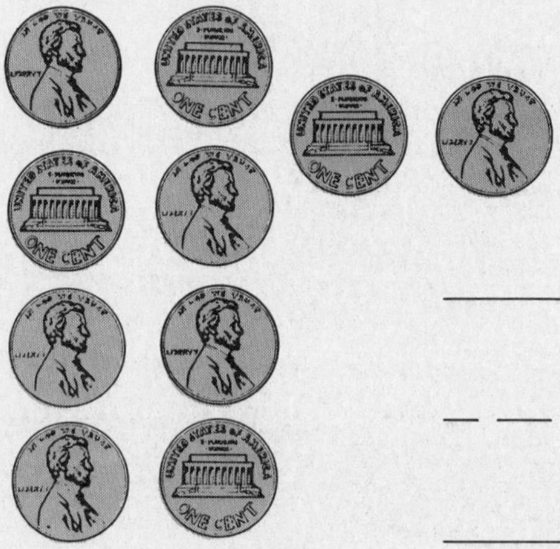

____

_ _ _ _ ¢

____

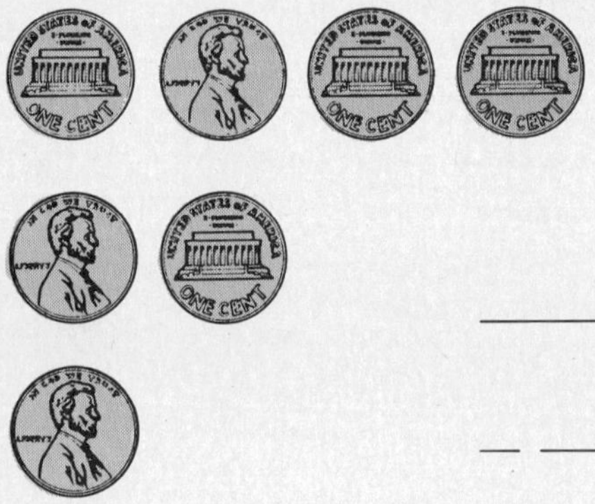

____

_ _ _ _ ¢

____

____

_ _ _ _ ¢

____

____

_ _ _ _ ¢

____

____

_ _ _ _ ¢

____

Count the pennies and write how much money.

Name ____________________

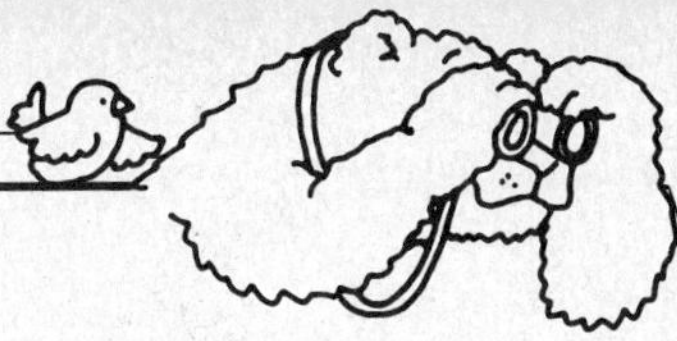

5¢

5¢

______

_ _ _ _ ¢

______

______

_ _ _ _ ¢

______

______

_ _ _ _ ¢

______

______

_ _ _ _ ¢

______

______

_ _ _ _ ¢

______

______

_ _ _ _ ¢

______

Count the nickels and pennies and write how much money.

Circle the coins needed to buy each item.

Name ______________________________

10¢

10¢

10¢

_______ ¢

_______ ¢

_______ ¢

_______ ¢

_______ ¢

_______ ¢

Count the dimes, nickels and pennies. Write how much money.

____ ¢

____ ¢

____ ¢

____ ¢

____ ¢

____ ¢

Count the dimes, nickels and pennies. Write how much money.

Name ______________________________

Circle the coins needed to buy each item.

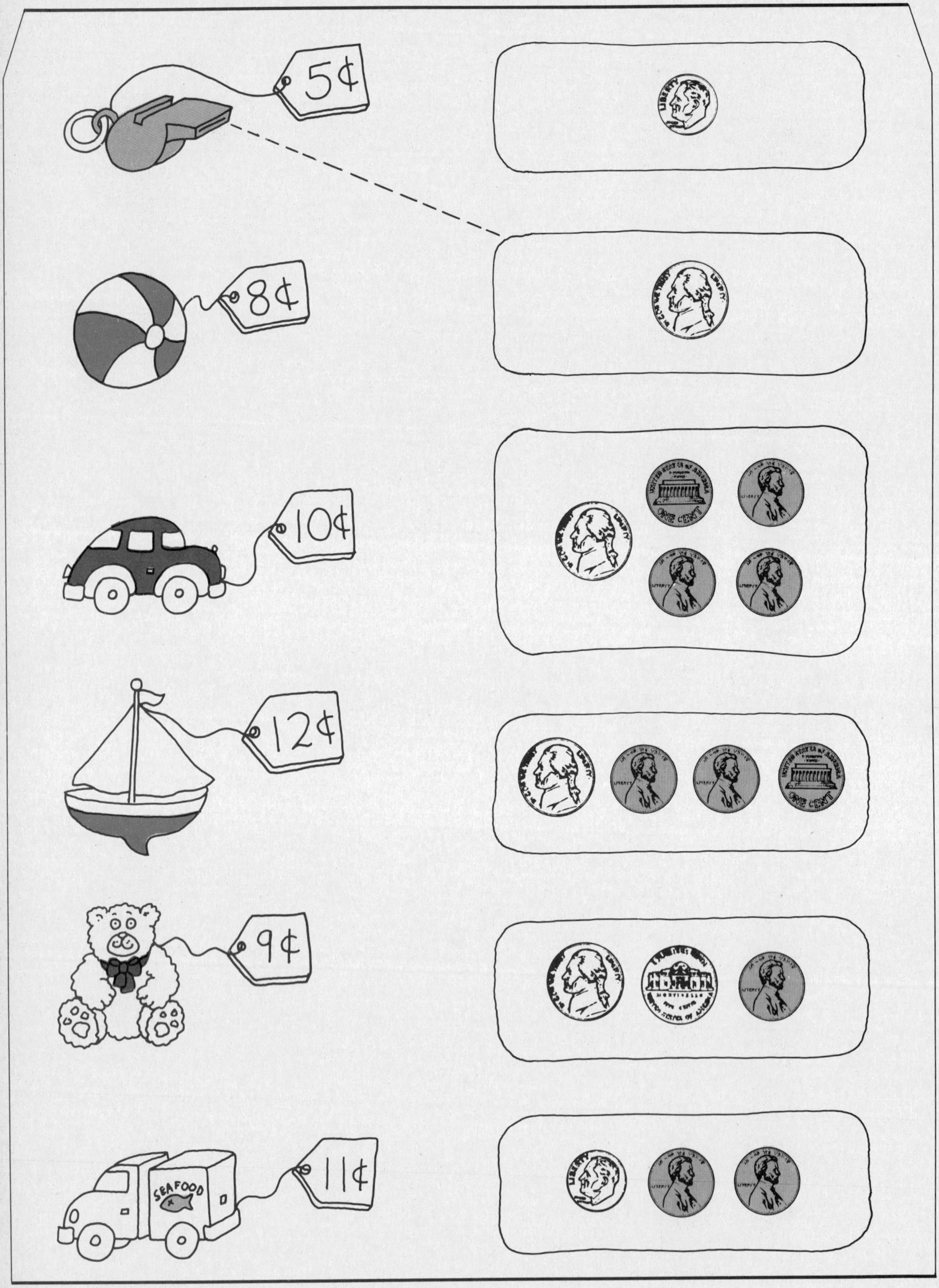

Draw a line from each toy to the set of coins needed to buy it.

Name ______________________________

____

_ _ _ _ _ ¢

____

____

_ _ _ _ _ ¢

____

Chapter Checkup Circle the action which happened first. Circle the correct digital clocks. Count the dimes, nickels and pennies. Write how much money. Circle the coins needed to buy each item.

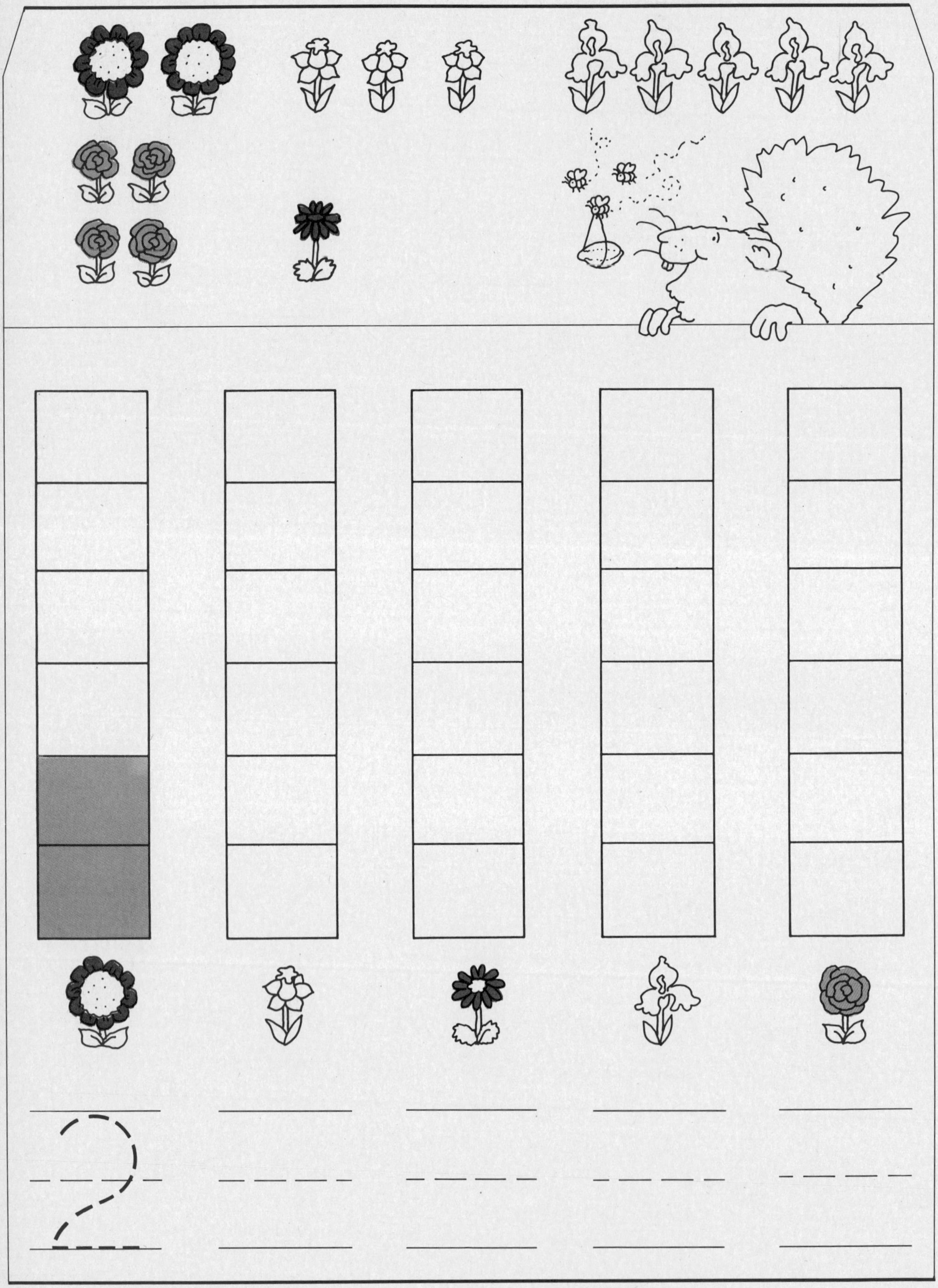

Field Trip Color one square for each kind of flower in the picture. Write the number of each kind.

Name ______________________________

6 NUMBERS THROUGH 20

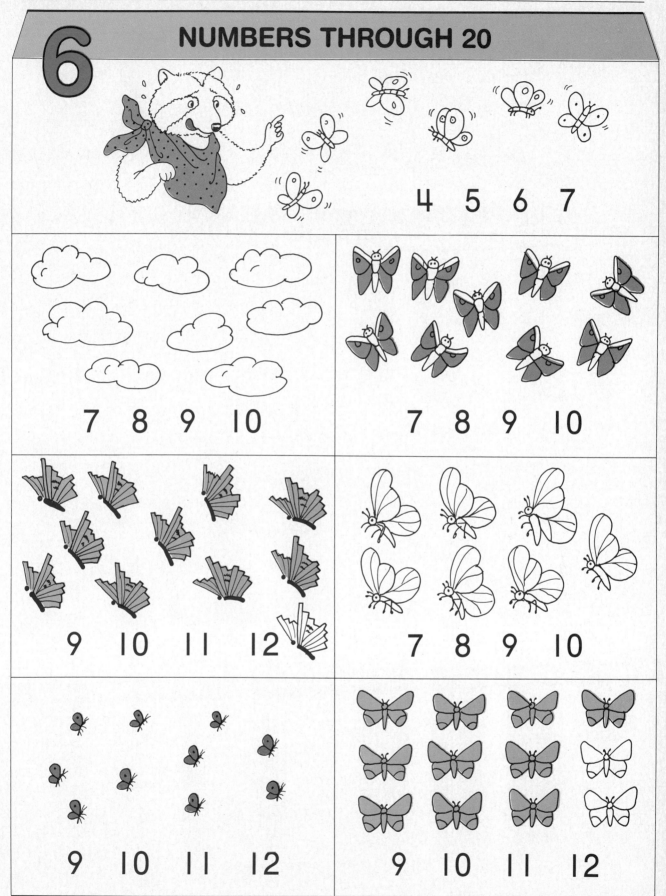

4 5 6 7

7 8 9 10

7 8 9 10

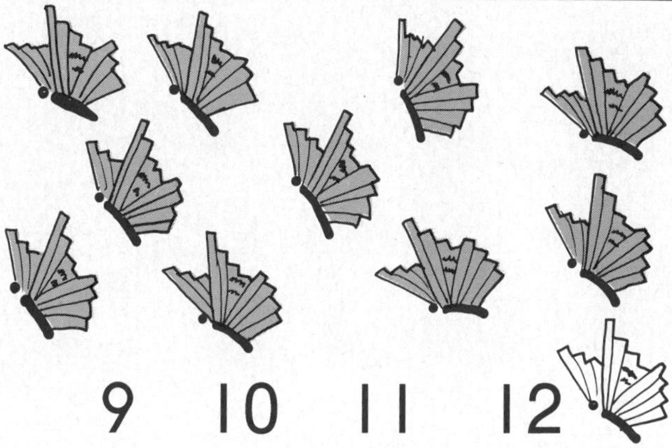

9 10 11 12

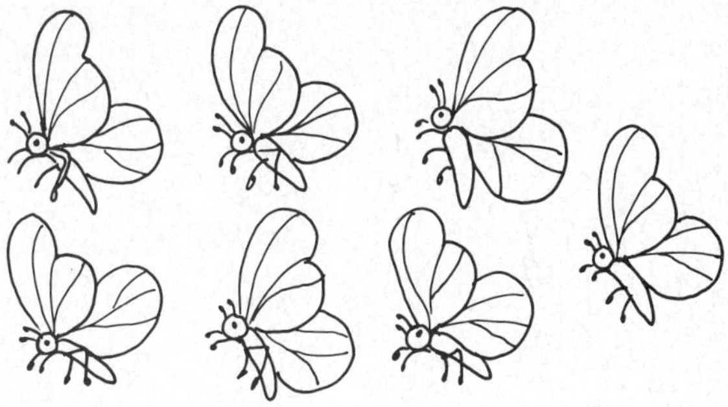

7 8 9 10

9 10 11 12

9 10 11 12

Circle the number that tells how many objects in each set.

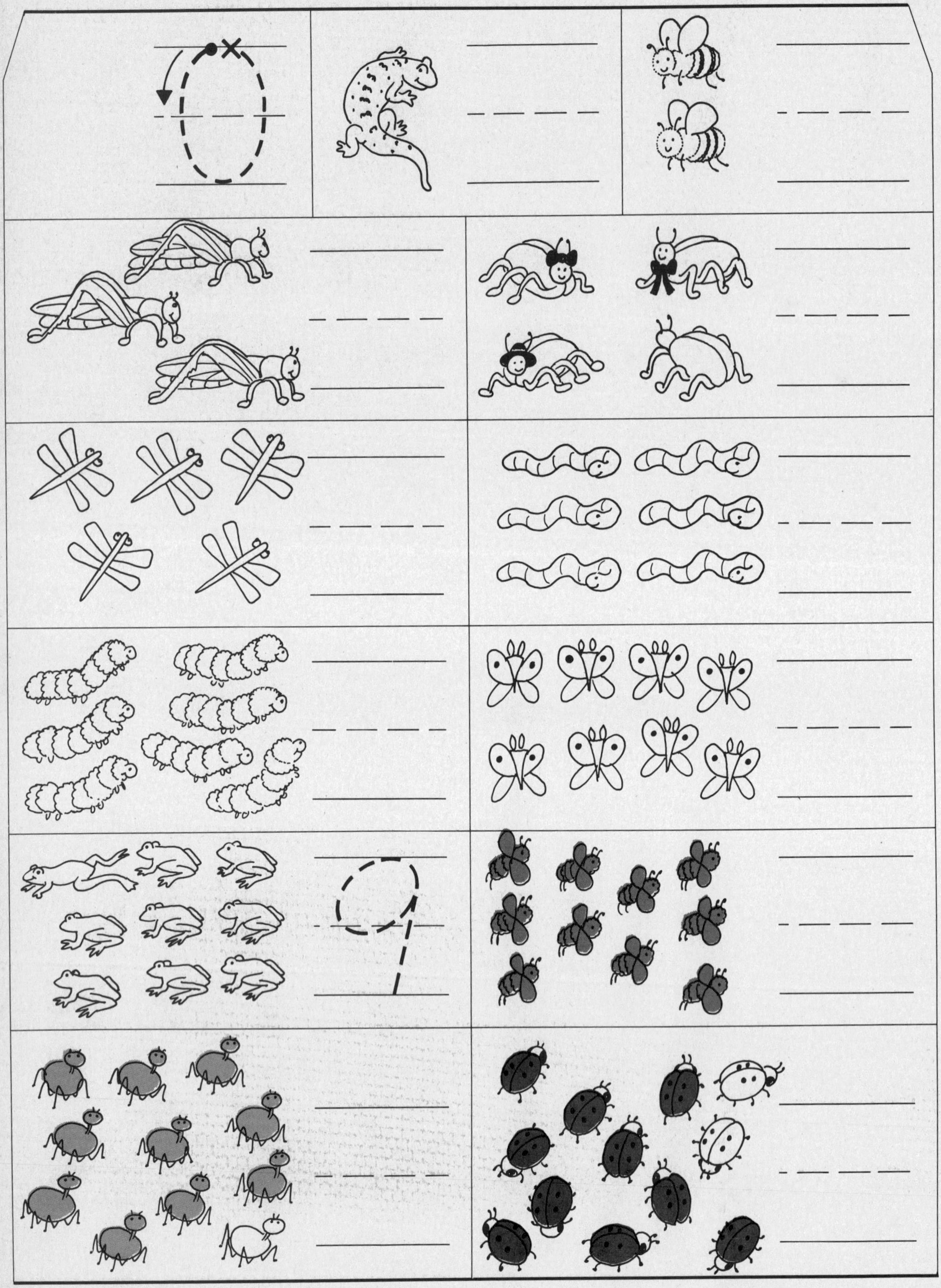

Count the objects in each set and write the number.

Name ________________________________

9 10 11 12

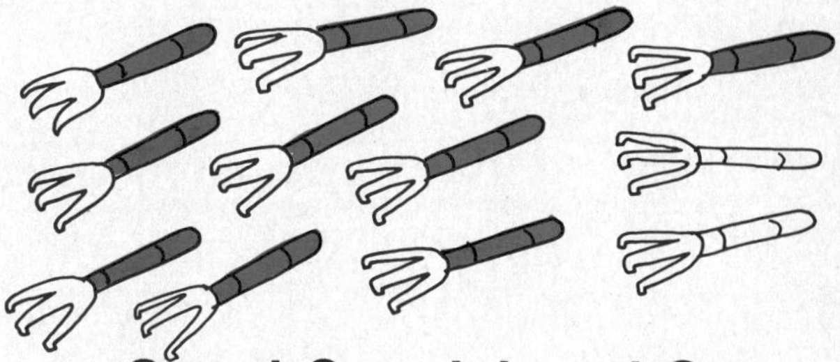

9 10 11 12

10 11 12 13

10 11 12 13

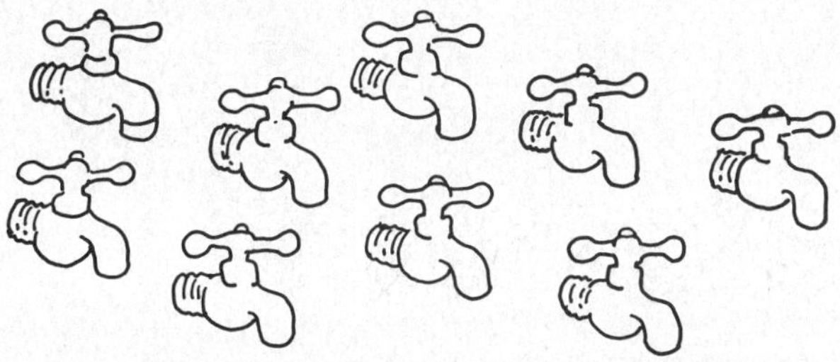

9 10 11 12

10 11 12 13

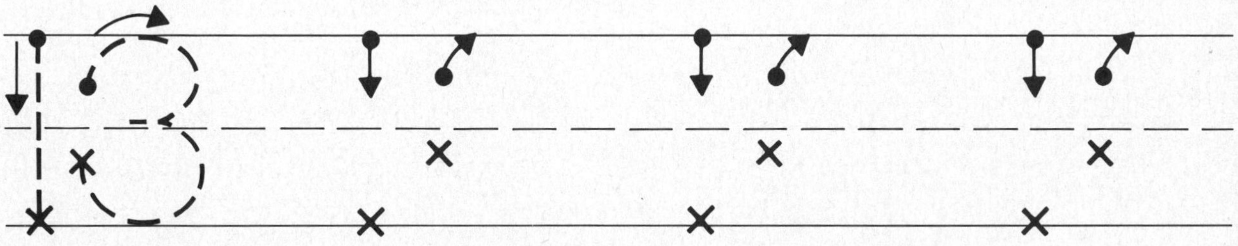

Trace the path for writing 13. Circle the number that tells how many objects in each set. Write the number 13.

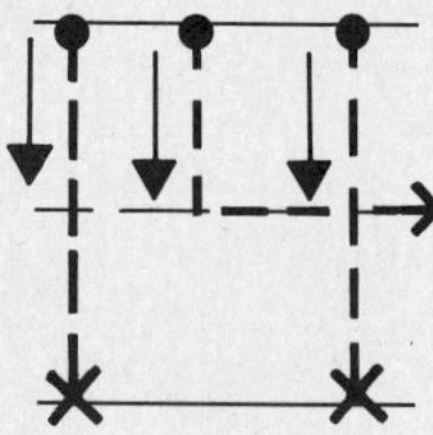

9 10 11 12

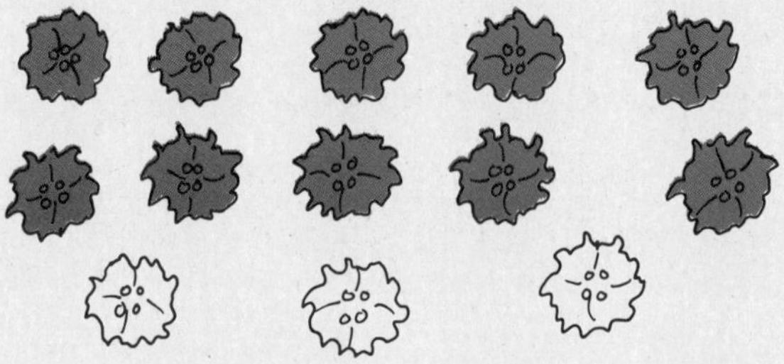

11 12 13 14

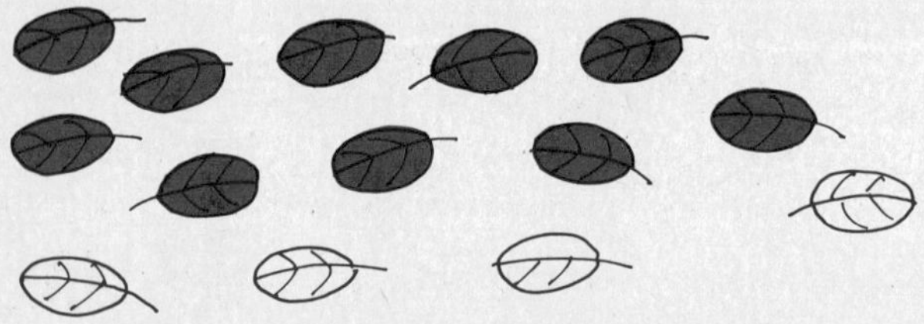

11 12 13 14

11 12 13 14

11 12 13 14

11 12 13 14

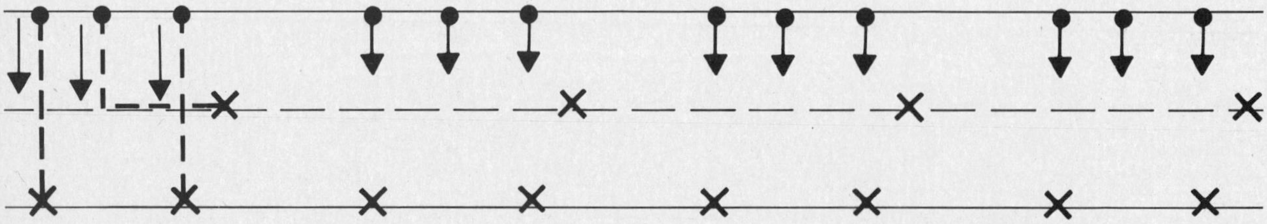

Trace the path for writing 14. Circle the number that tells how many objects in each set. Write the number 14.

Name ______________________________

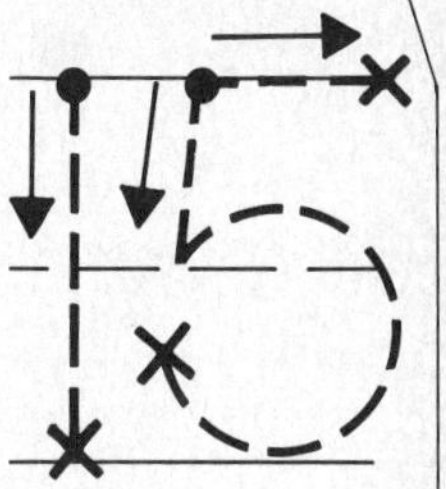

12 13 14 15

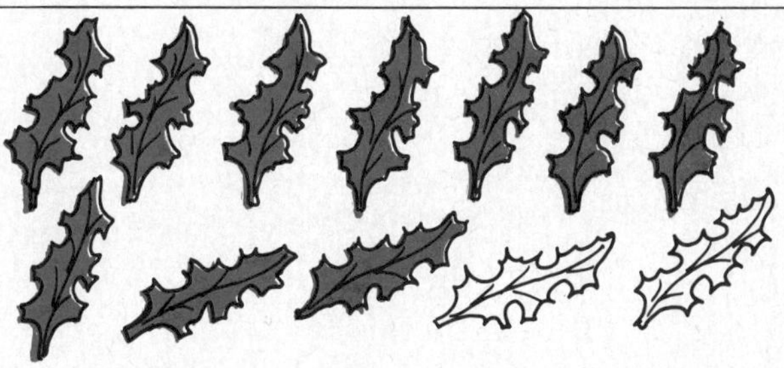

12 13 14 15

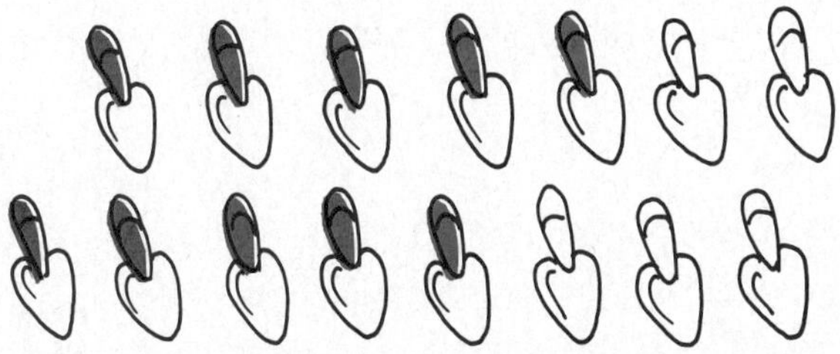

12 13 14 15

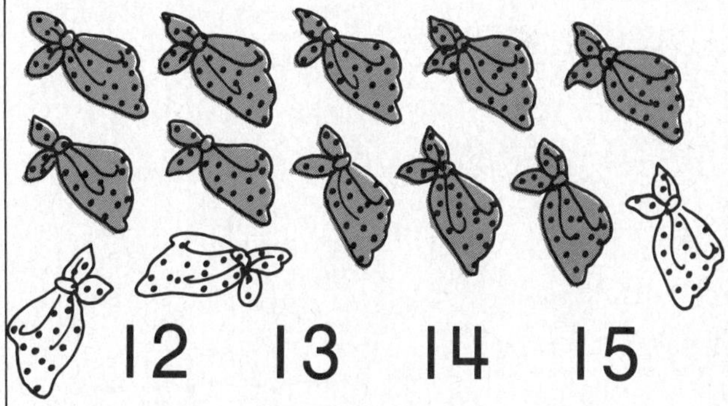

12 13 14 15

10 11 12 13

12 13 14 15

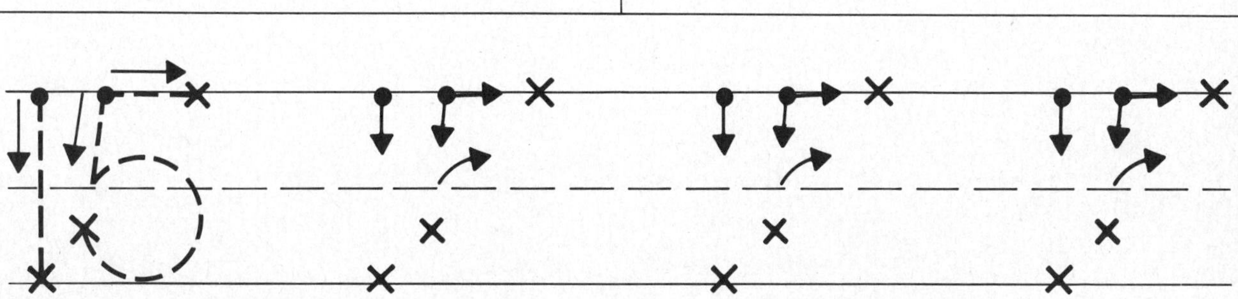

Trace the path for writing 15. Circle the number that tells how many objects in each set. Write the number 15.

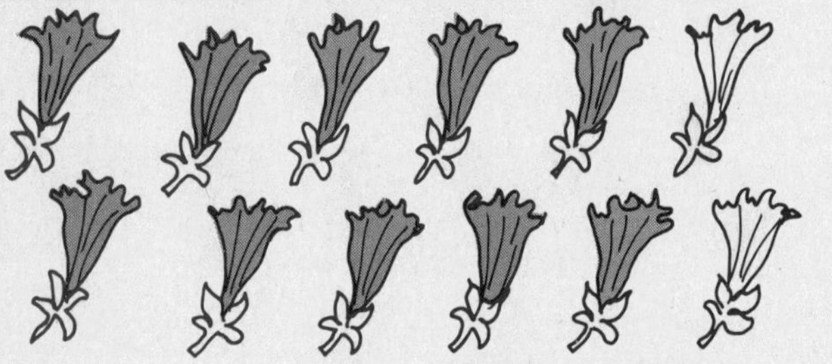

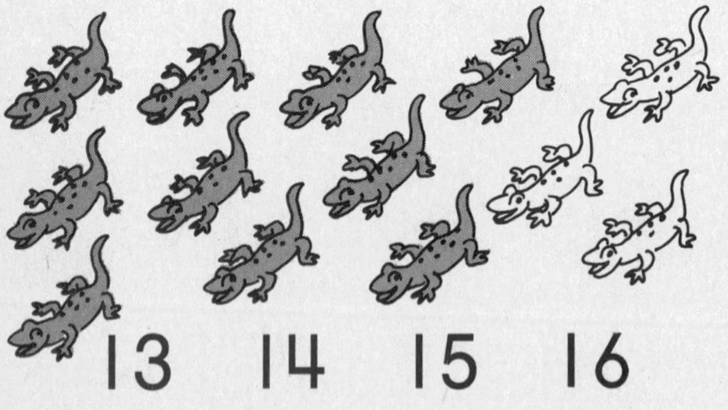

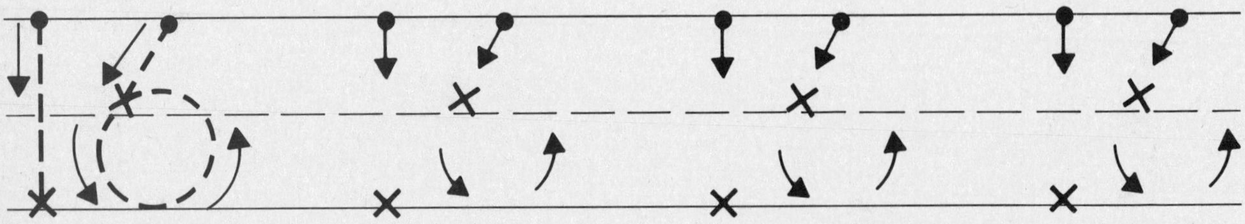

Trace the path for writing 16. Circle the number that tells how many objects in each set. Write the number 16.

Name ______________________________

16 ¢

____ ¢

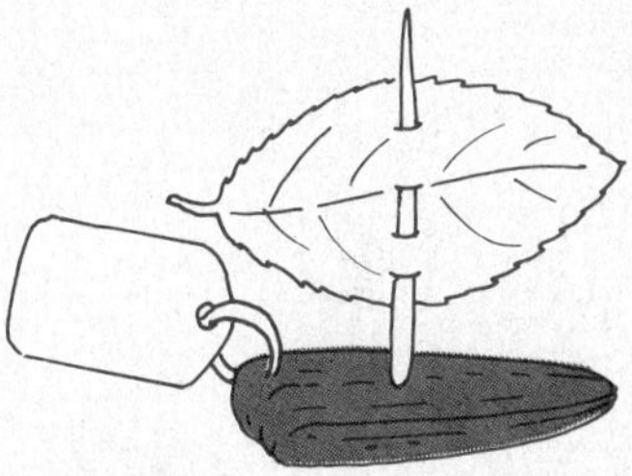

____ ¢

____ ¢

____ ¢

Count the coins and write how much money.

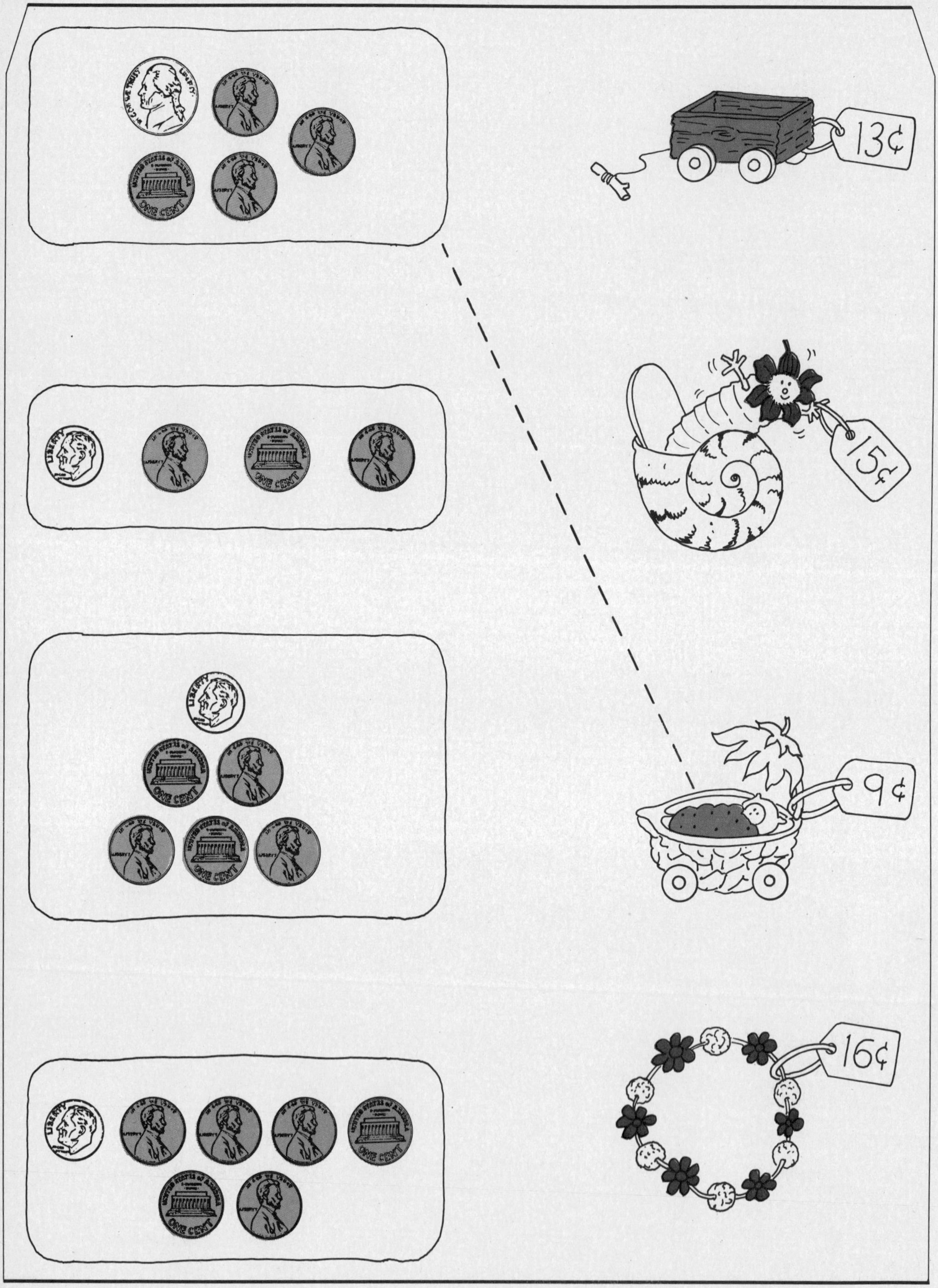

Draw a line from the set of coins to the object they can buy.

Name ______________________________

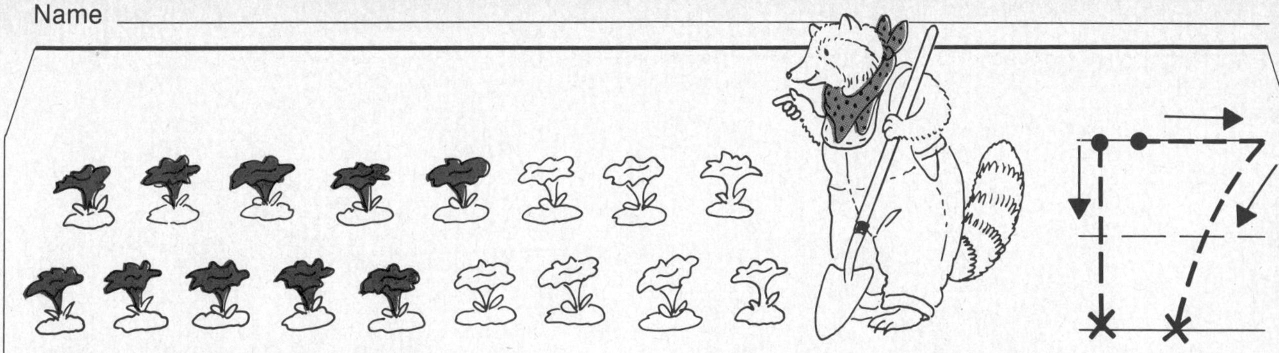

13 14 15 16

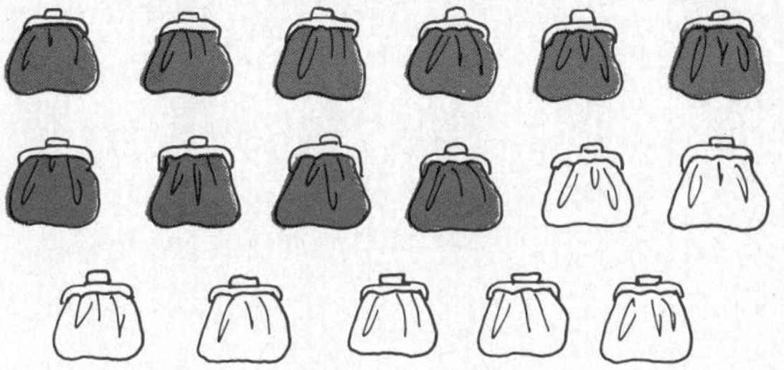

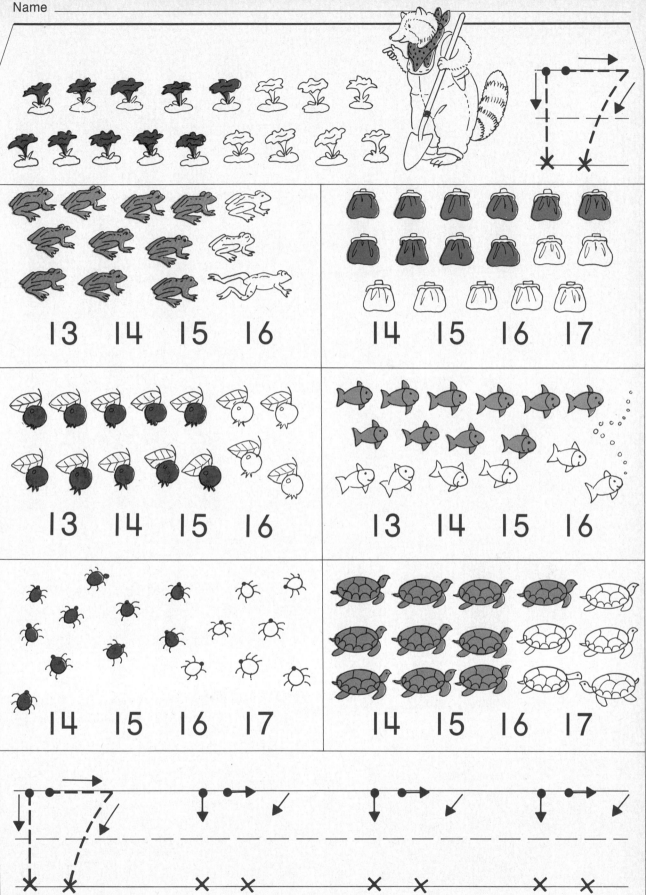

14 15 16 17

13 14 15 16

13 14 15 16

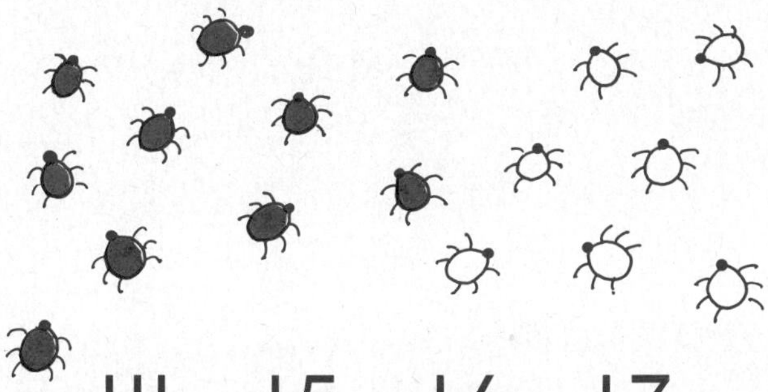

14 15 16 17

14 15 16 17

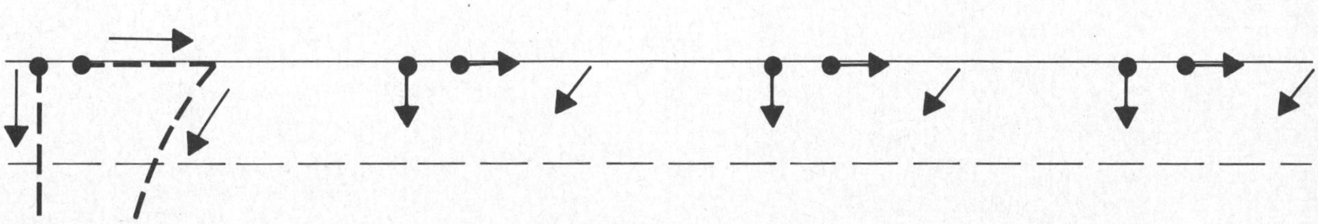

Trace the path for writing 17. Circle the number that tells how many objects in each set. Write the number 17.

15 16 17 18

15 16 17 18

15 16 17 18

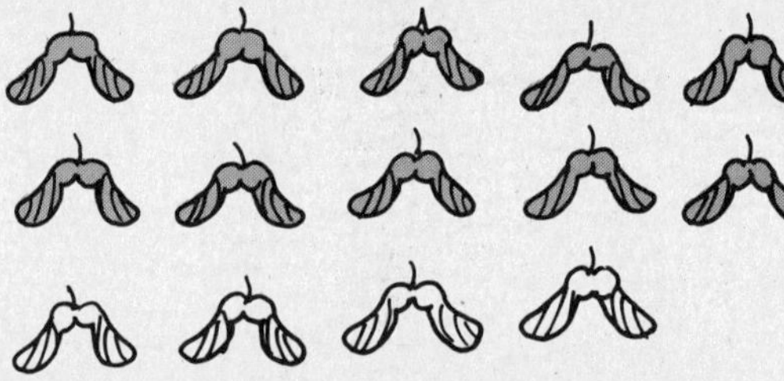

14 15 16 17

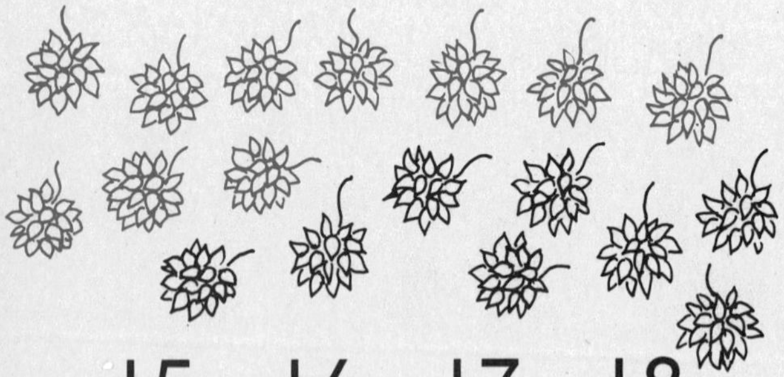

15 16 17 18

14 15 16 17

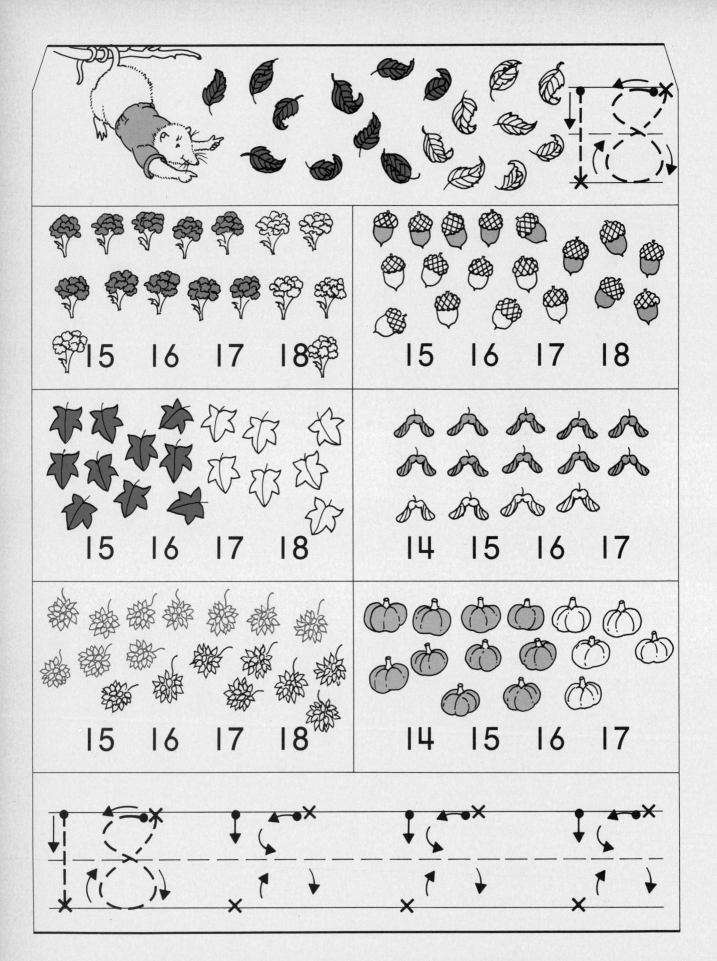

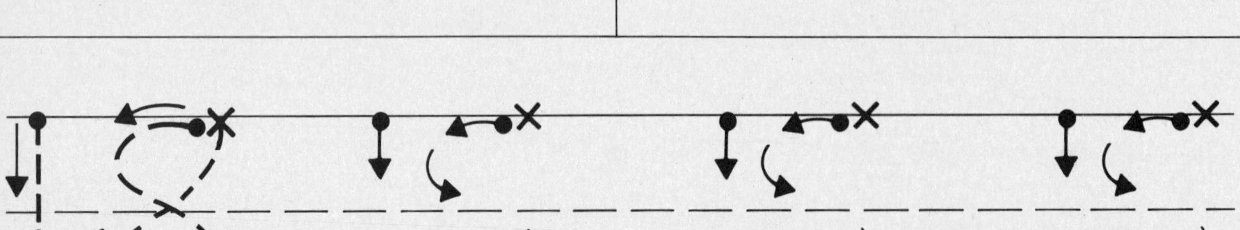

Trace the path for writing 18. Circle the number that tells how many objects in each set. Write the number 18.

Name ______________________________

16 17 18 19

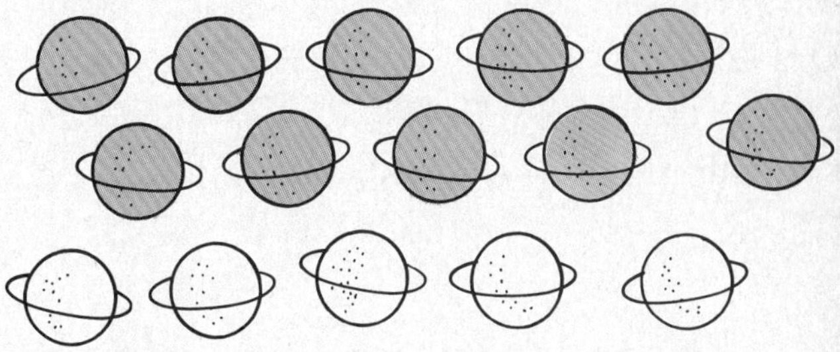

14 15 16 17

16 17 18 19

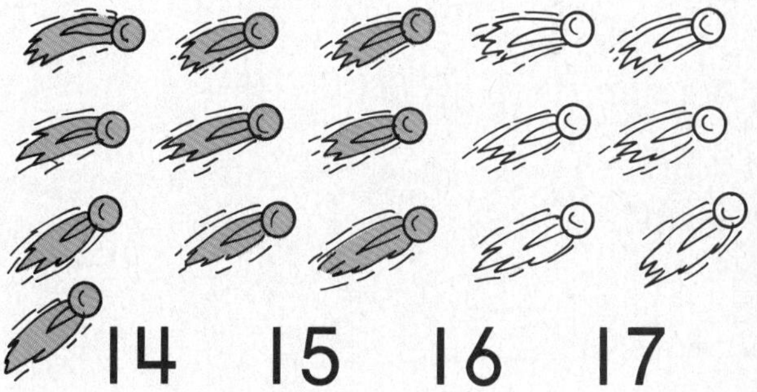

14 15 16 17

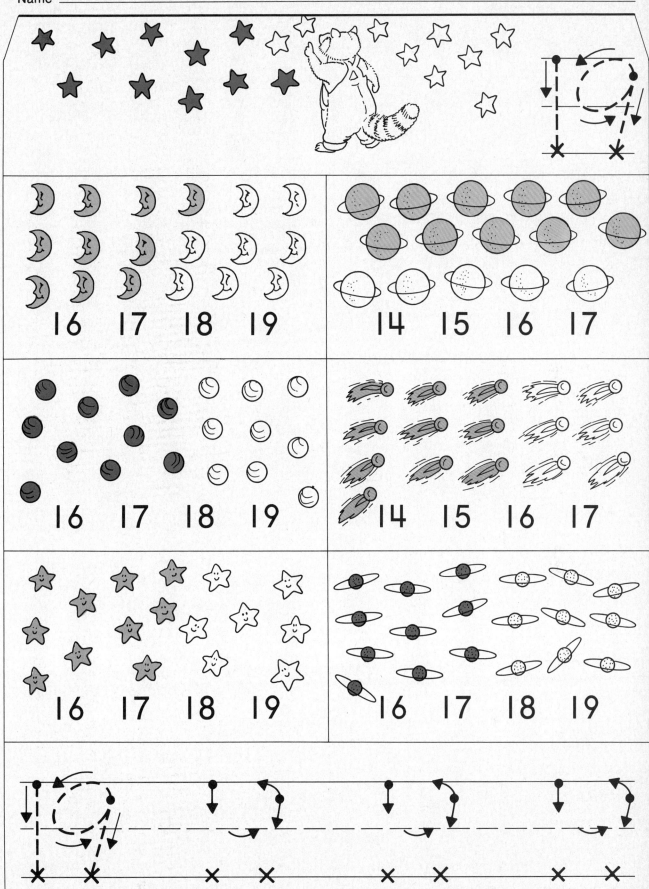

16 17 18 19

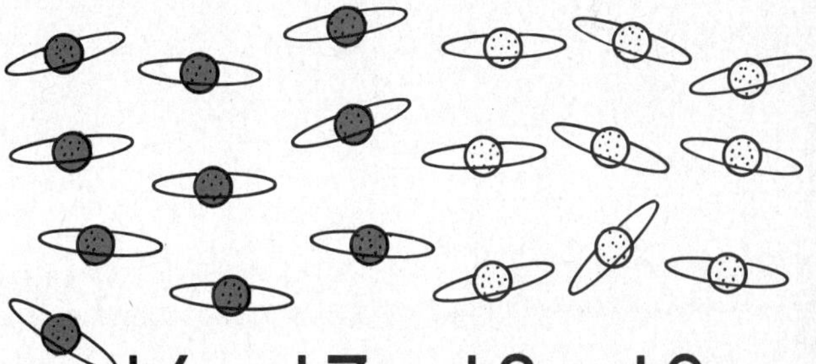

16 17 18 19

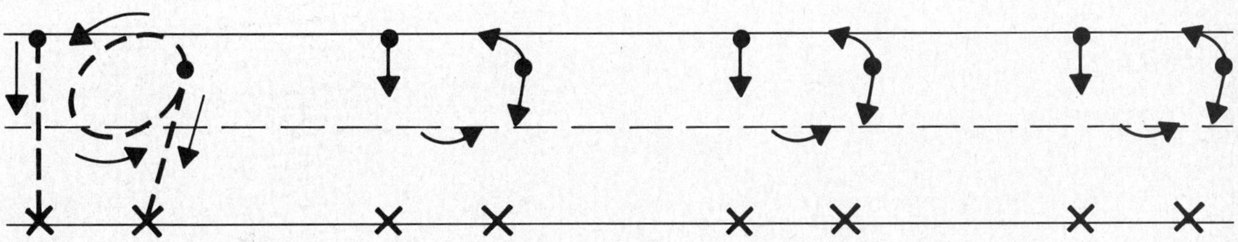

Trace the path for writing 19. Circle the number that tells how many objects in each set. Write the number 19.

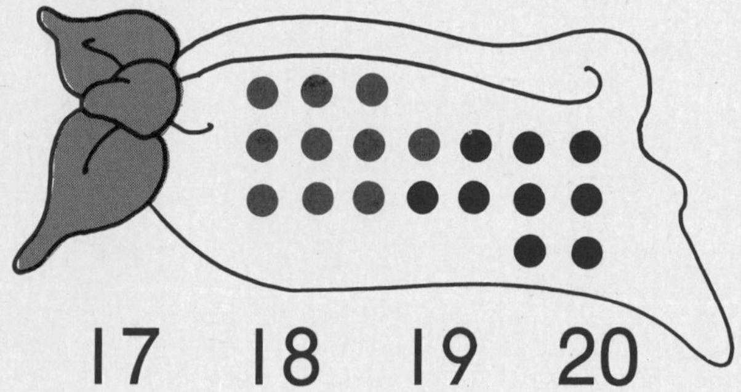

17 18 19 20

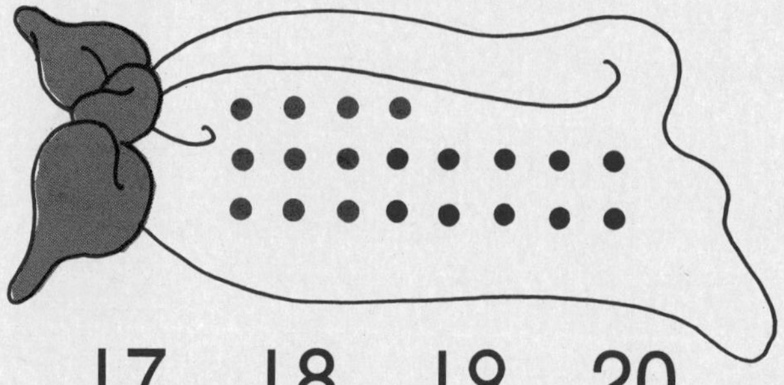

17 18 19 20

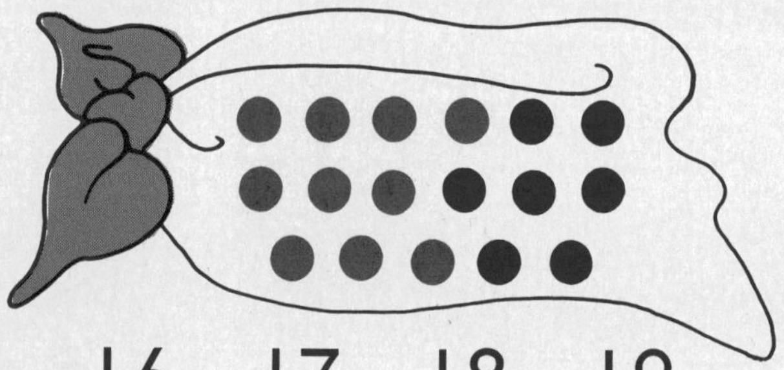

16 17 18 19

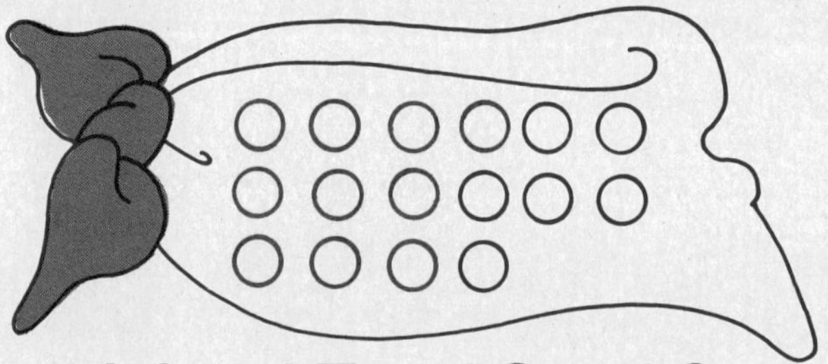

16 17 18 19

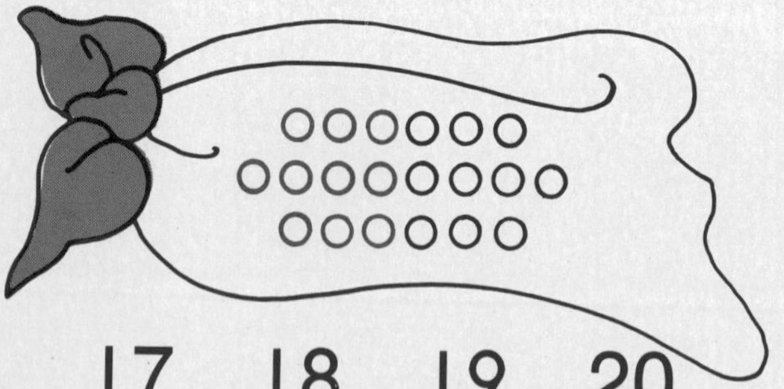

17 18 19 20

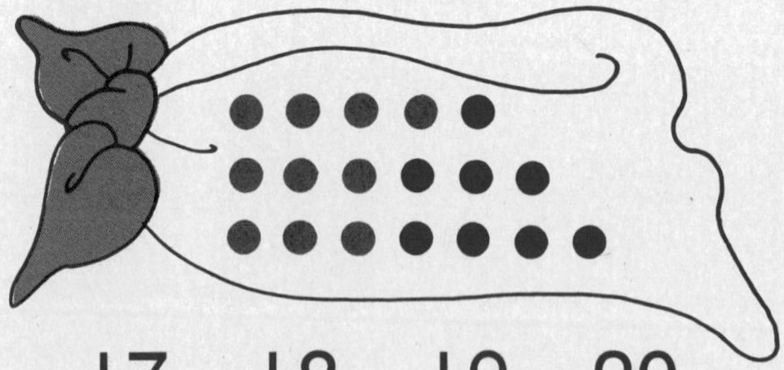

17 18 19 20

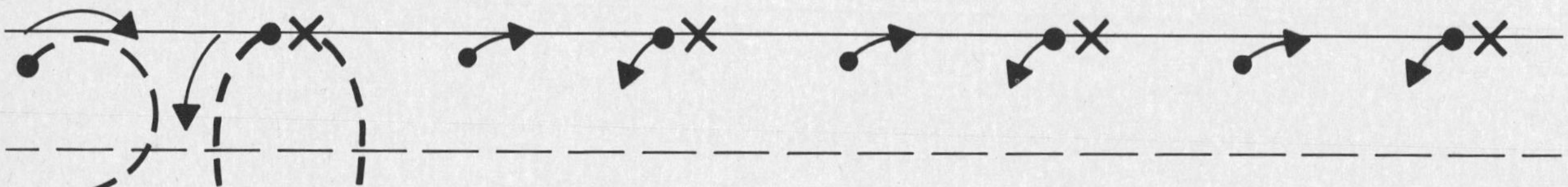

Trace the path for writing 20. Circle the number that tells how many objects in each set. Write the number 20.

Name ______________________________

7¢ 9¢ 12¢

8¢ 11¢ 12¢

10¢ 5¢ 15¢

5¢ 13¢ 8¢

10¢ 15¢ 16¢

15¢ 19¢ 20¢

Circle the number that tells how much money in each set of coins.

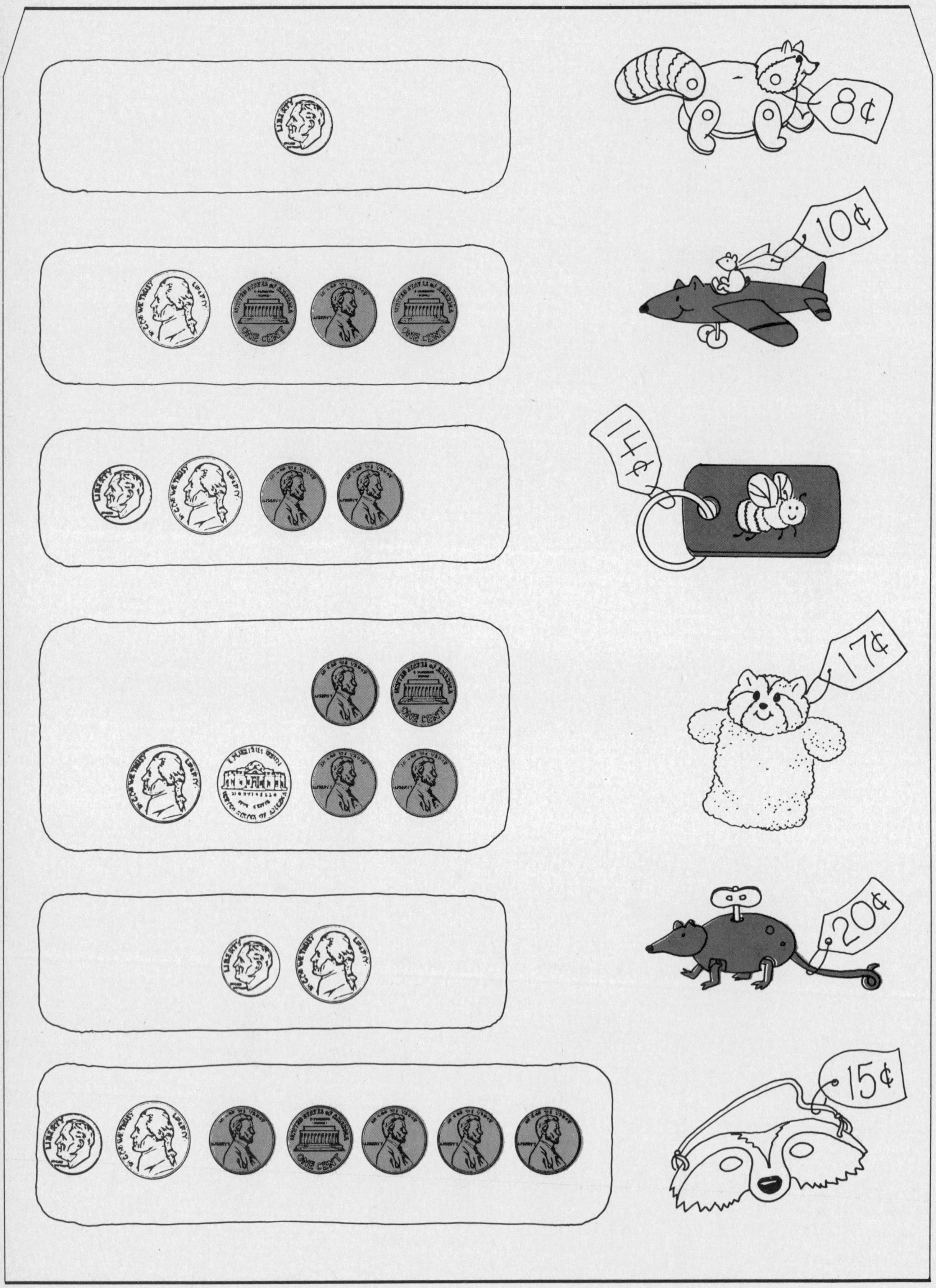

Draw a line from the set of coins to the object they can buy.

Name ______________________________

1 2 5

6 10

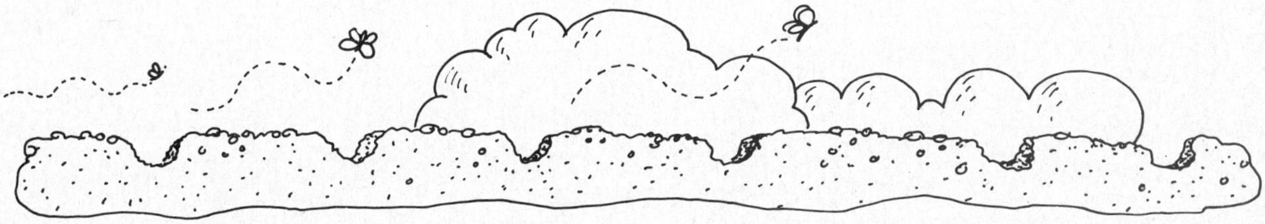

11 15

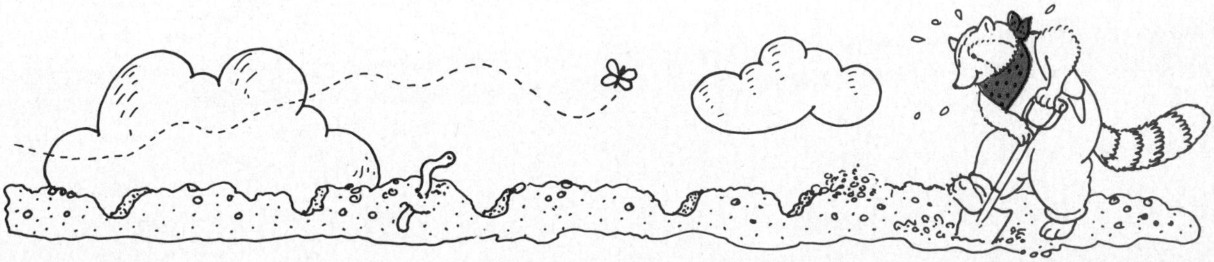

16 20

Write the numbers 1 through 20 in order.

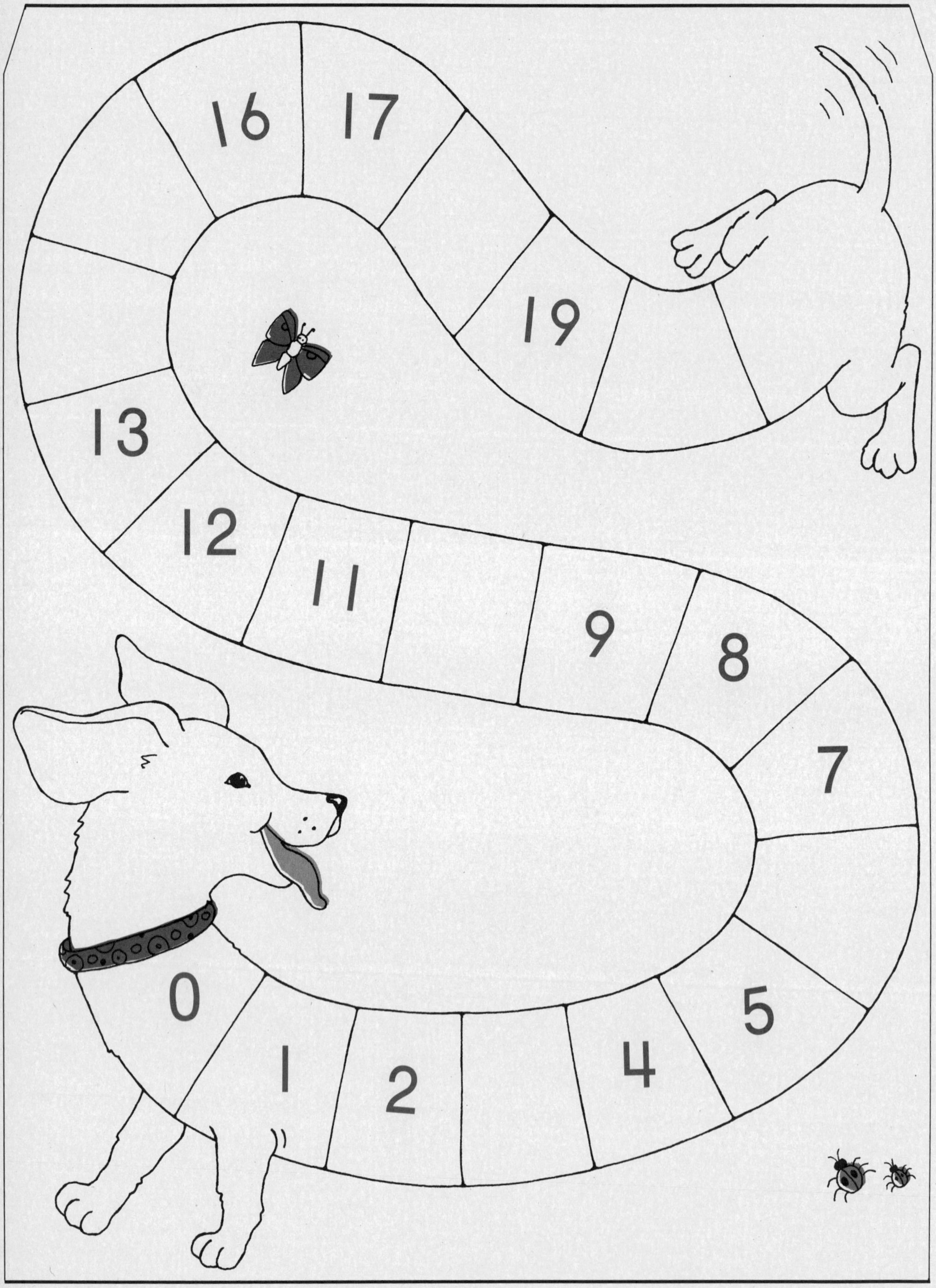

Write the missing numbers to count from 0 through 20.

Name ______________________________

12 13 14 15

13 14 15 16

17 18 19 20

17 18 19 20

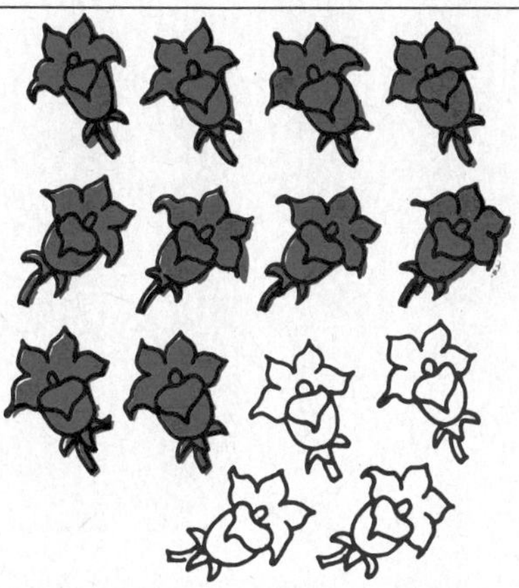

______

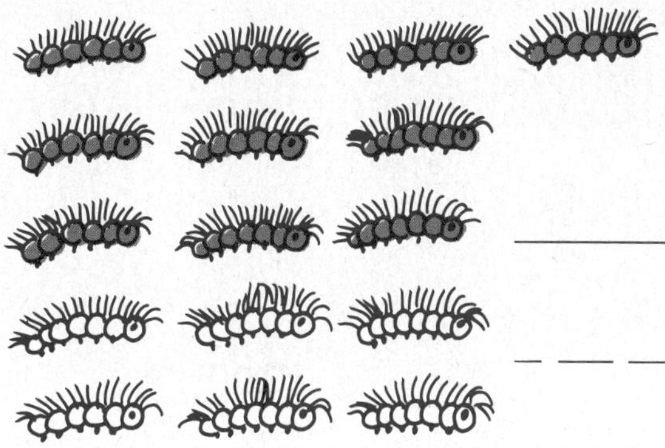

______

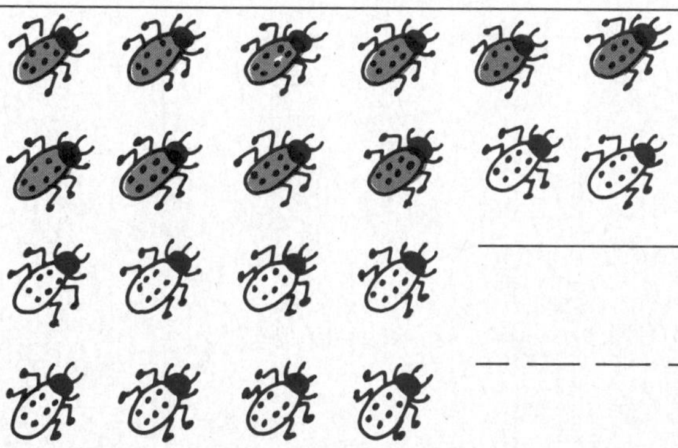

______

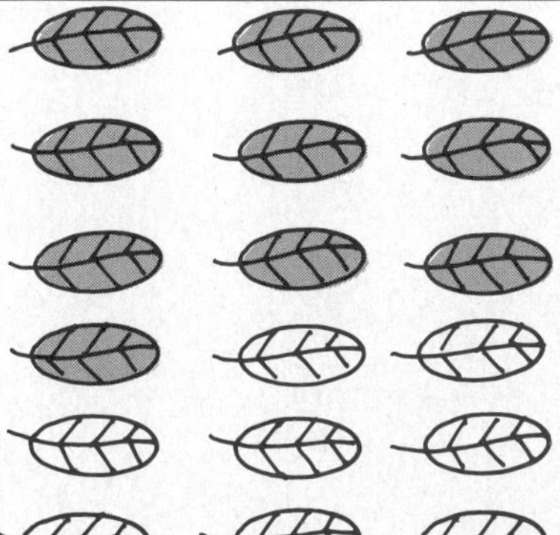

______

Chapter Checkup Circle the number that tells how many objects in each set. Count the objects in each set and write the number.

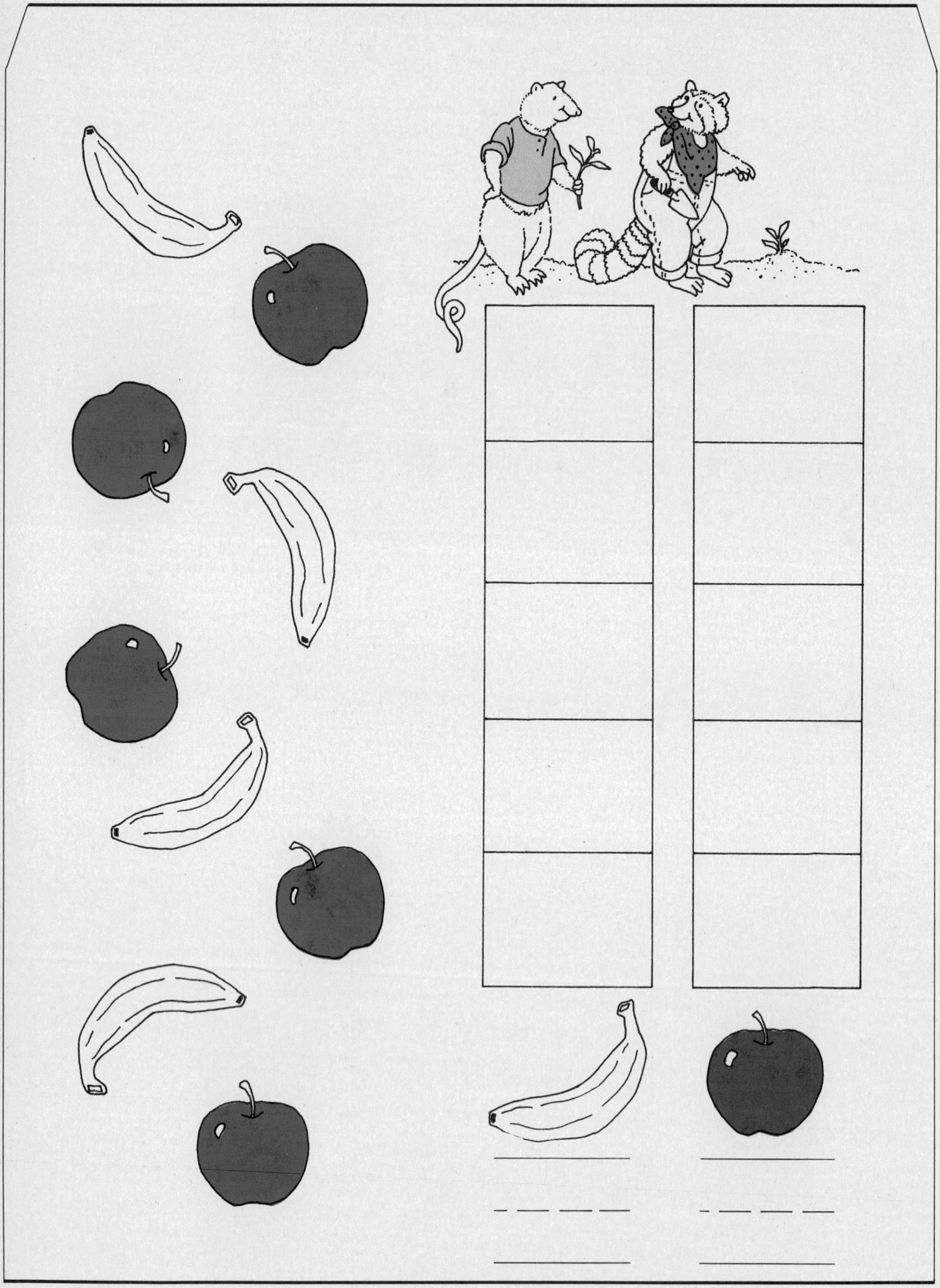

Field Trip Count the number of each kind of fruit; write that number and color that many boxes.

Name ______________________________

7 ORDER AND PLACE VALUE

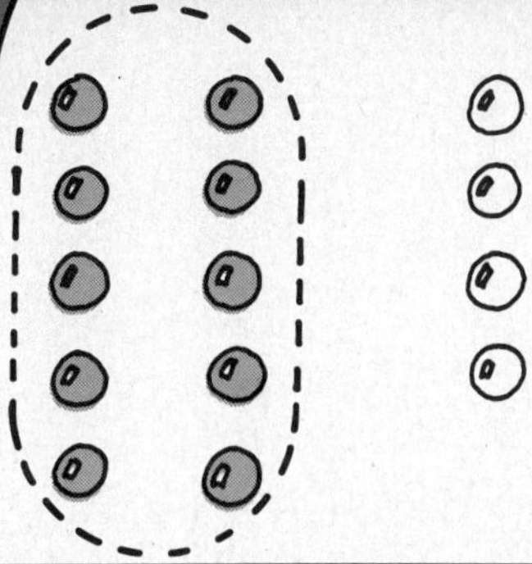

14

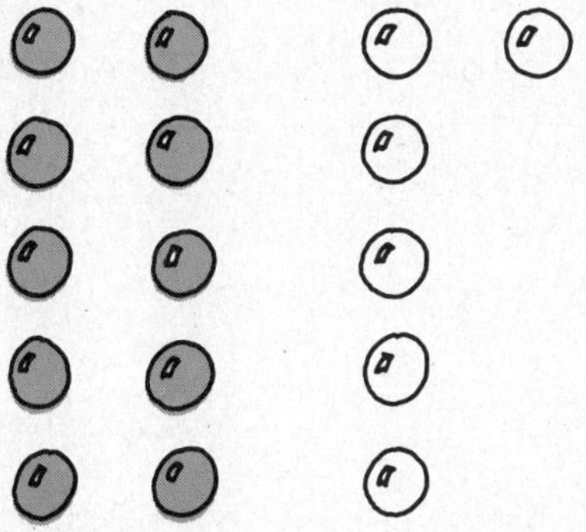

______

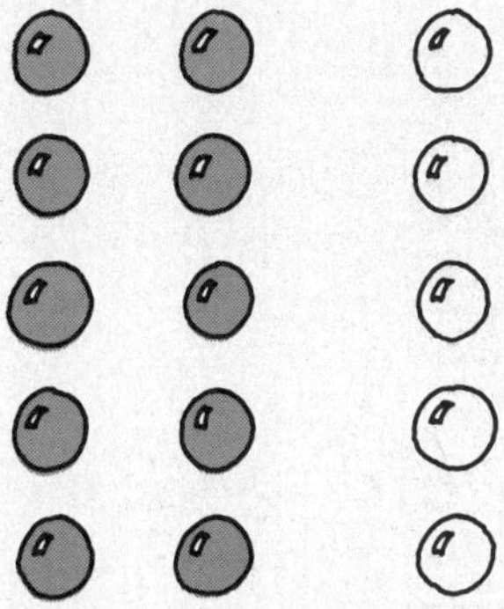

______

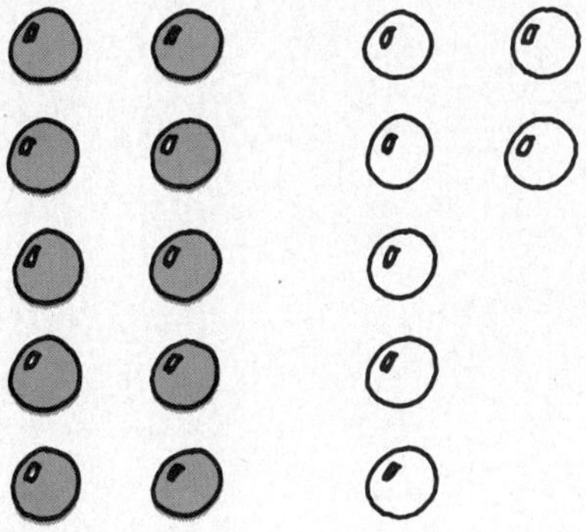

______

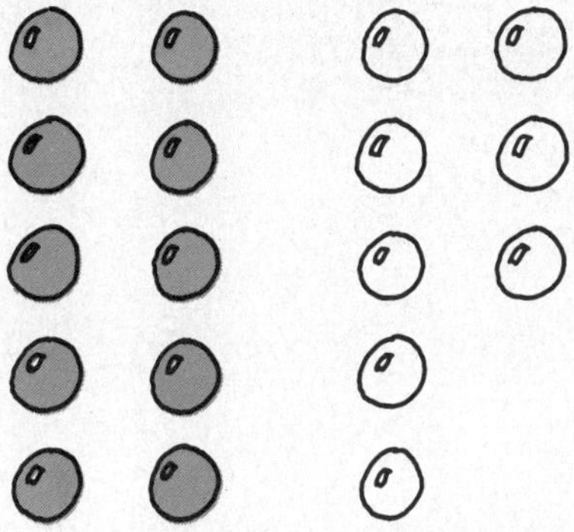

______

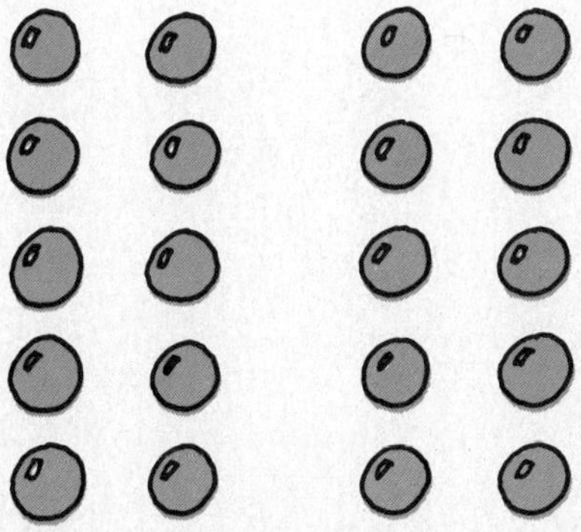

______

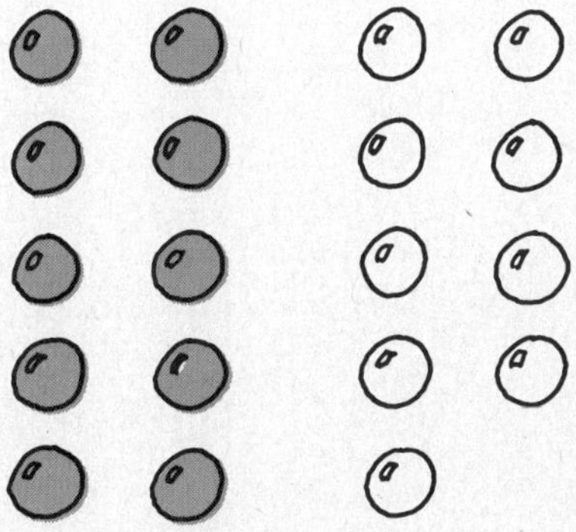

______

Circle each set of 10. Write the total number of objects in each set.

Connect the dots in order from 0 through 20.

Name ______________________________

6

8

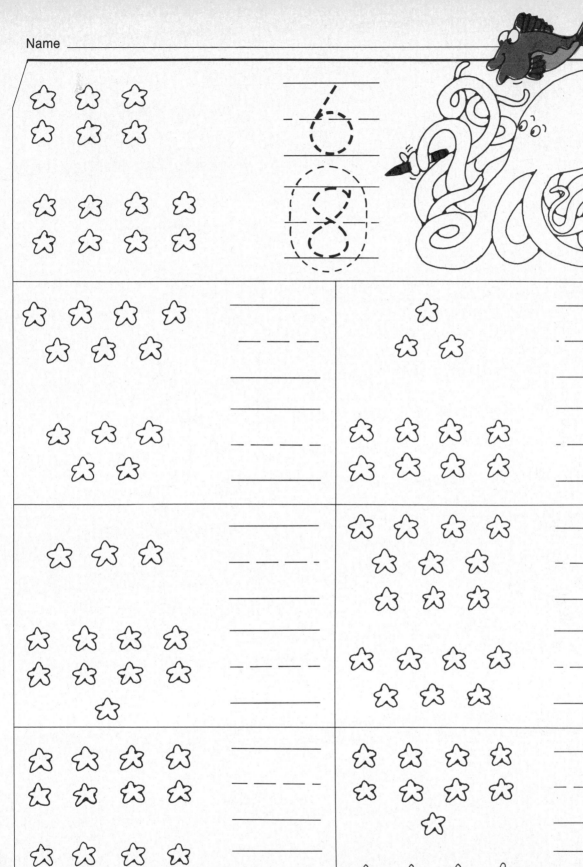

Count the objects in each set and write the number.
Circle the greater number.

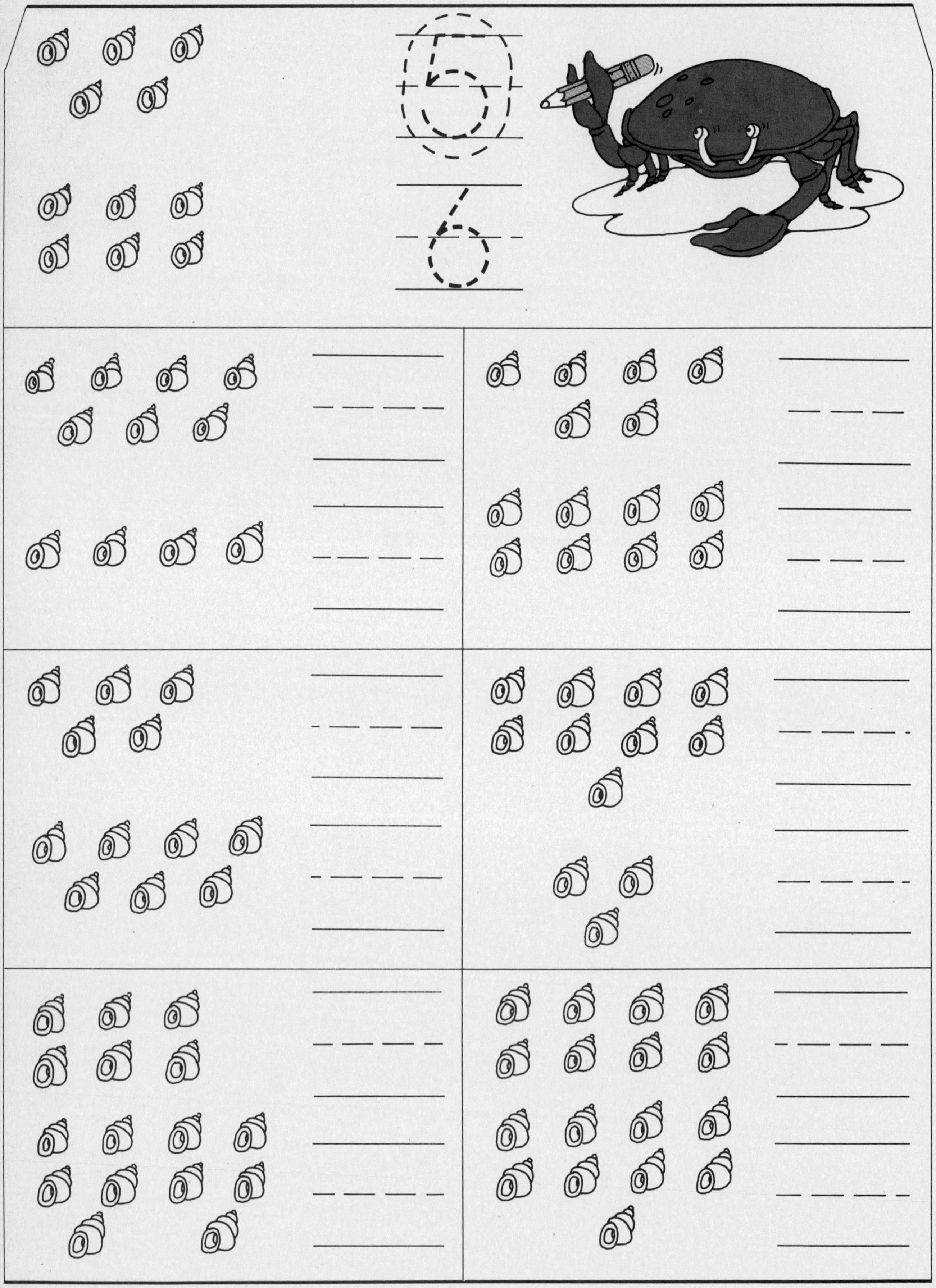

Count the objects in each set and write the number.
Circle the lesser number.

Name ______________________________

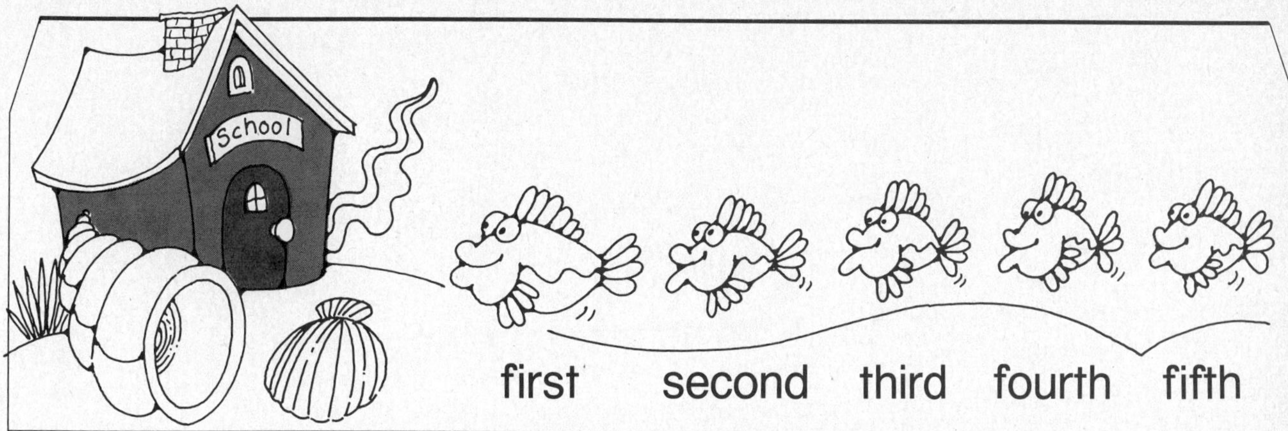

first second third fourth fifth

second

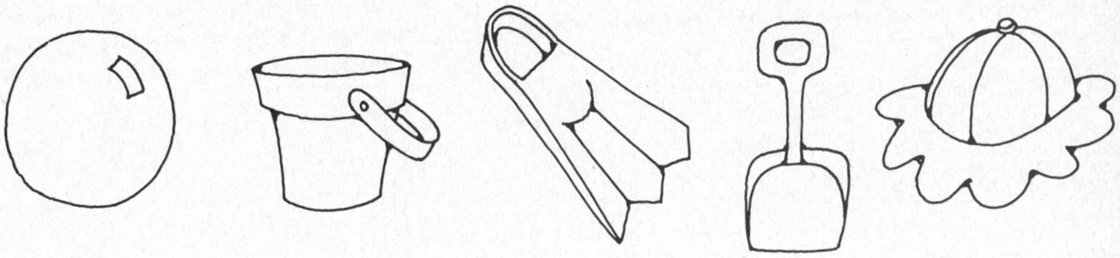

first

fourth

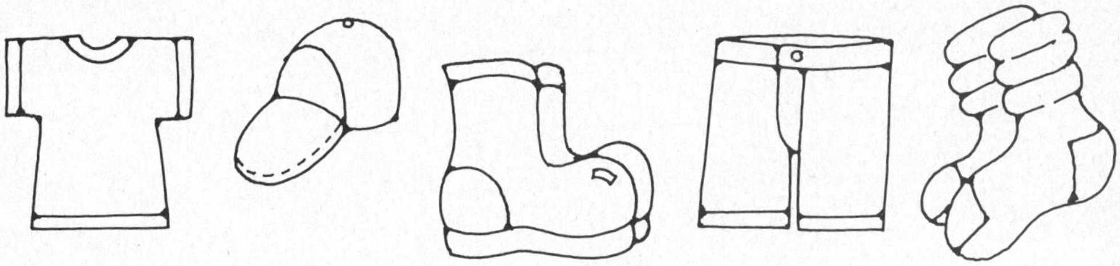

fifth

third

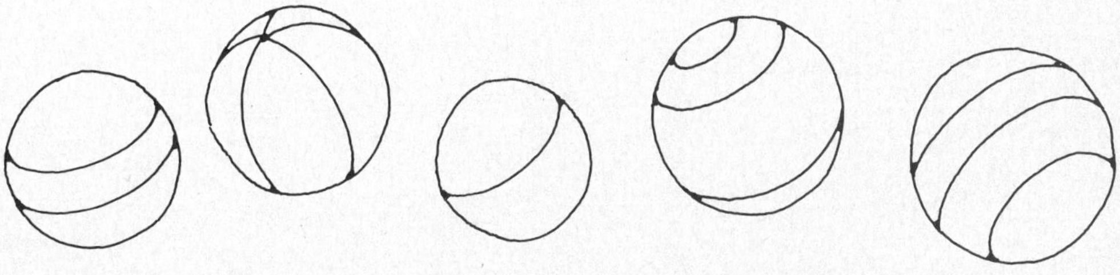

Circle the object in the position named by the ordinal number.

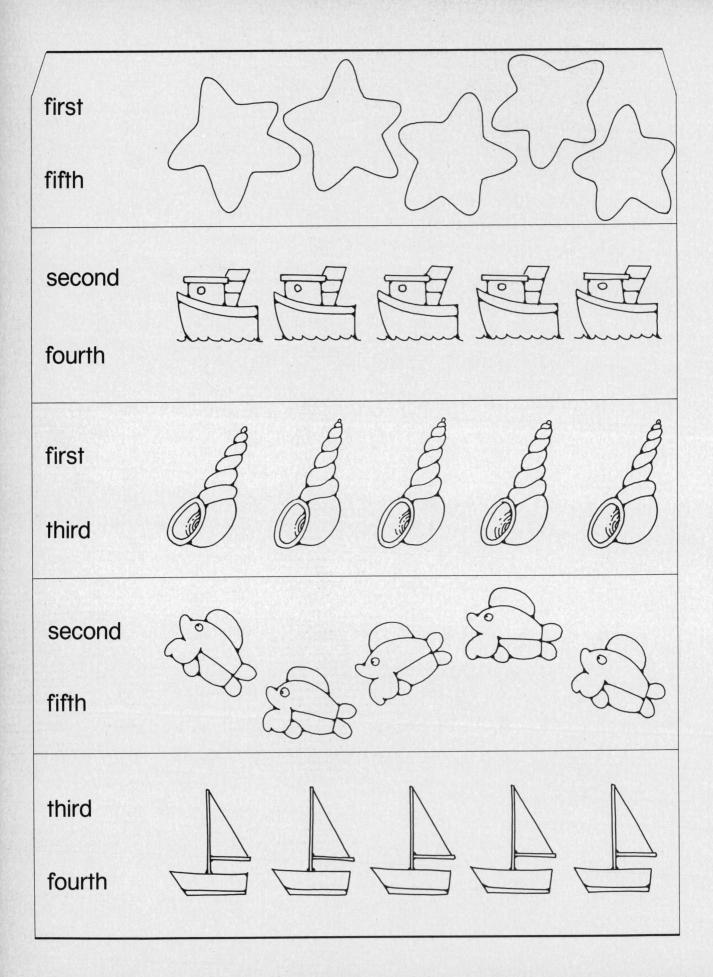

first

fifth

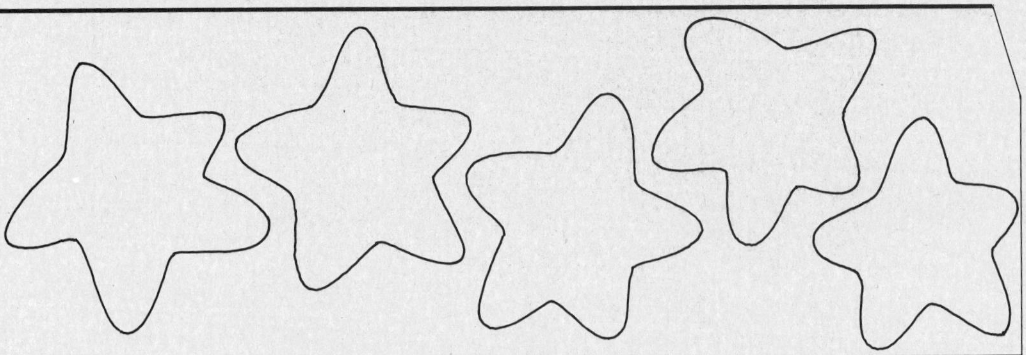

second

fourth

first

third

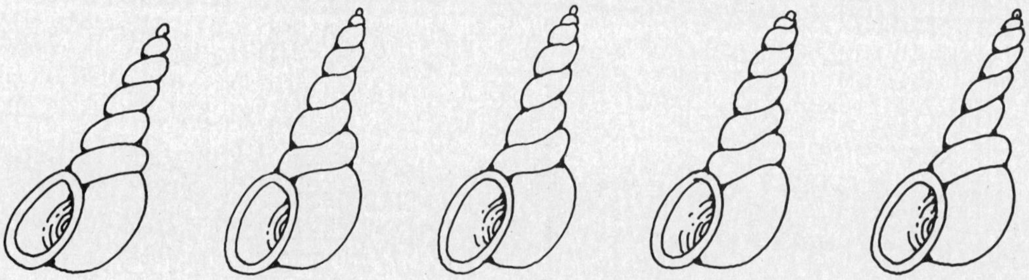

second

fifth

third

fourth

Circle the objects in the positions named by the ordinal numbers.

Name ____________________

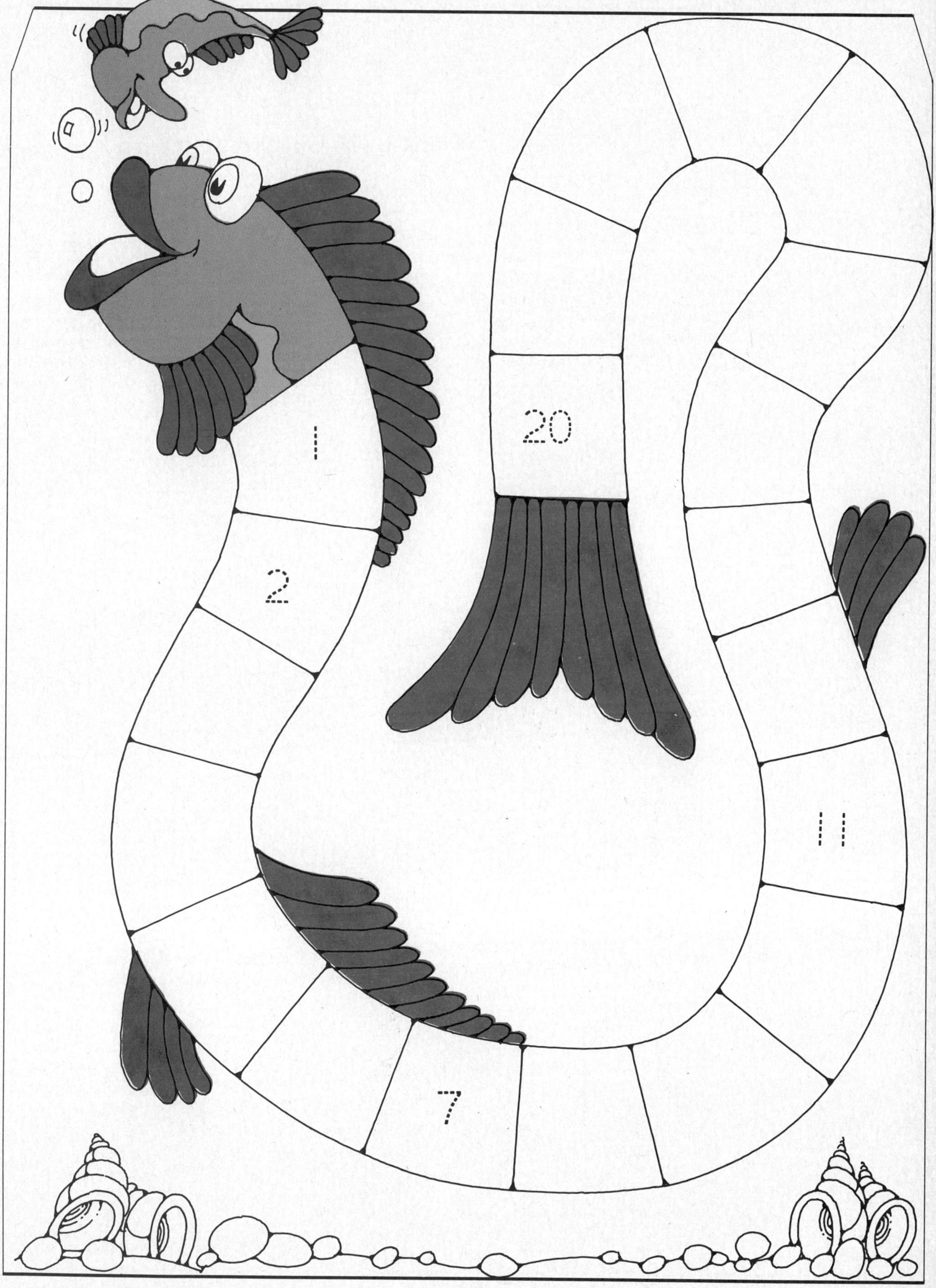

Write the numbers 1 through 20 in order.

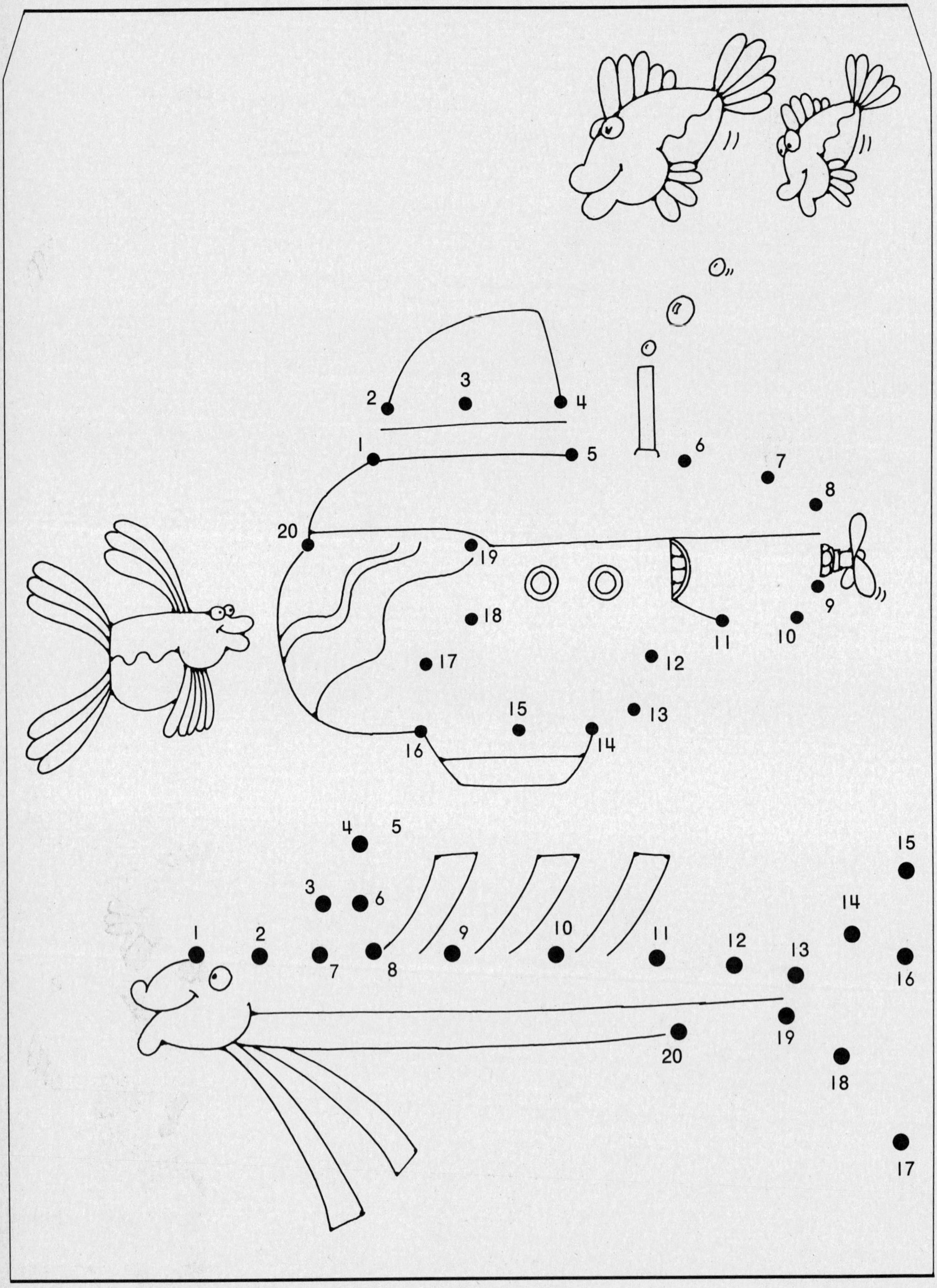

Connect the dots in order from 1 through 20 in each picture.

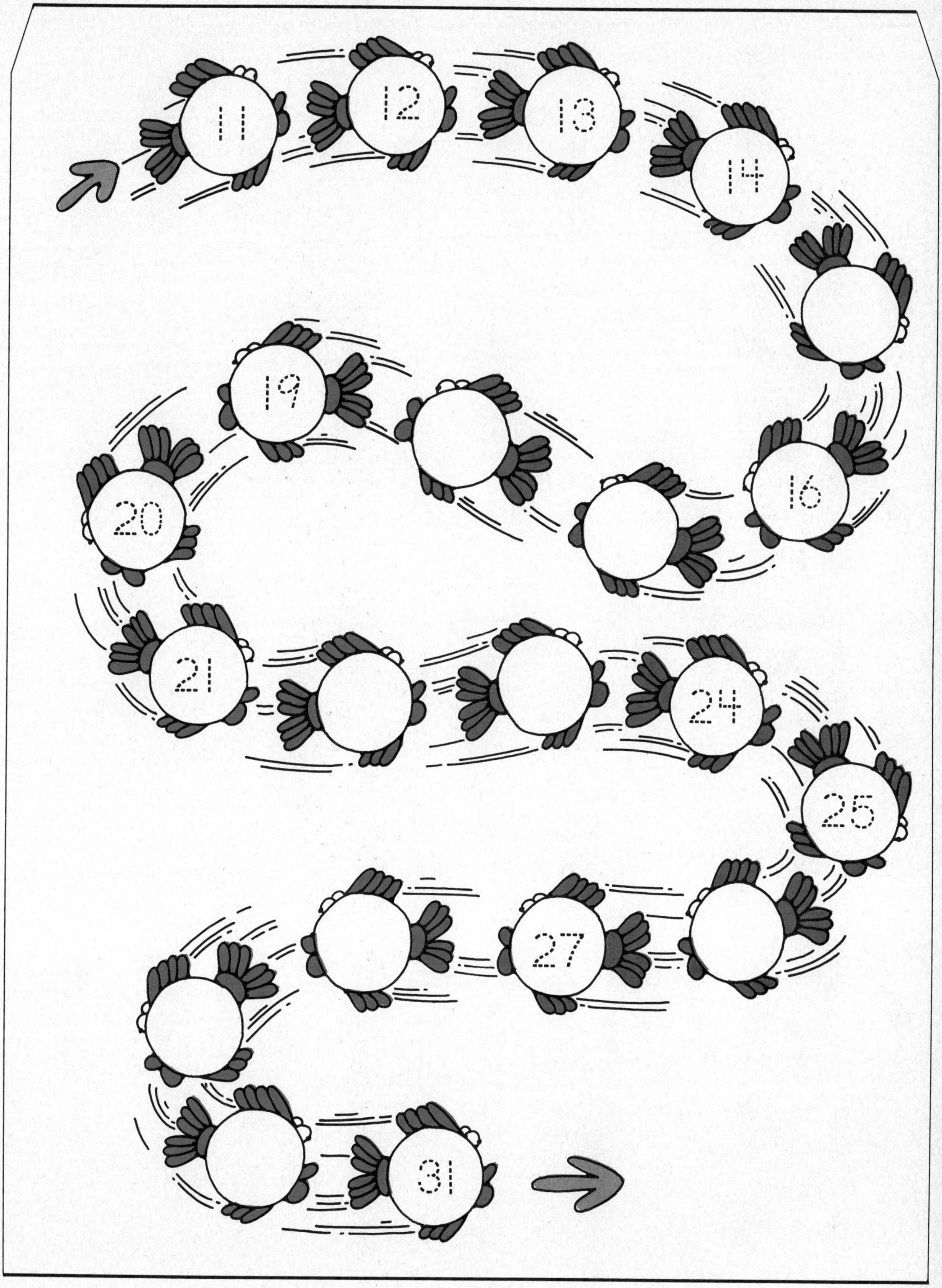

Write the numbers 11 through 31 in order.

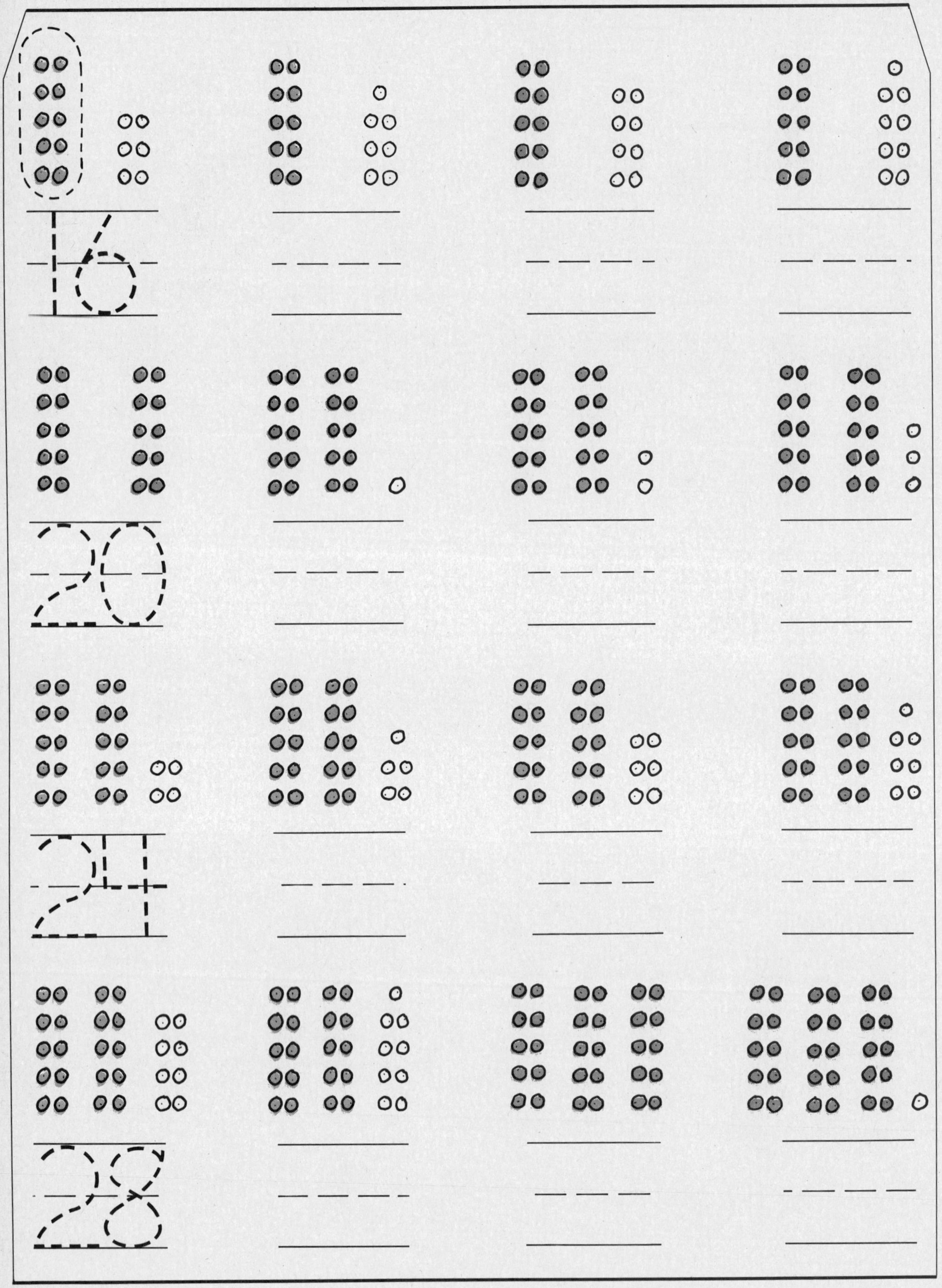

Circle each set of 10. Write the total number of objects in each set.

Name ______________________________

Sunday	Monday	Tuesday	Wednesday	Thursday	Friday	Saturday
		1	2	3	4	5
6	7	8	9	10	11	12
13	14	15	16	17	18	19
20	21	22	23	24	25	26
27	28	29	30	31		

Use the vocabulary **calendar, month, week** and **day,** and the names for each day of the week. Associate the days of the month with their dates, 1 through 31.

Sunday	Monday	Tuesday	Wednesday	Thursday	Friday	Saturday

Sunday ☐ Monday ☐ Tuesday ☐

Wednesday ☐ Thursday ☐ Friday ☐

Saturday ☐

Write the numbers 1 through 31 on the calendar. Count the number of times each day occurs that month and write the number.

Name ______________________________

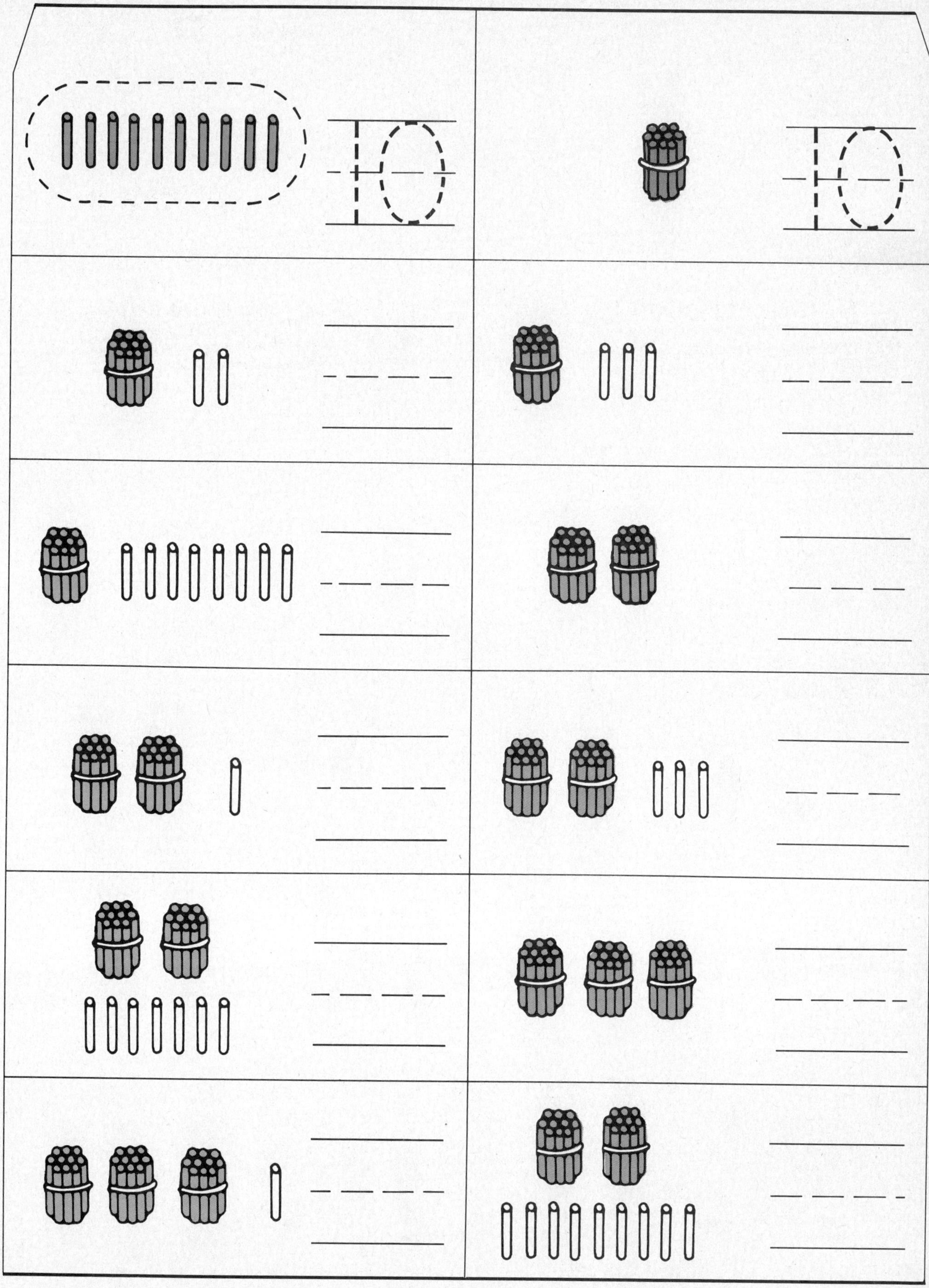

Write the number that tells how many.

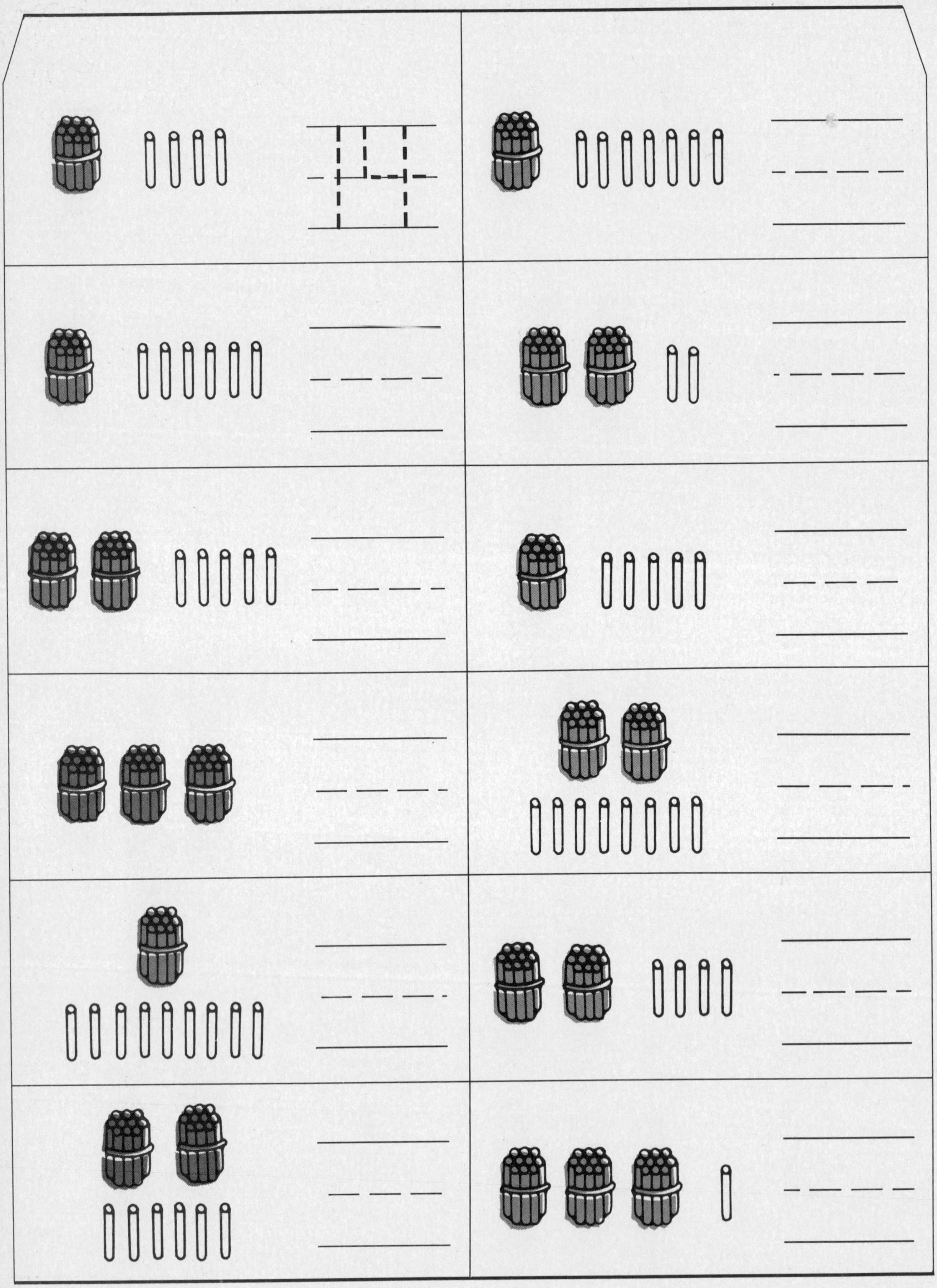

Write the number that tells how many.

Name ______________________

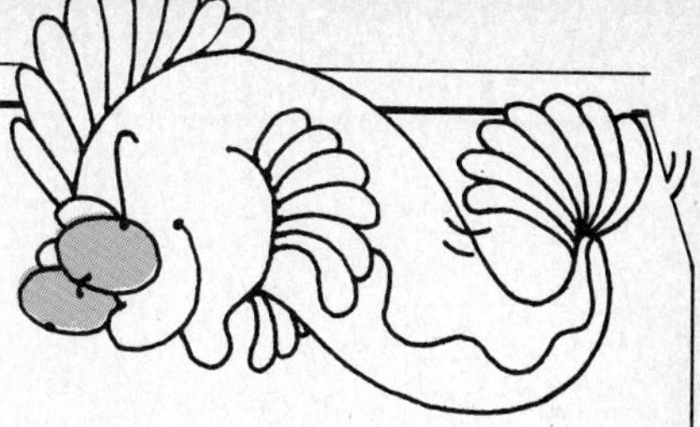

7	8			11	
13		15			18
19			22		24
25		27			30

Write the missing counting numbers in each number line.

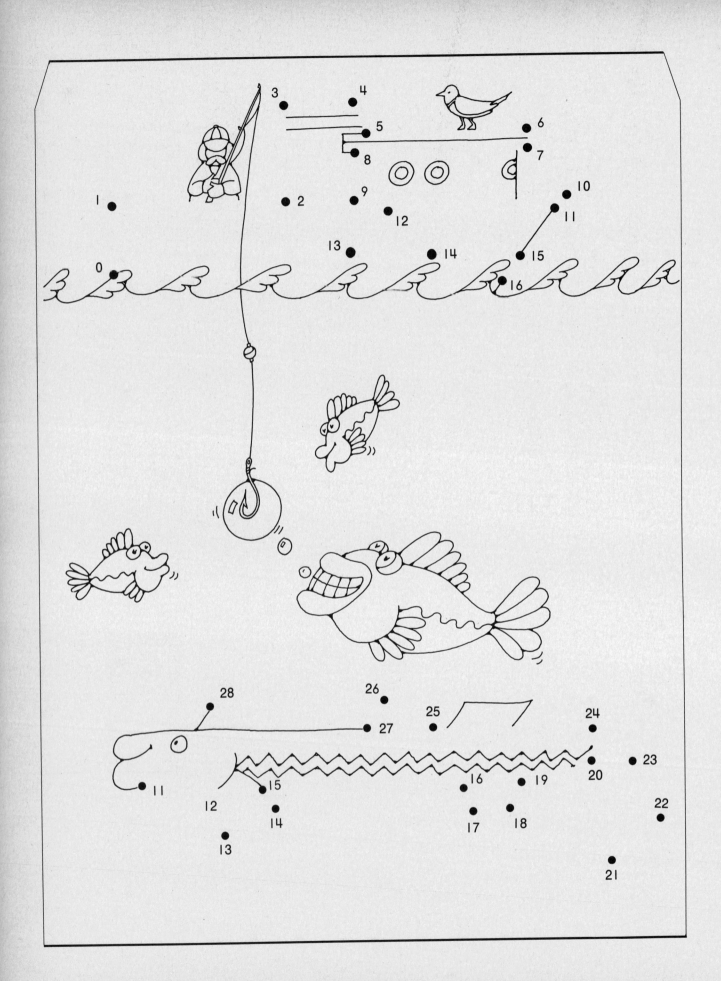

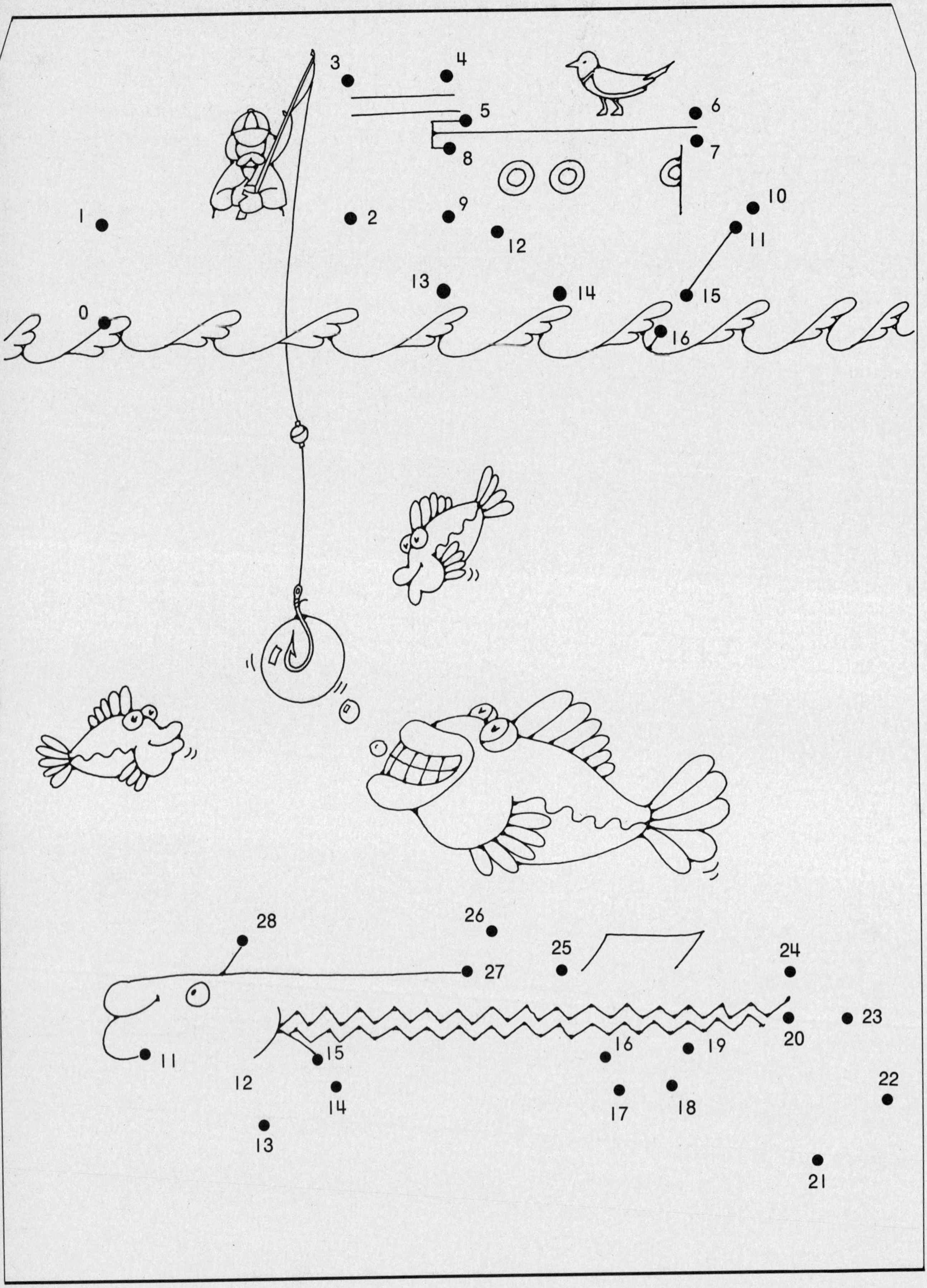

Connect the dots in order from 0 through 16 and from 11 through 28.

Name ______________________________

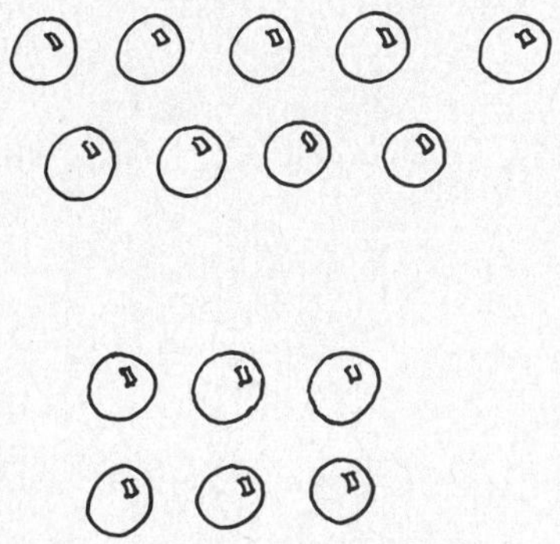

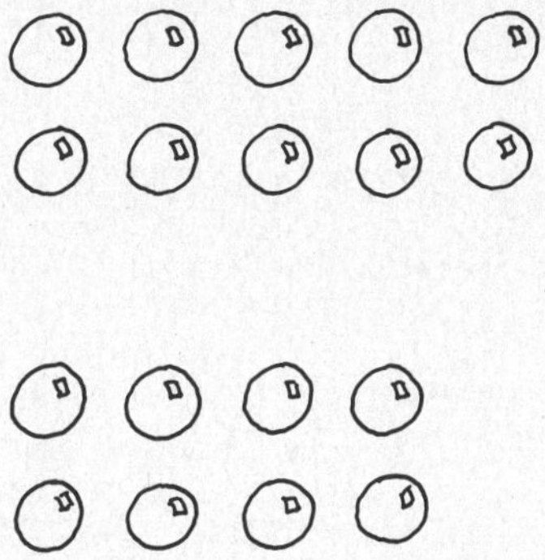

second

fifth

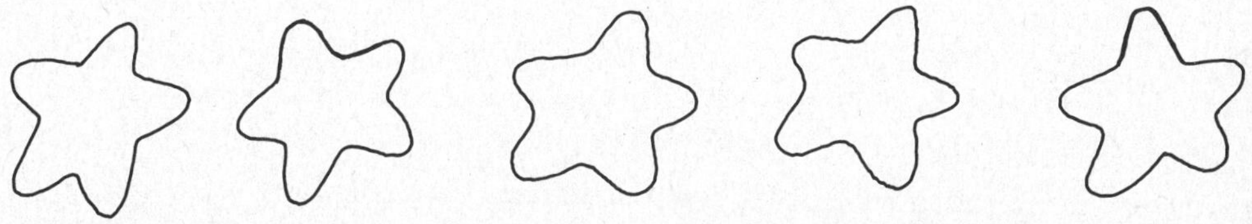

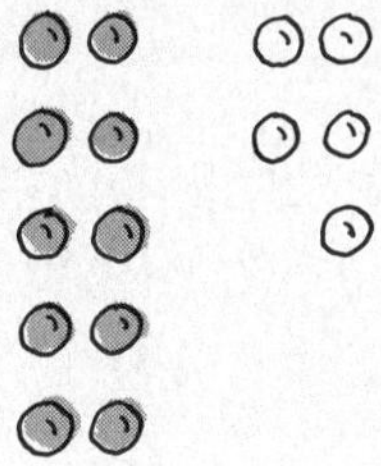

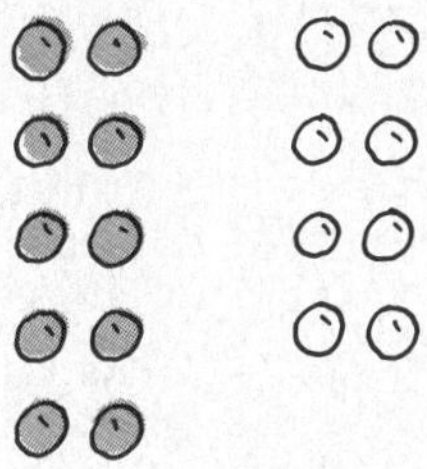

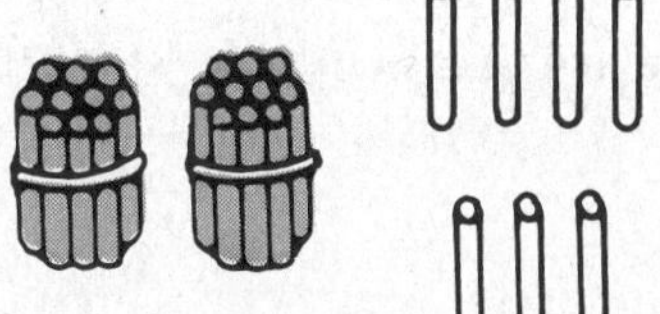

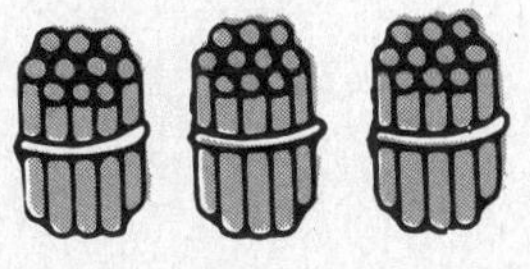

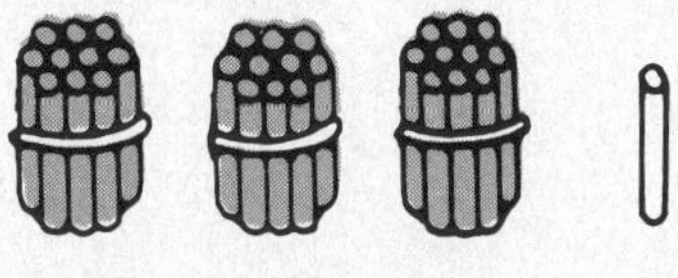

Chapter Checkup Count the objects in each set and write the number.
Circle the number that is less and the number that is greater.
Circle the object in the position named by the ordinal number.
Write the number that tells how many.

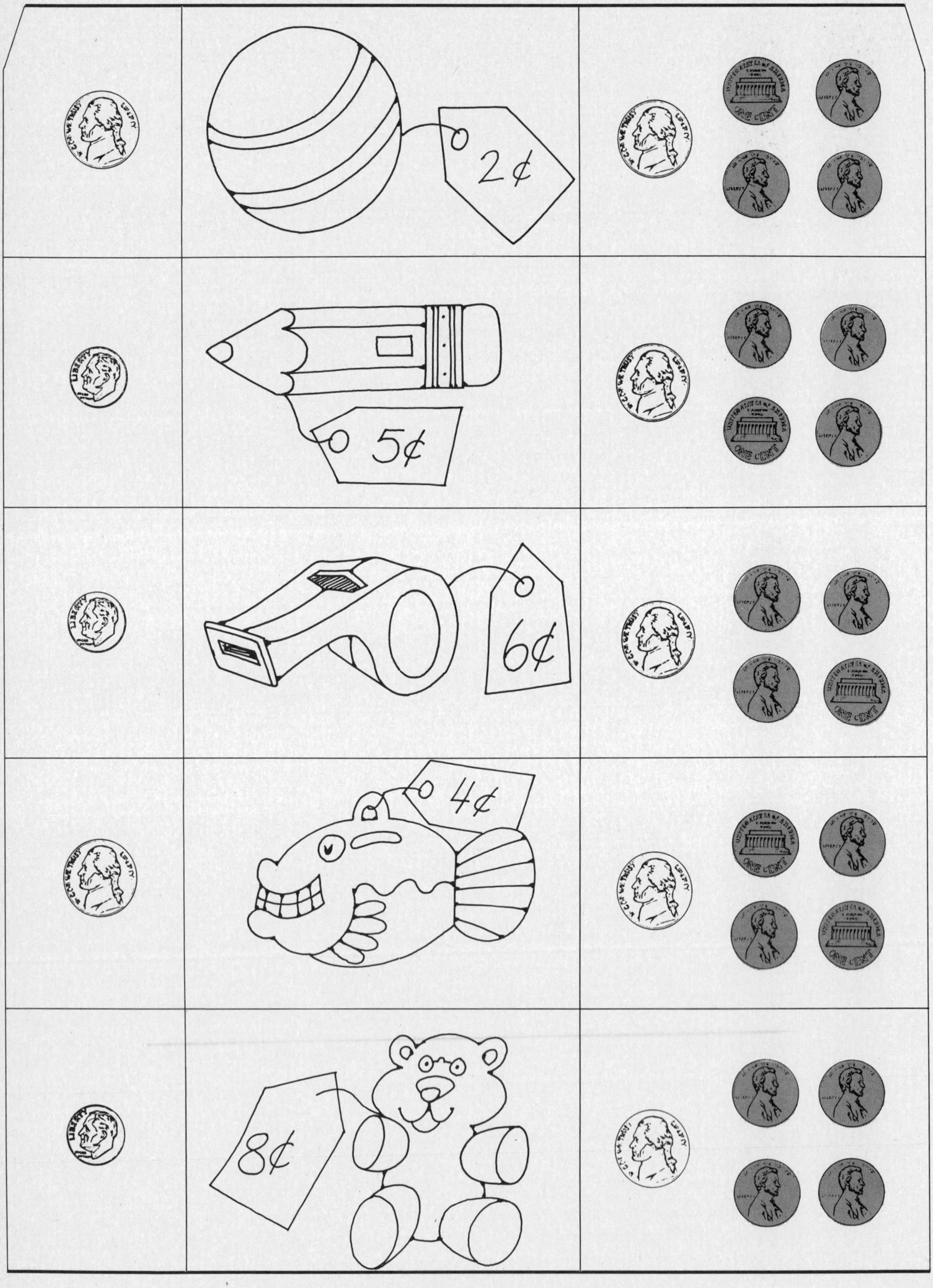

Field Trip Use the first coin to buy the object. Circle the coins you get back for change.

Name ______________________

8 FRACTIONS AND MEASUREMENT

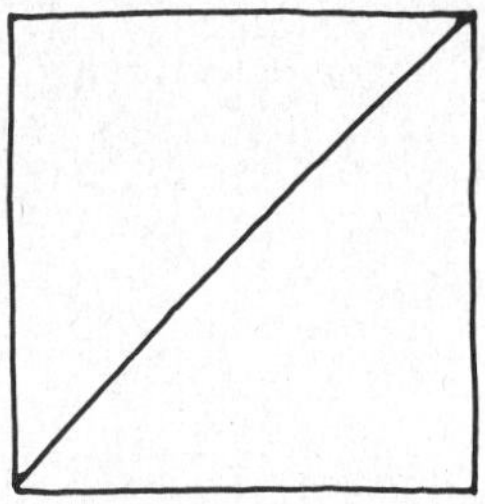

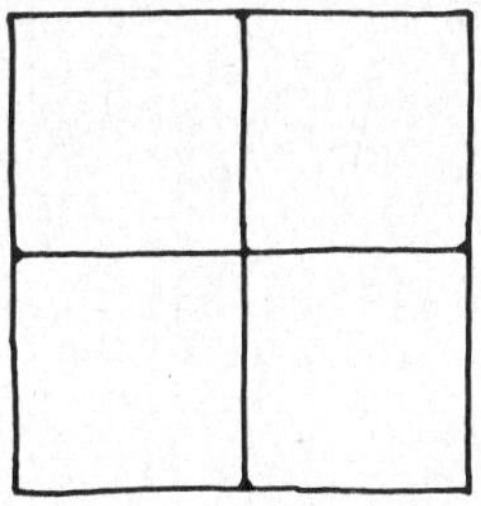

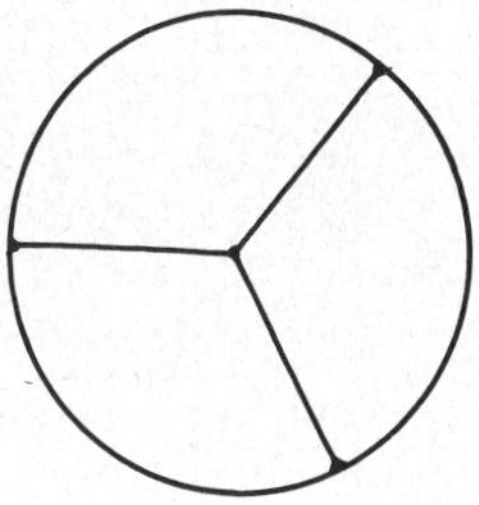

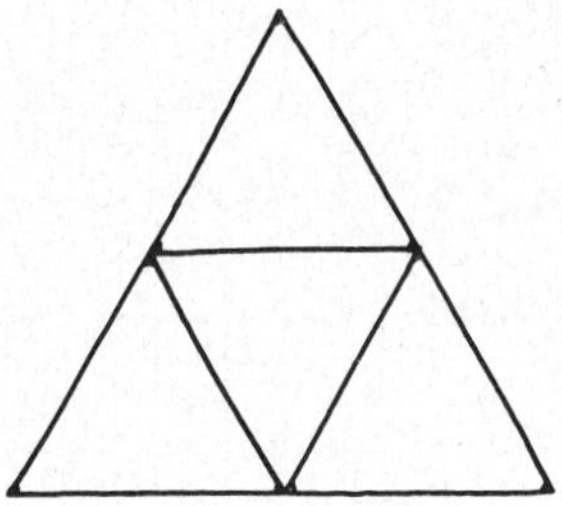

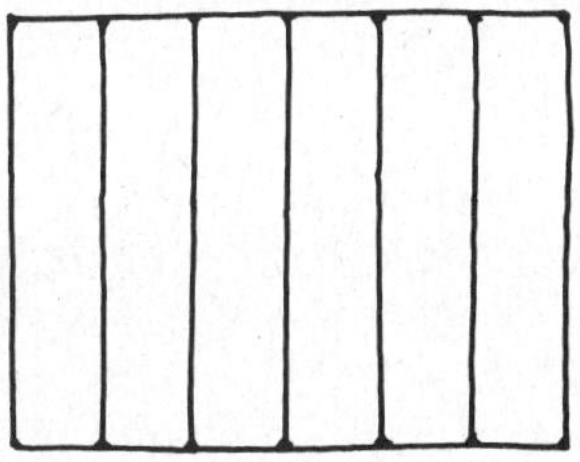

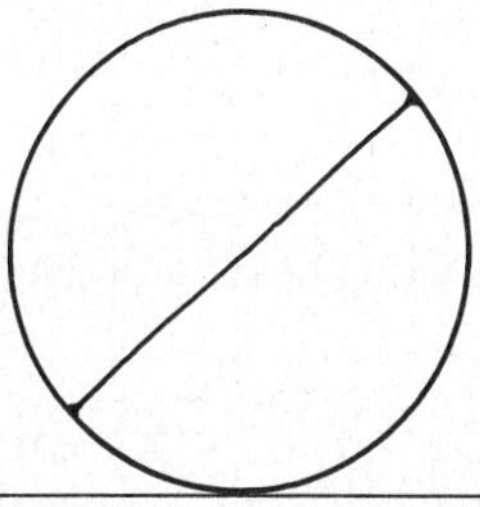

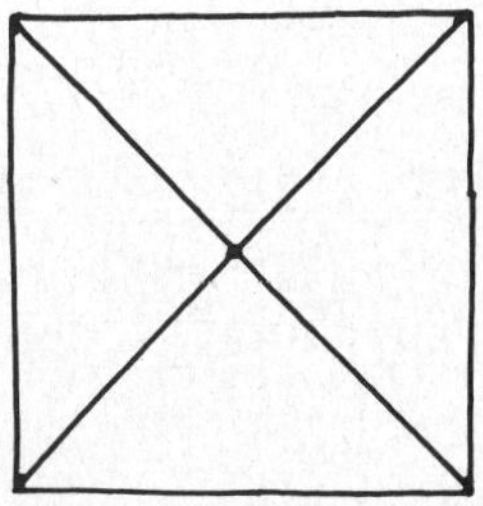

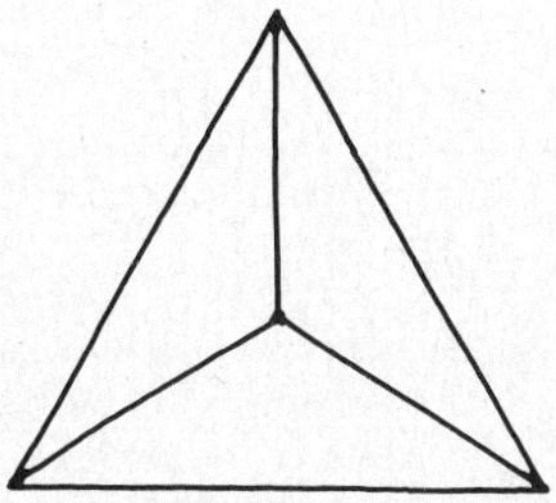

Write the number of equal parts.

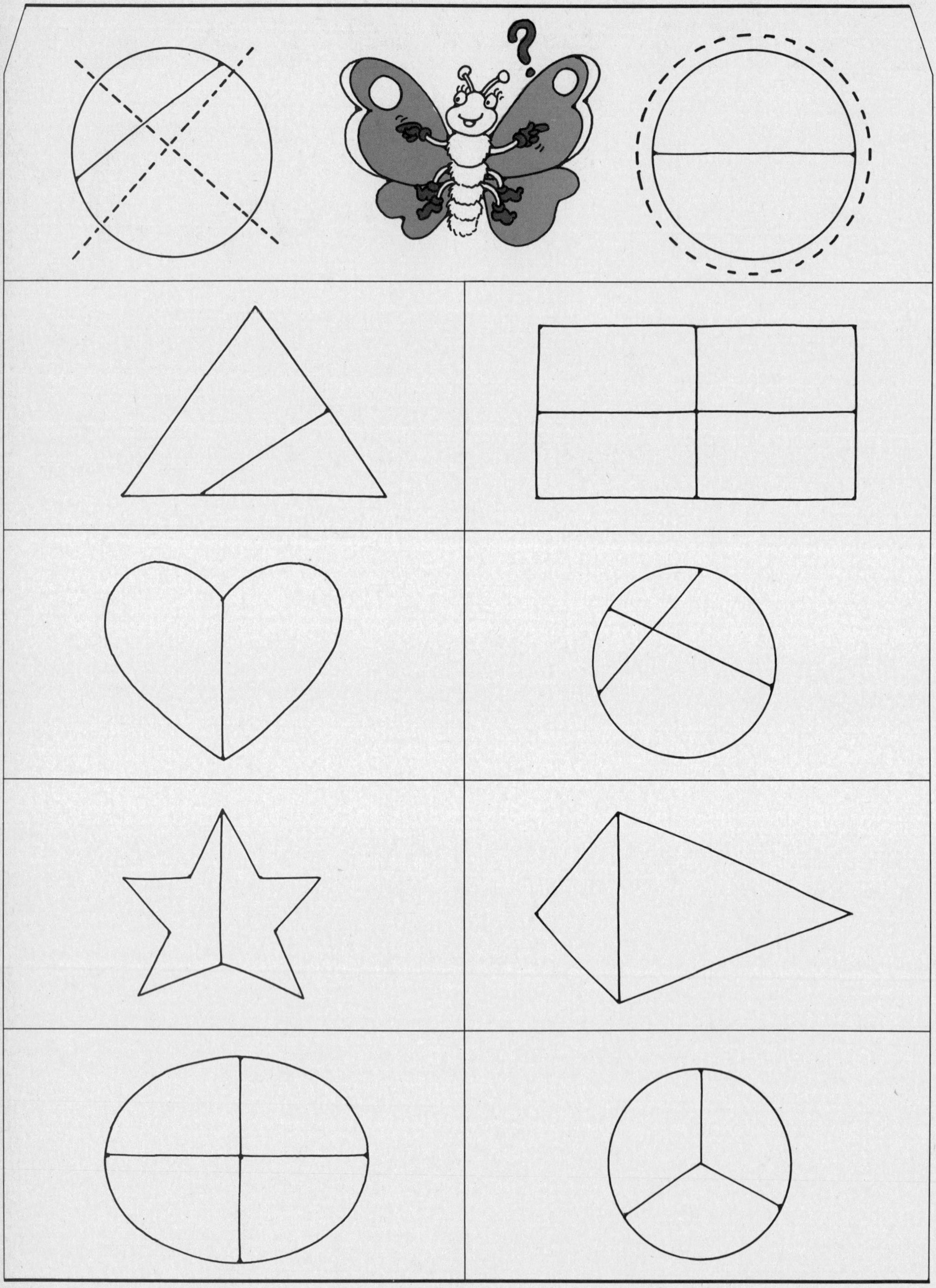

Circle the figure with equal parts. Put an X on the figure that does not have equal parts.

Name ______________________________

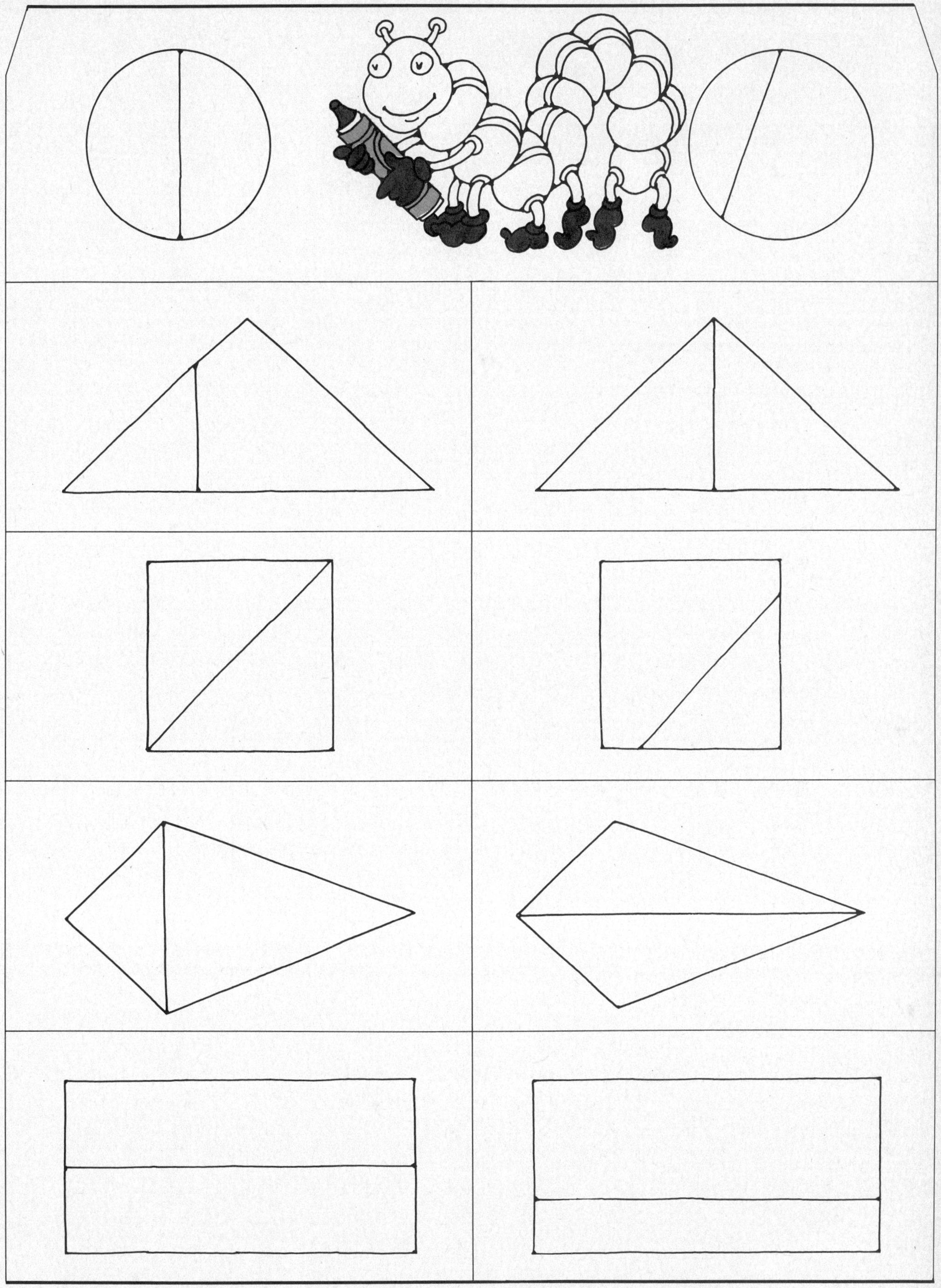

Circle each figure that is cut into equal halves. Put an X on any that do not show two equal halves.

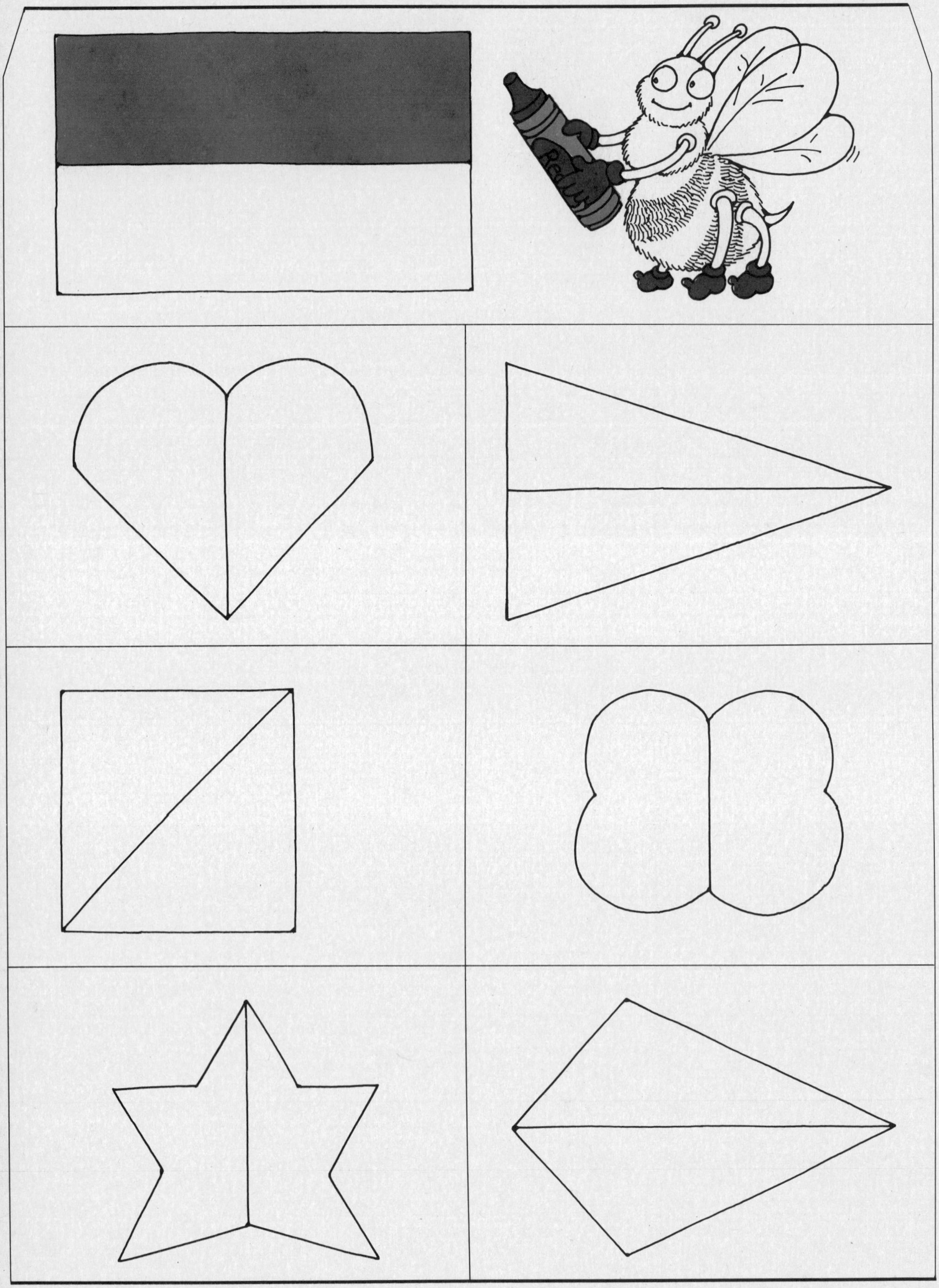

Color one half of each figure.

Name ______________________________

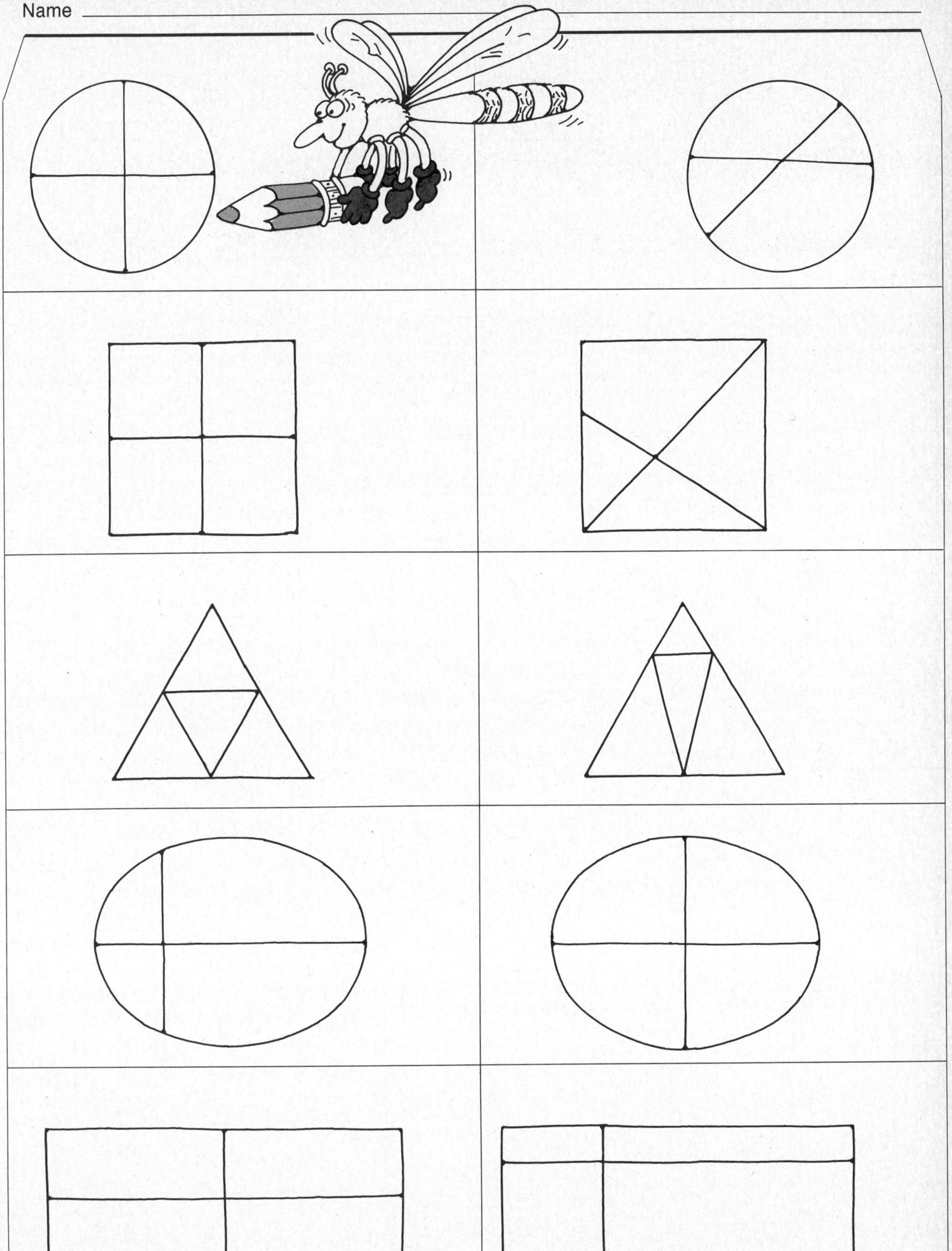

Circle each figure that is divided into 4 equal parts. Put an X through any figure divided into 4 unequal parts.

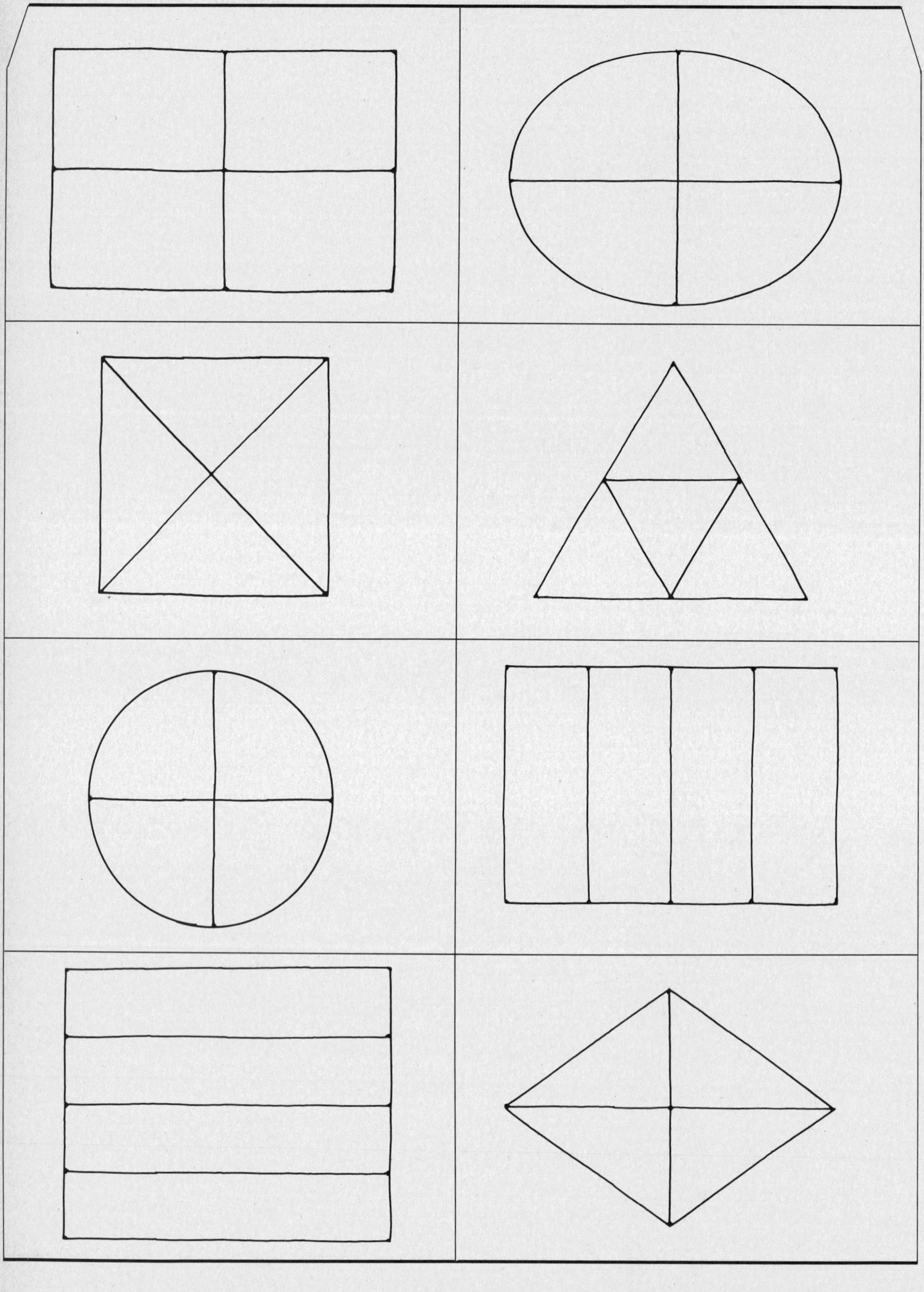

Color one fourth of each figure.

Name ______________________________

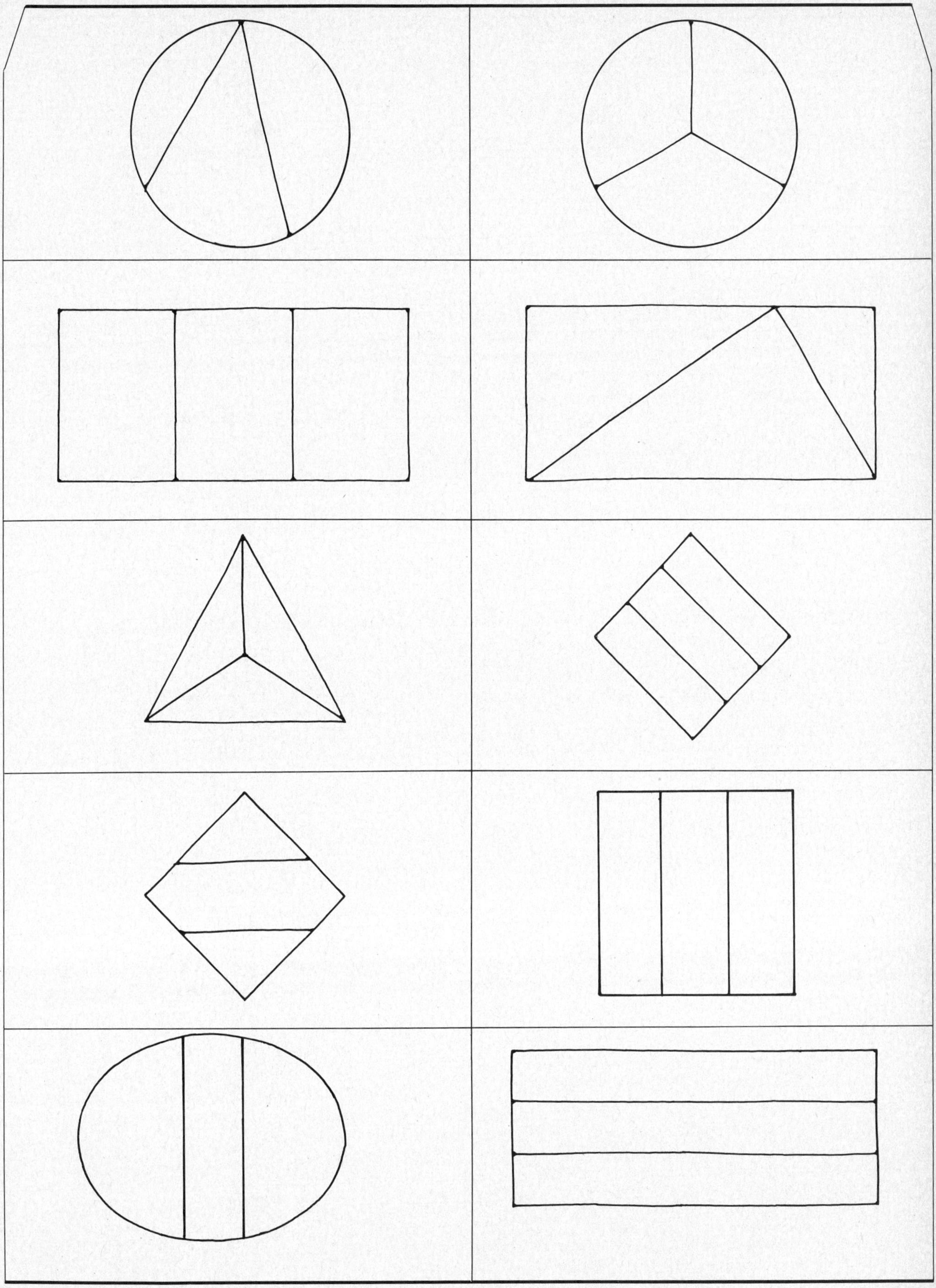

Circle each figure that is divided into 3 equal parts. Put an X through any figure that is divided into 3 unequal parts.

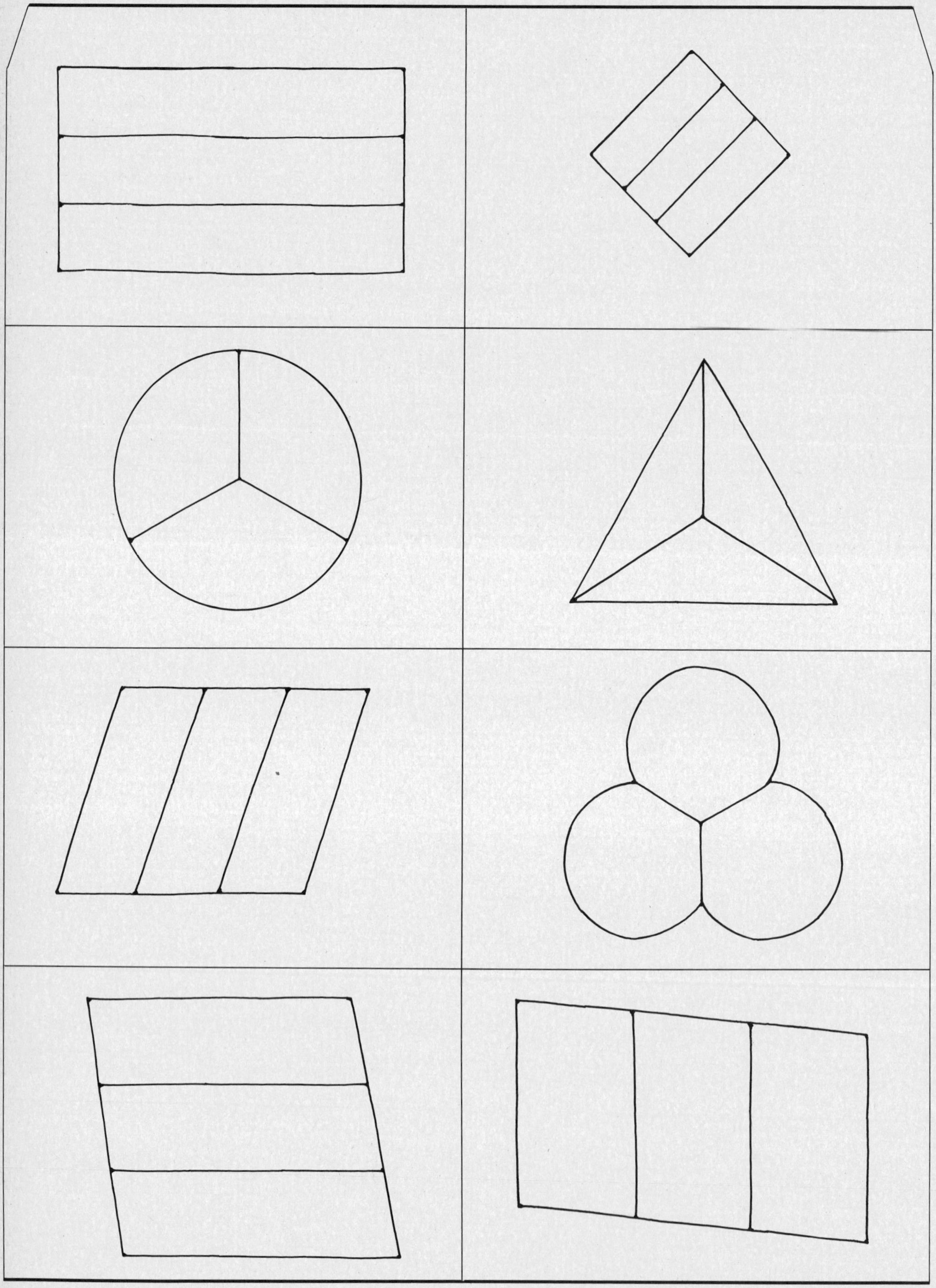

Color one third of each figure.

Name ______________________________

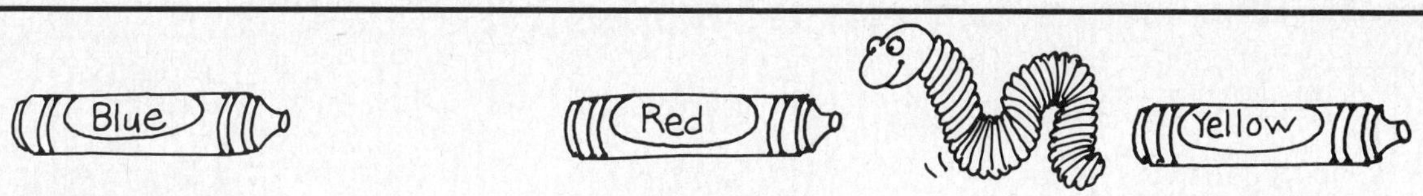

one half | one third | one fourth

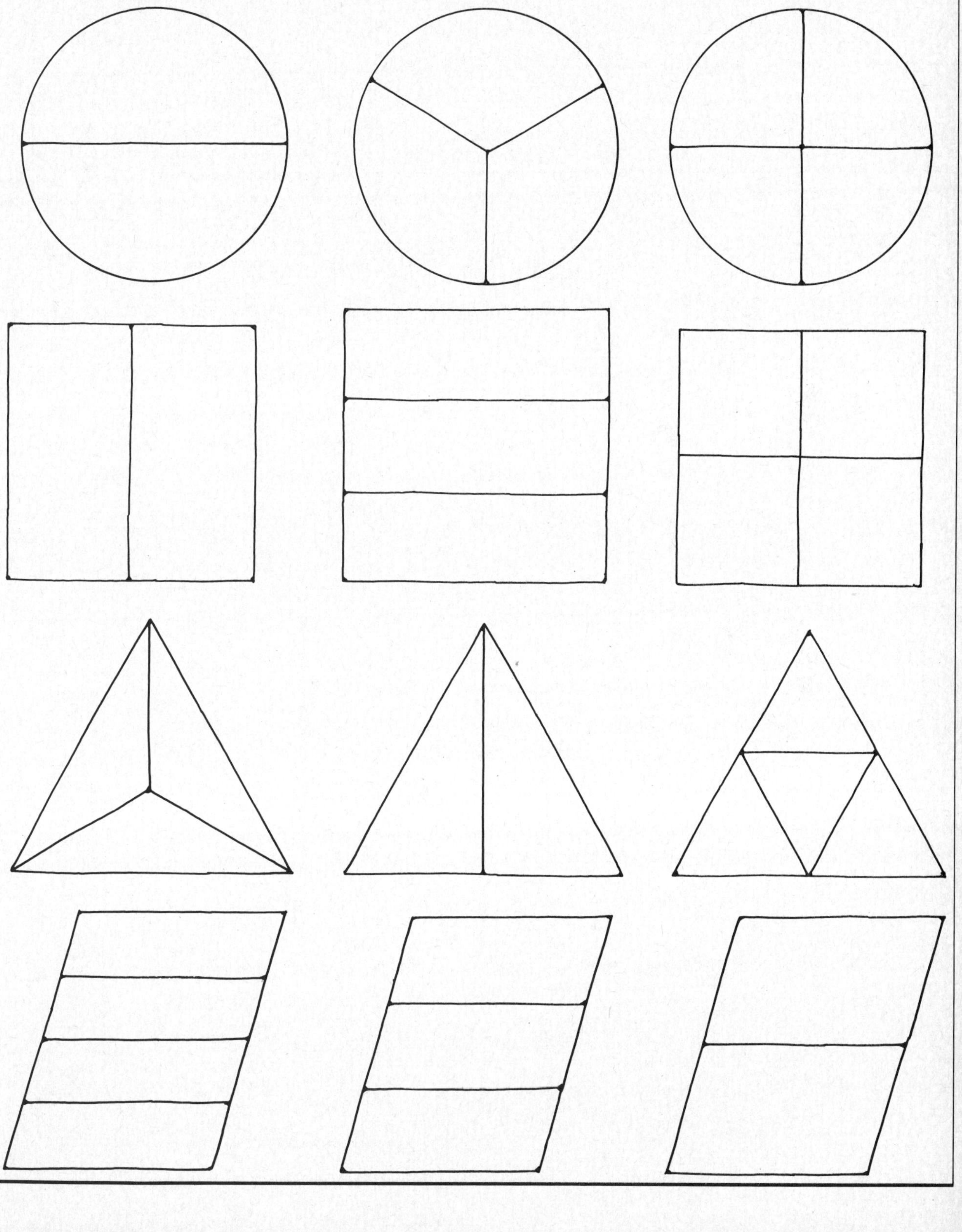

Name one part of each figure. Match it to the color at the top of the page. Color that part.

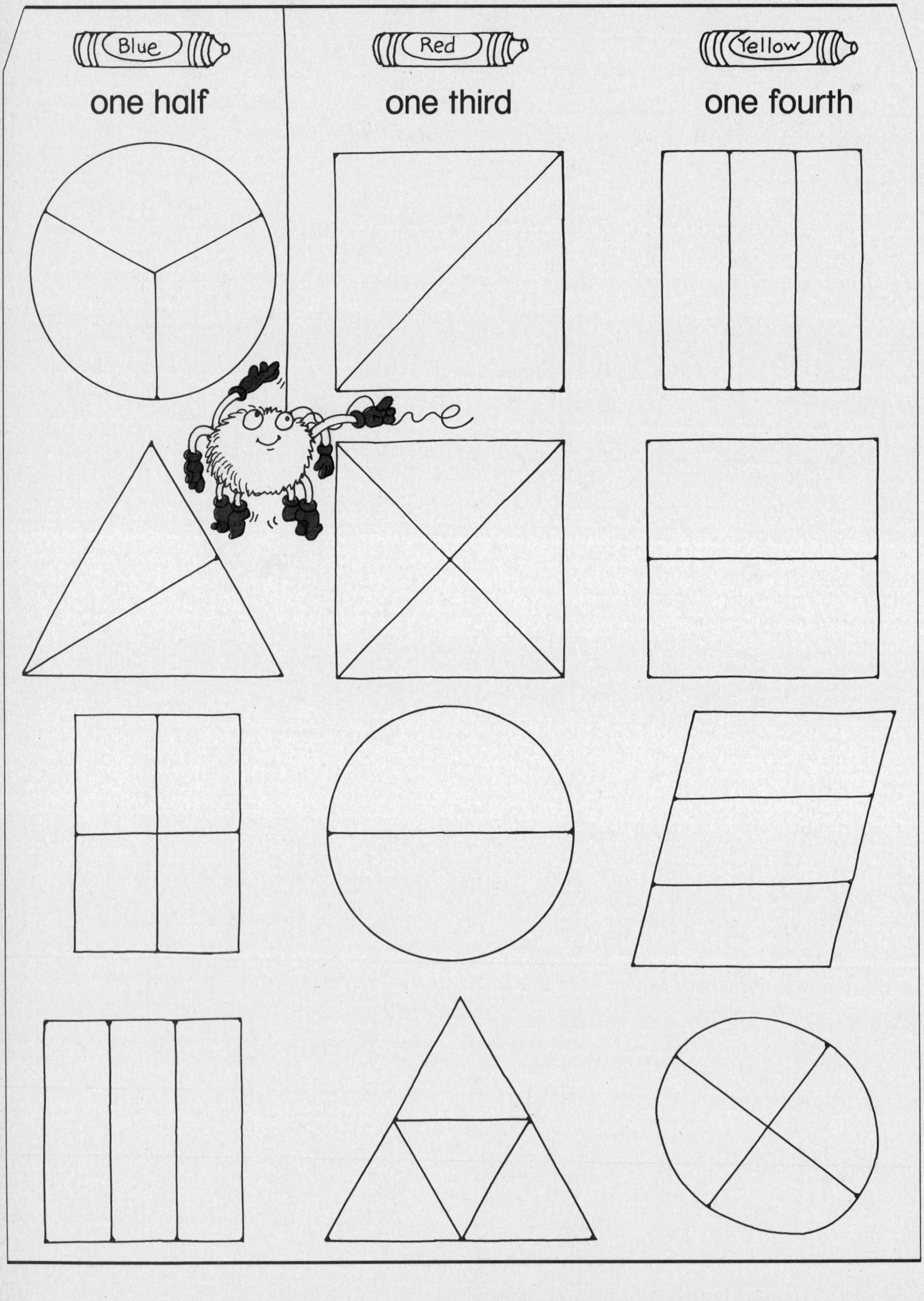

Name one part of each figure. Match it to the color at the top of the page. Color that part.

Name ______________________________

Circle the one that holds more.

Circle the one that holds less.

Name ______________________

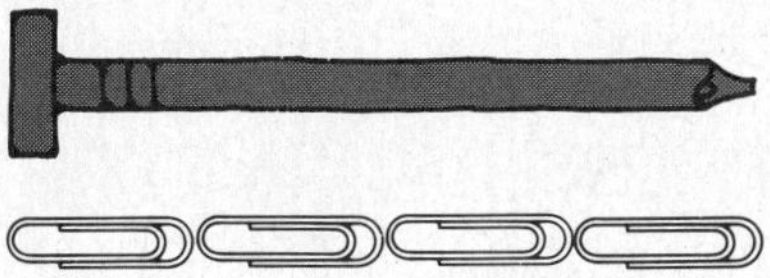

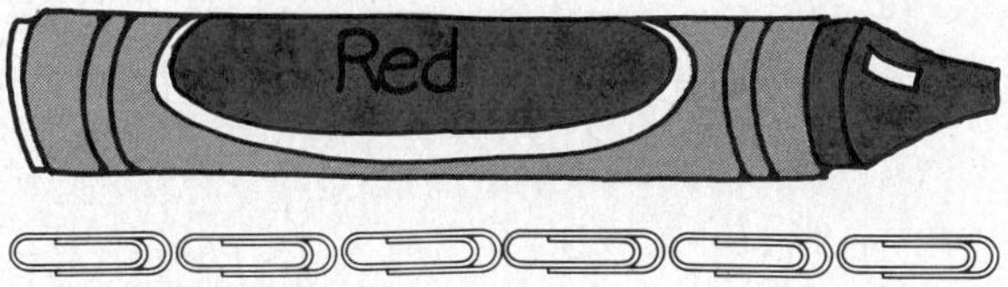

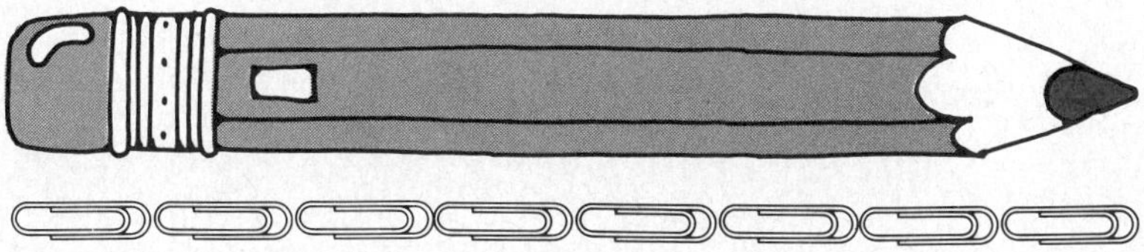

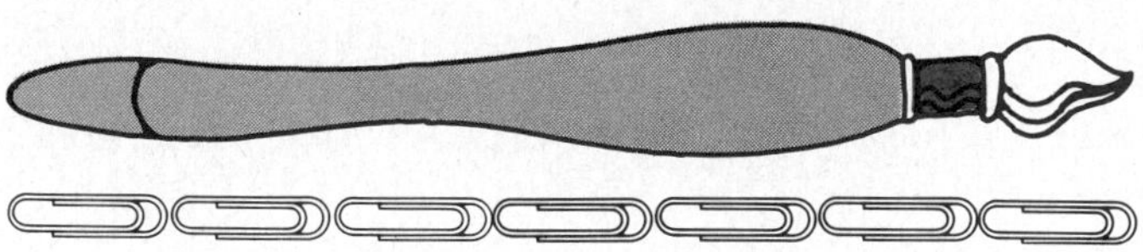

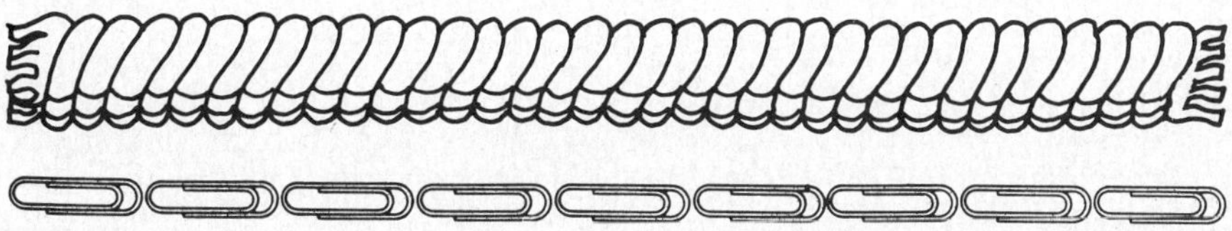

Count the number of paper clips in the length of each object.
Write the number.

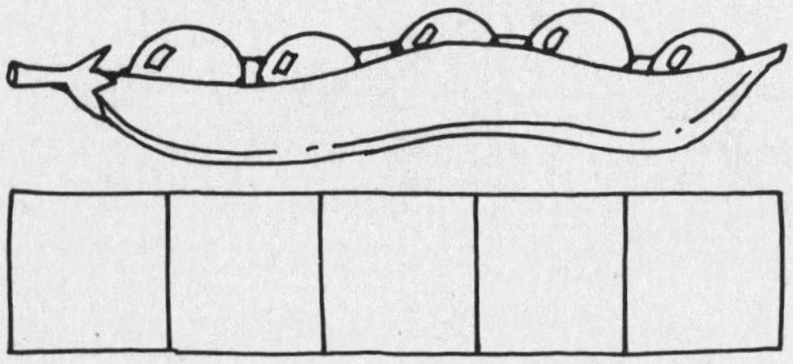

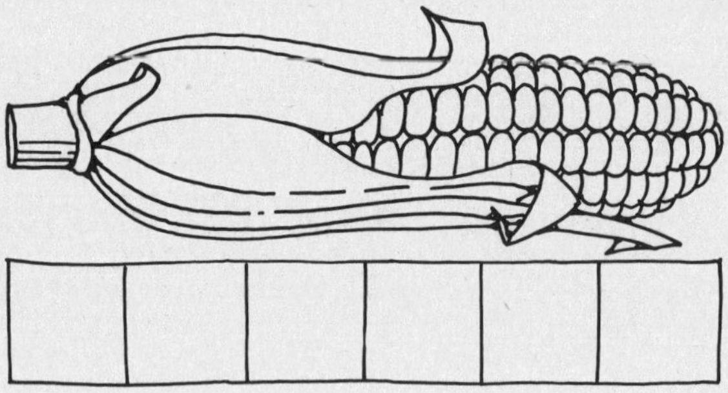

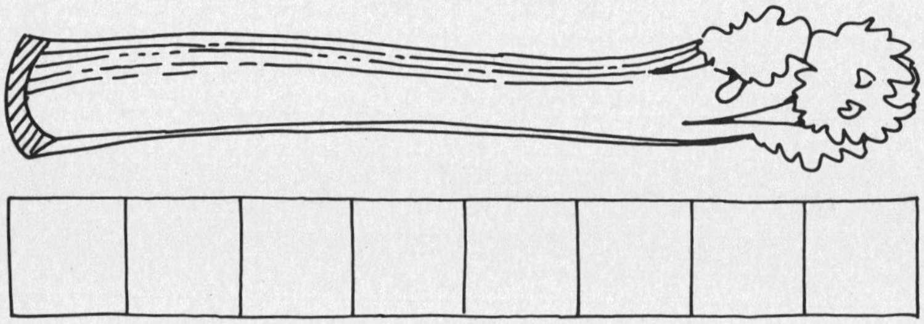

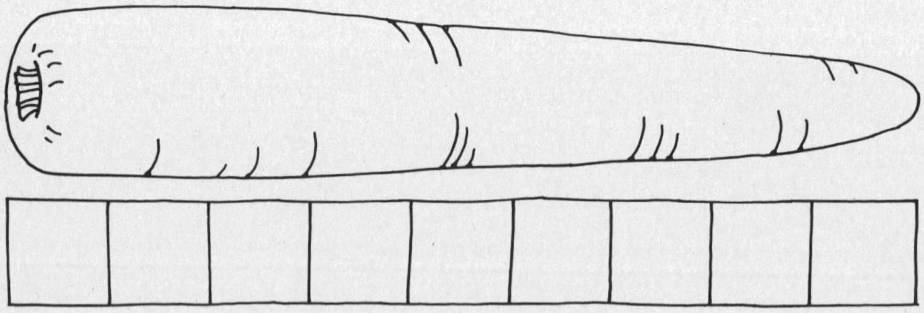

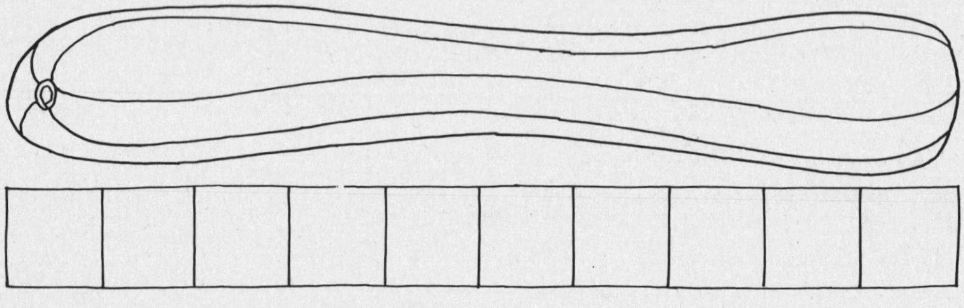

Count the number of squares in the length of each object.
Write the number.

Name ____________________

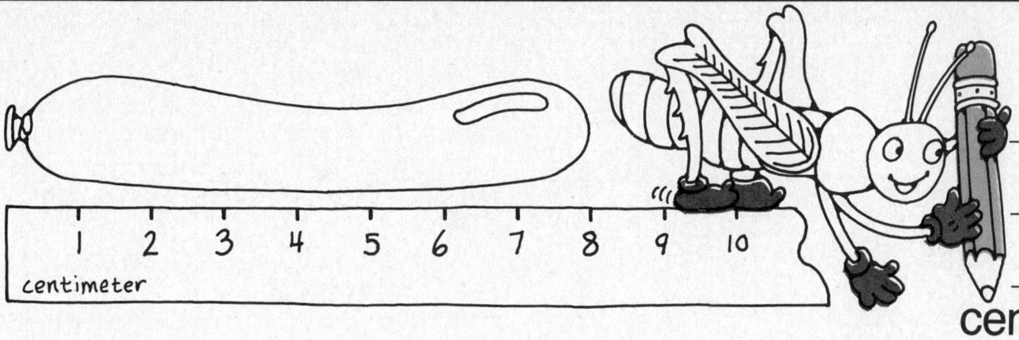

8 centimeters

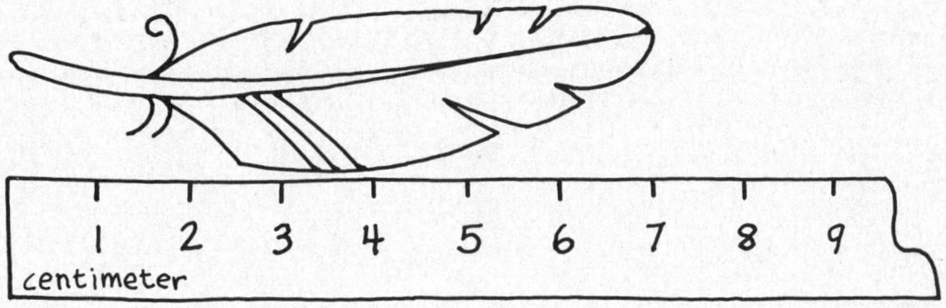

____ centimeters

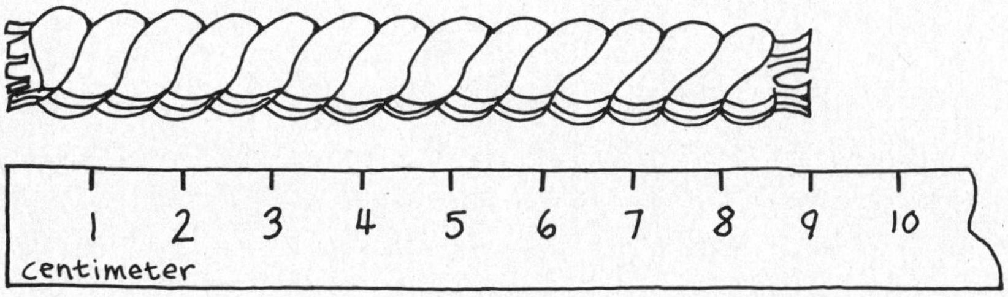

____ centimeters

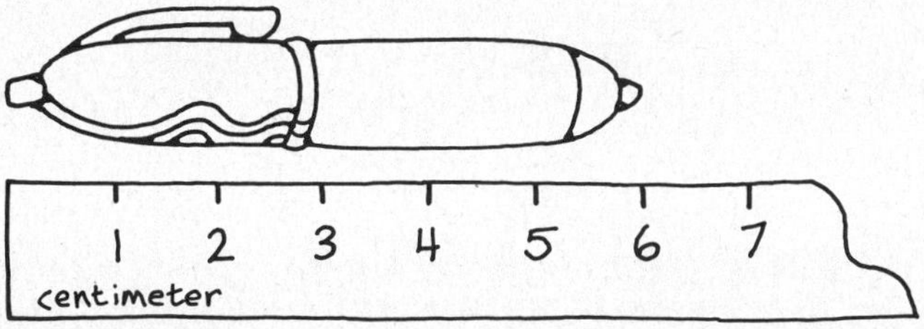

____ centimeters

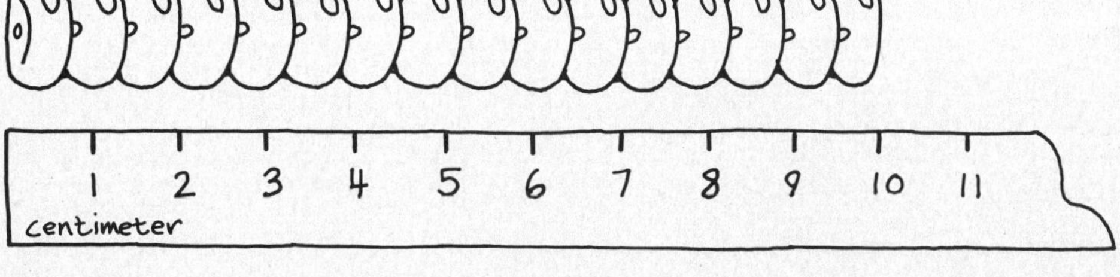

____ centimeters

Use the ruler to measure the length of each object in centimeters.
Write the number.

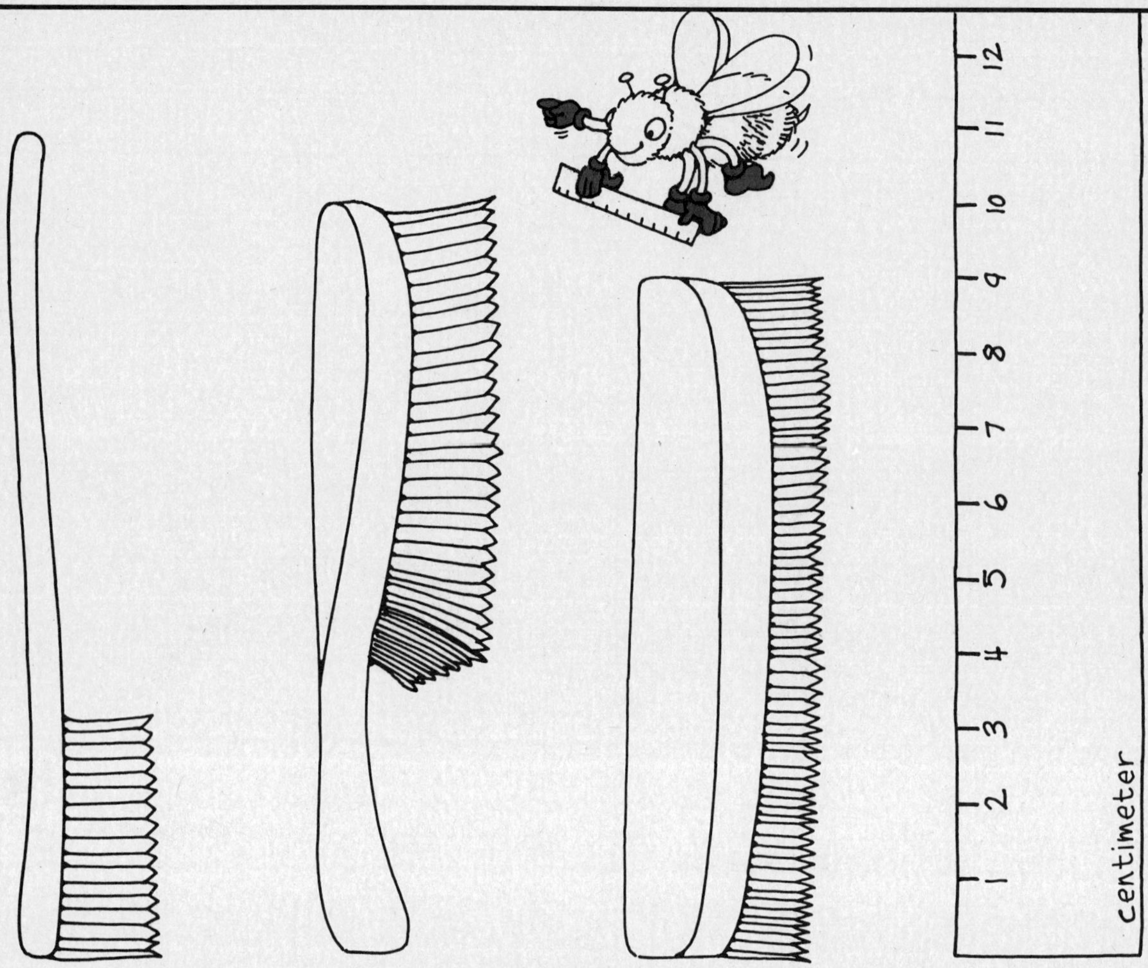

centimeters centimeters centimeters

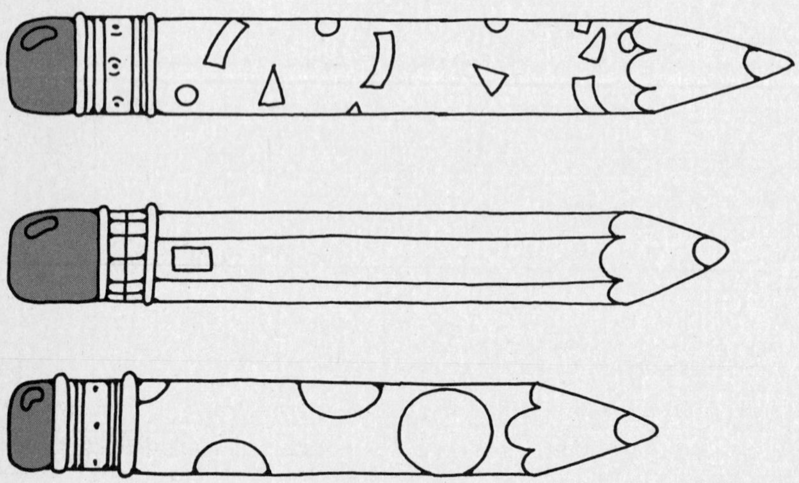

centimeters

centimeters

centimeters

Use a ruler to measure the length of each object in centimeters.
Write the number.

Name ______________________________

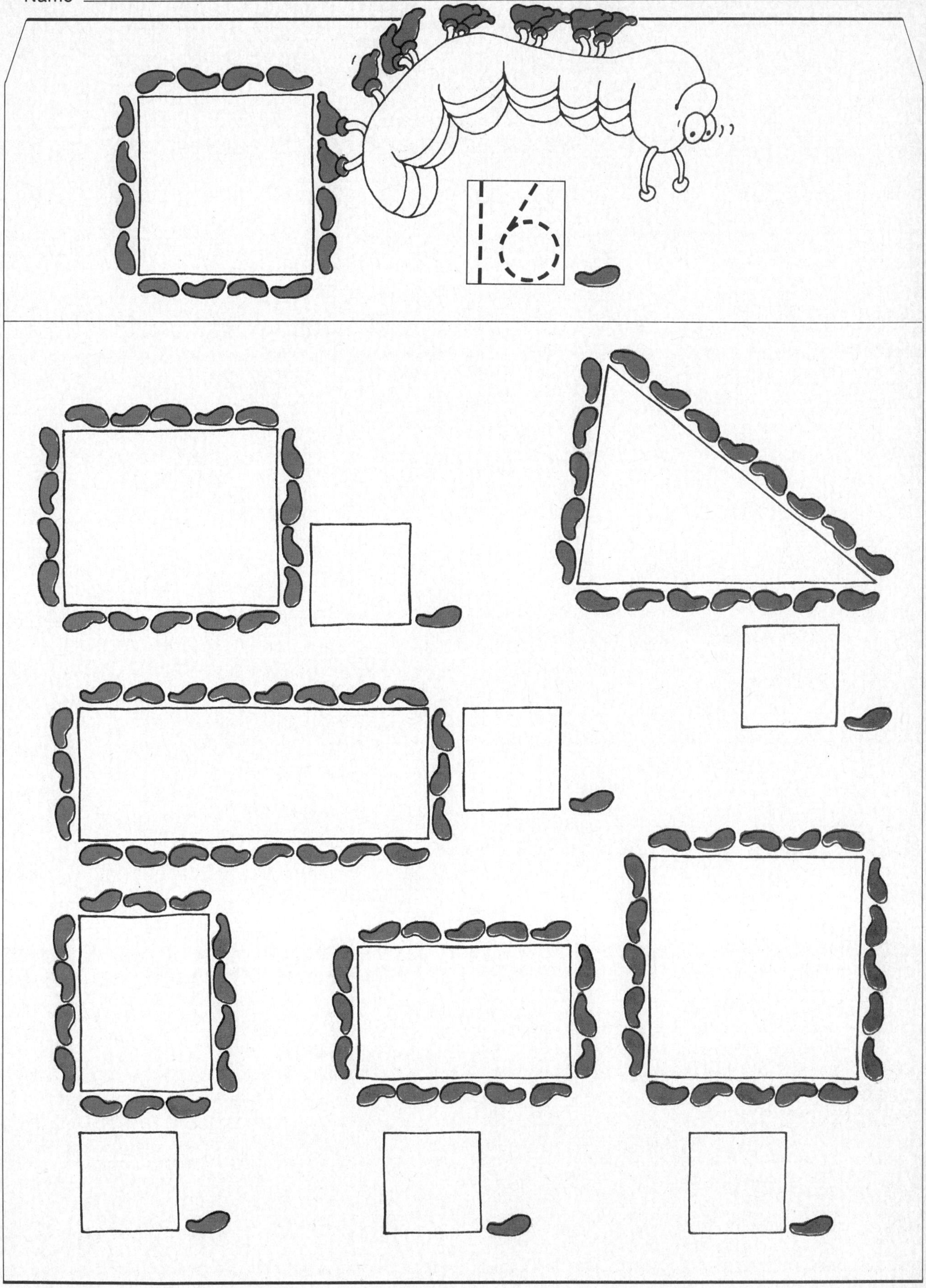

Count the number of footsteps around each figure. Write the number.

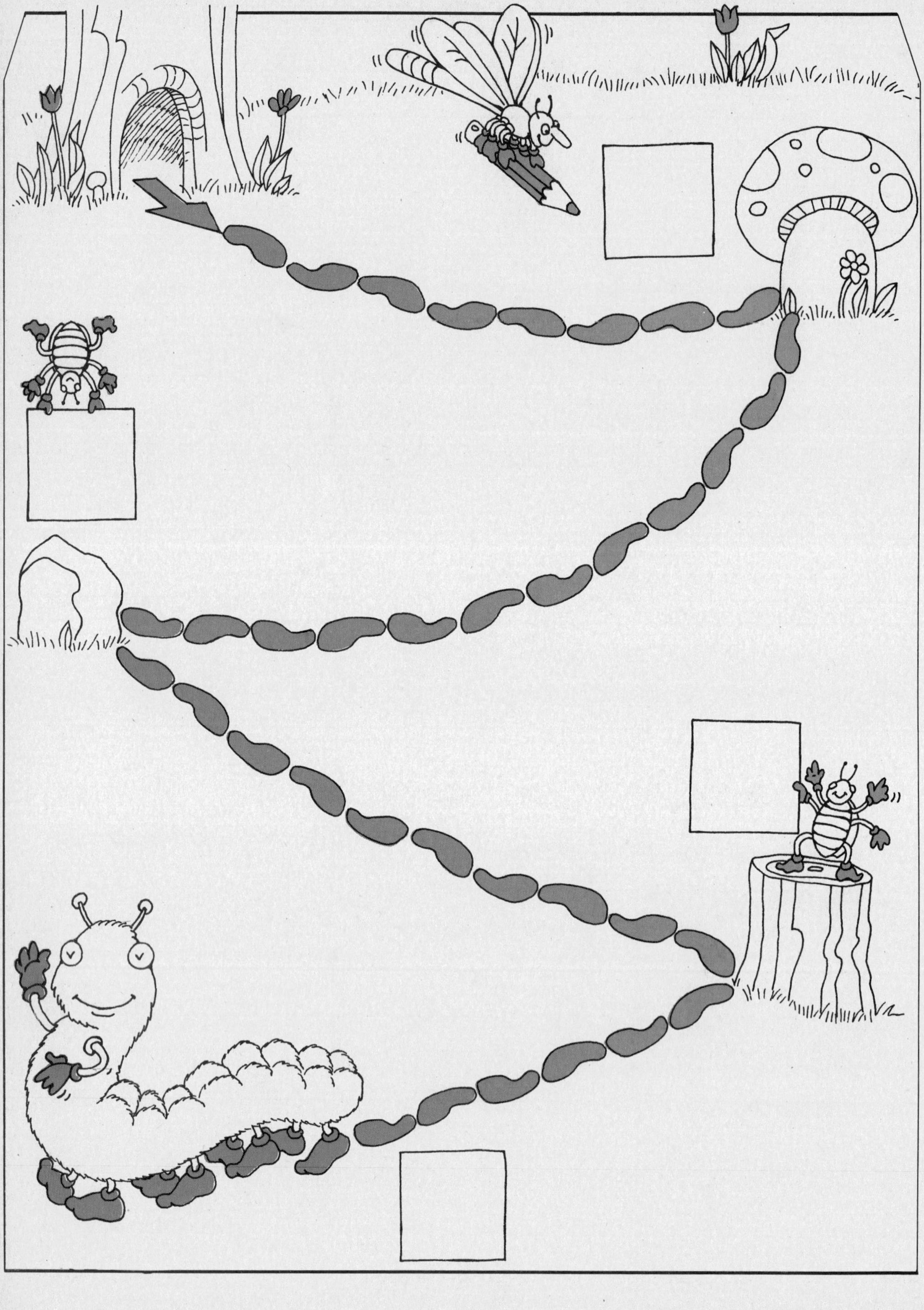

Count the number of footsteps between two points. Write the number.

Name ______________________________

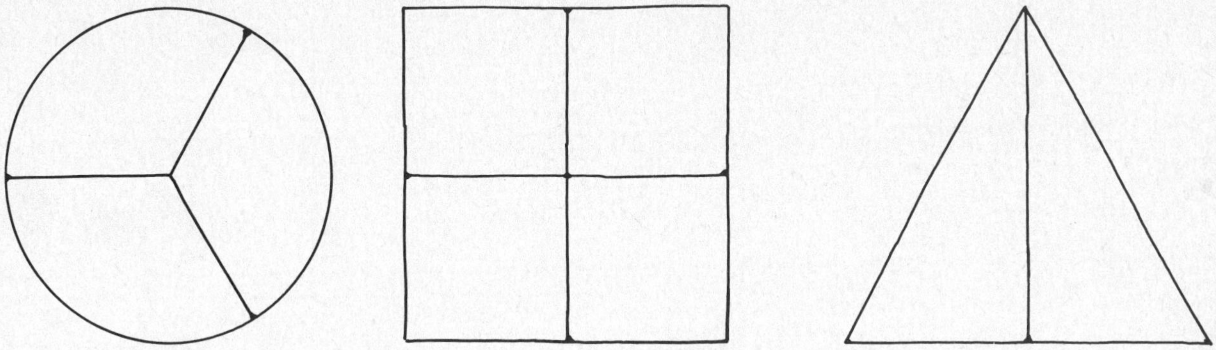

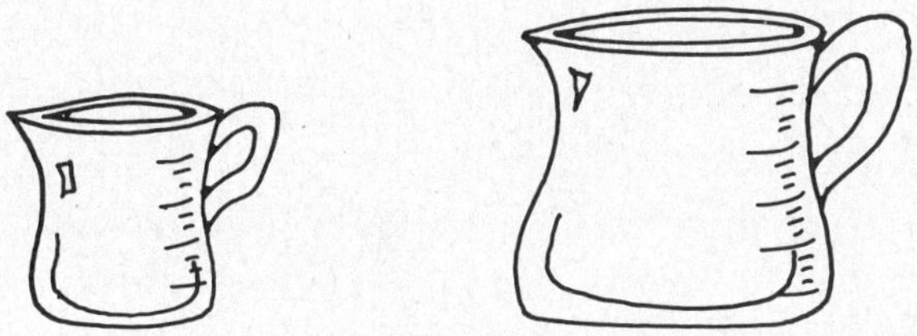

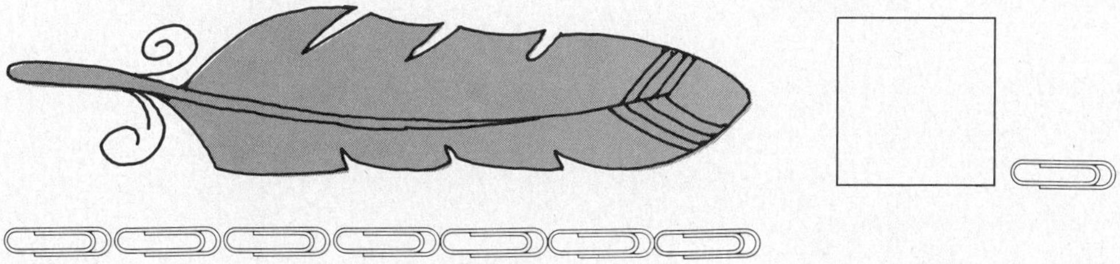

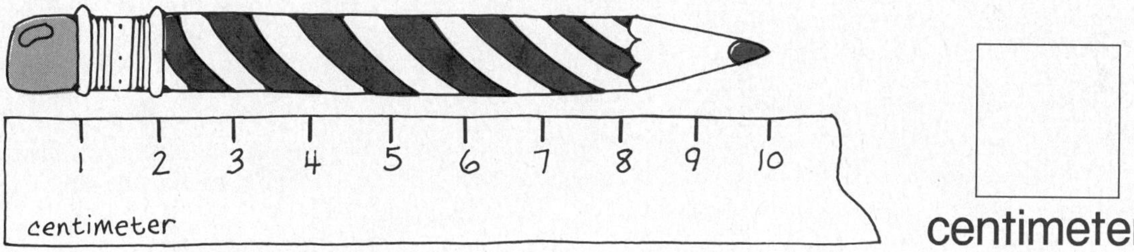

centimeters

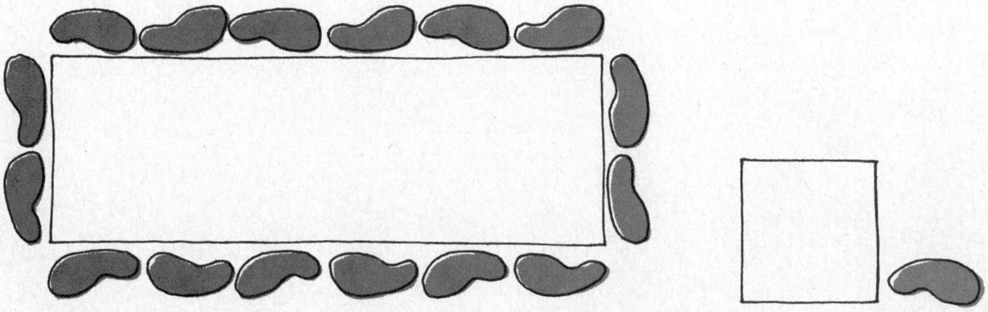

Chapter Checkup Color one third red, one fourth yellow and one half blue. Circle the pitcher that holds more. Circle the glass that holds less. Count the number of paper clips in the length of the feather. Use the ruler to measure the length of the pencil in centimeters. Count the number of footsteps around the figure. Write the numbers.

Field Trip Use the vocabulary **hotter** and **colder.** In the first two examples, circle the scene that is hotter. In the last two, circle the item that is colder.

Name ______________________________

9 ADDITION

1 and 1 are 2

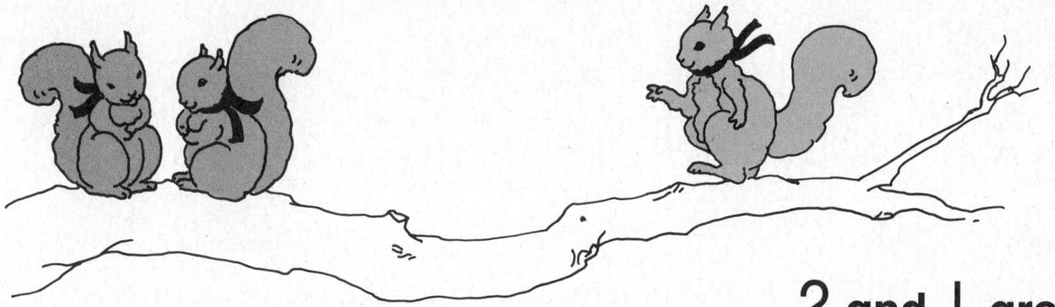

2 and 1 are ☐

2 and 2 are ☐

3 and 2 are ☐

Write the number that tells how many in all.

2 and 2 are

3 and 3 are

2 and 4 are

4 and 2 are

Write the number that tells how many in all.

Name ______________________________

1 and 1 are 2

☐ and ☐ are ☐

☐ and ☐ are ☐

☐ and ☐ are ☐

Write the number that tells how many animals are sitting, how many are joining them and how many in all.

☐ and ☐ are ☐

☐ and ☐ are ☐

☐ and ☐ are ☐

☐ and ☐ are ☐

Write the number that tells how many animals are sitting, how many are joining them and how many in all.

Name ______________________________

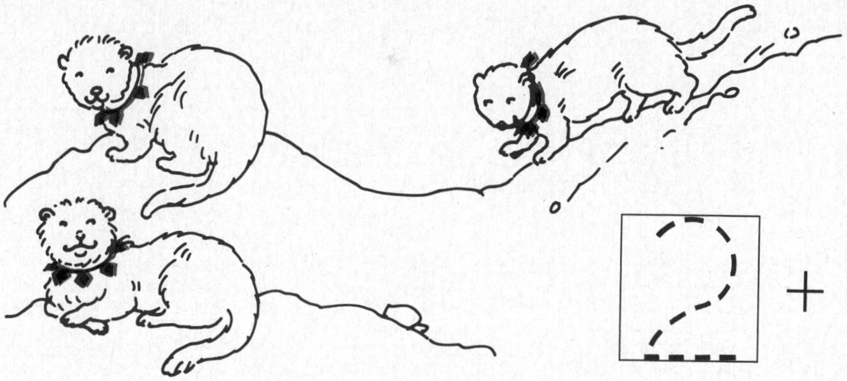

$2 + 1 = 3$

$\square + \square = \square$

$\square + \square = \square$

$\square + \square = \square$

Write the number that tells how many animals are sitting, how many are joining them and how many in all.

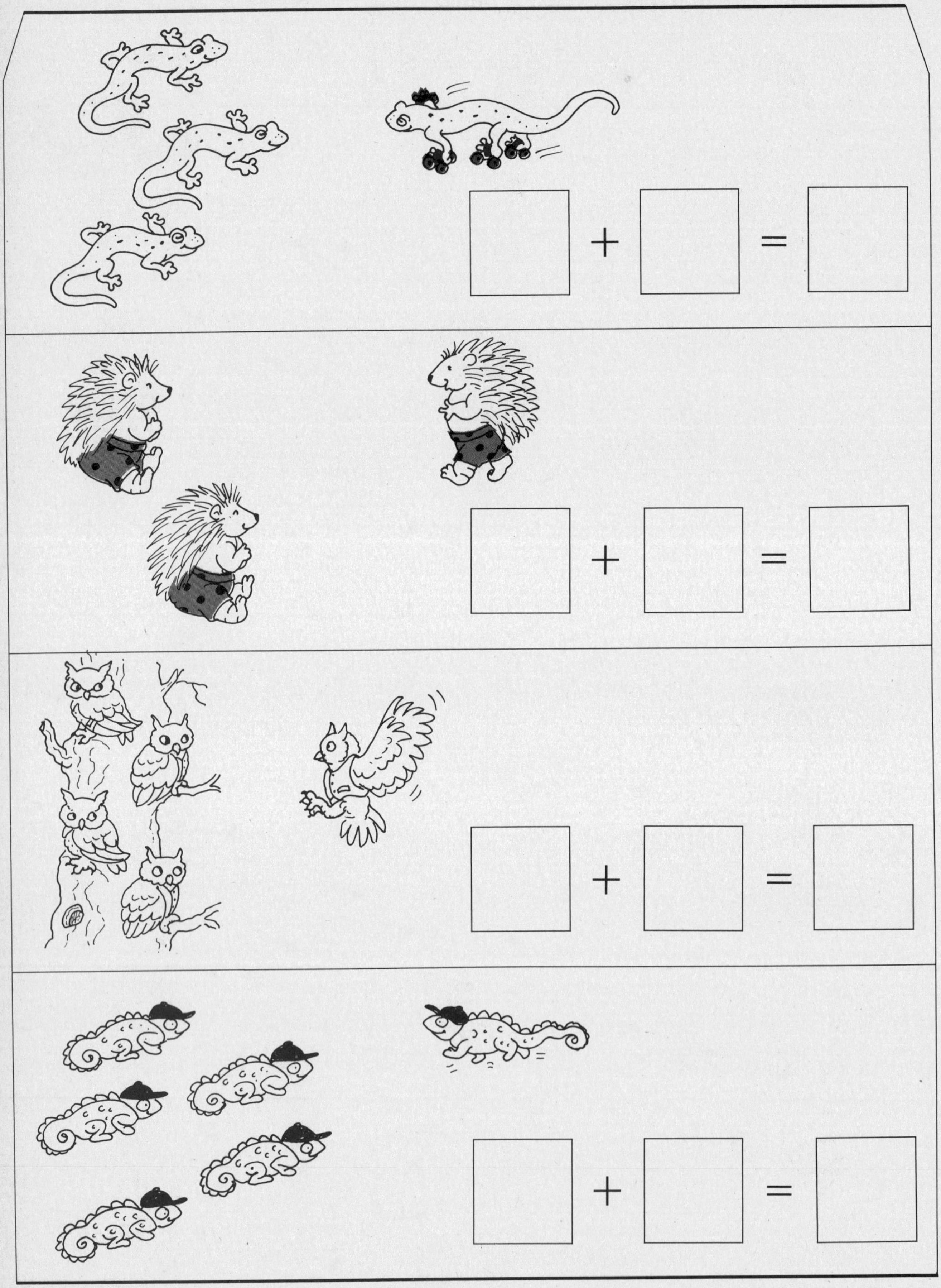

Write the number that tells how many animals are sitting, how many are joining them and how many in all.

Name ______________________________

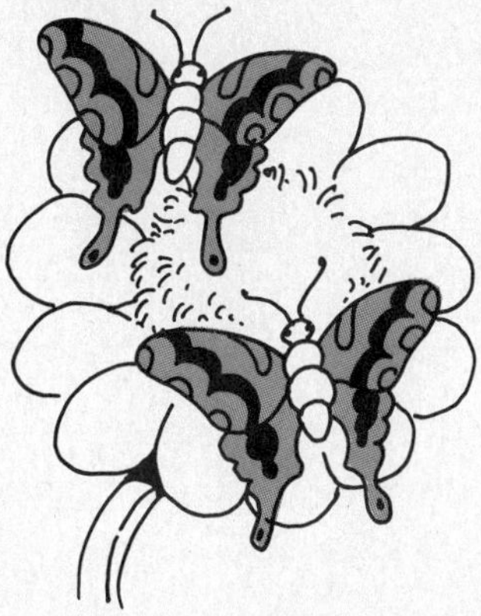

___ + ___ = ___

___ + ___ = ___

___ + ___ = ___

___ + ___ = ___

Write the number that tells how many animals are sitting, how many are joining them and how many in all.

$\square + \square = \square$

$\square + \square = \square$

$\square + \square = \square$

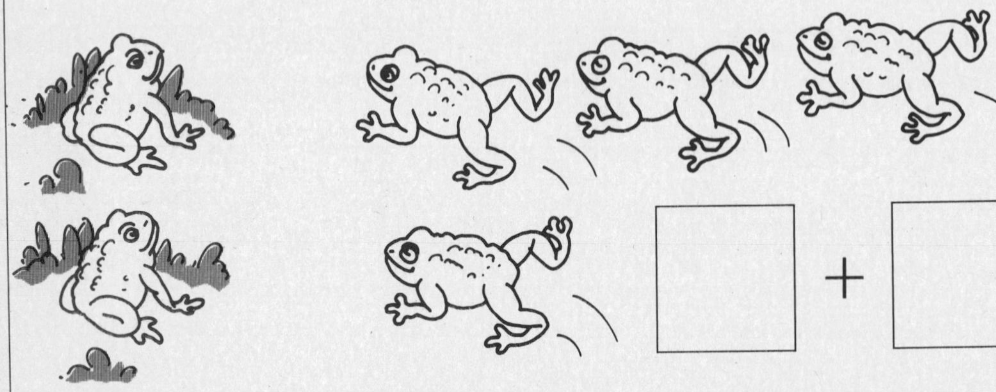

$\square + \square = \square$

Write the number that tells how many animals are sitting, how many are joining them and how many in all.

Name ______________________________

$$\begin{array}{r} 2 \\ +2 \\ \hline 4 \end{array}$$

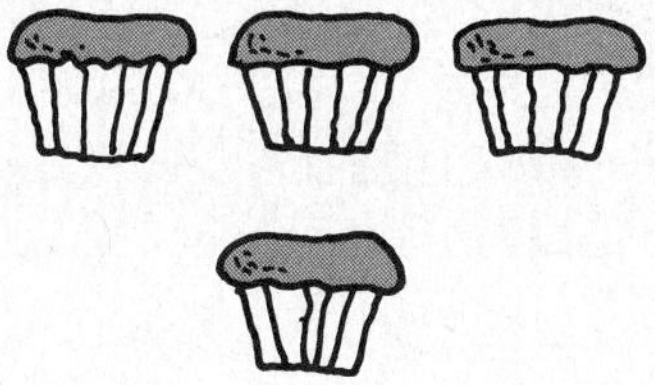

$$\begin{array}{r} 3 \\ +1 \\ \hline \square \end{array}$$

$$\begin{array}{r} 1 \\ +2 \\ \hline \square \end{array}$$

$$\begin{array}{r} 2 \\ +3 \\ \hline \square \end{array}$$

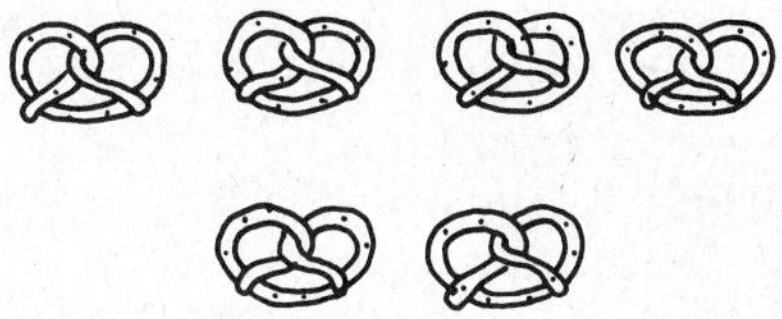

$$\begin{array}{r} 4 \\ +2 \\ \hline \square \end{array}$$

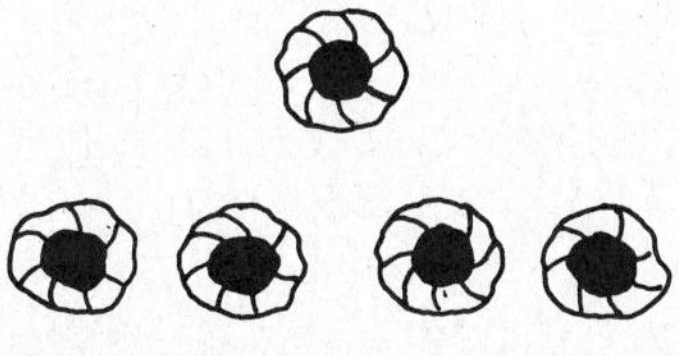

$$\begin{array}{r} 1 \\ +4 \\ \hline \square \end{array}$$

$$\begin{array}{r} 3 \\ +3 \\ \hline \square \end{array}$$

Use the objects to help find how many in all. Write the number.

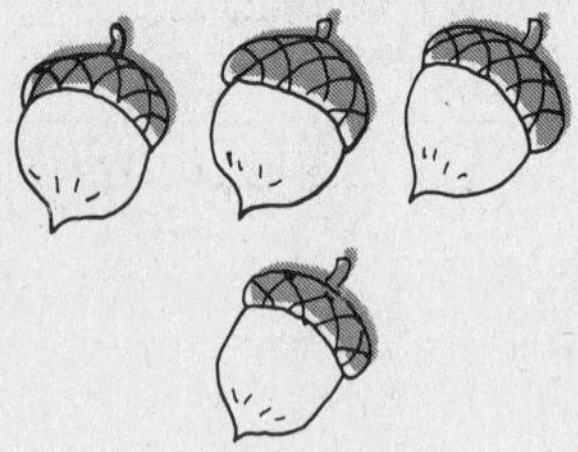

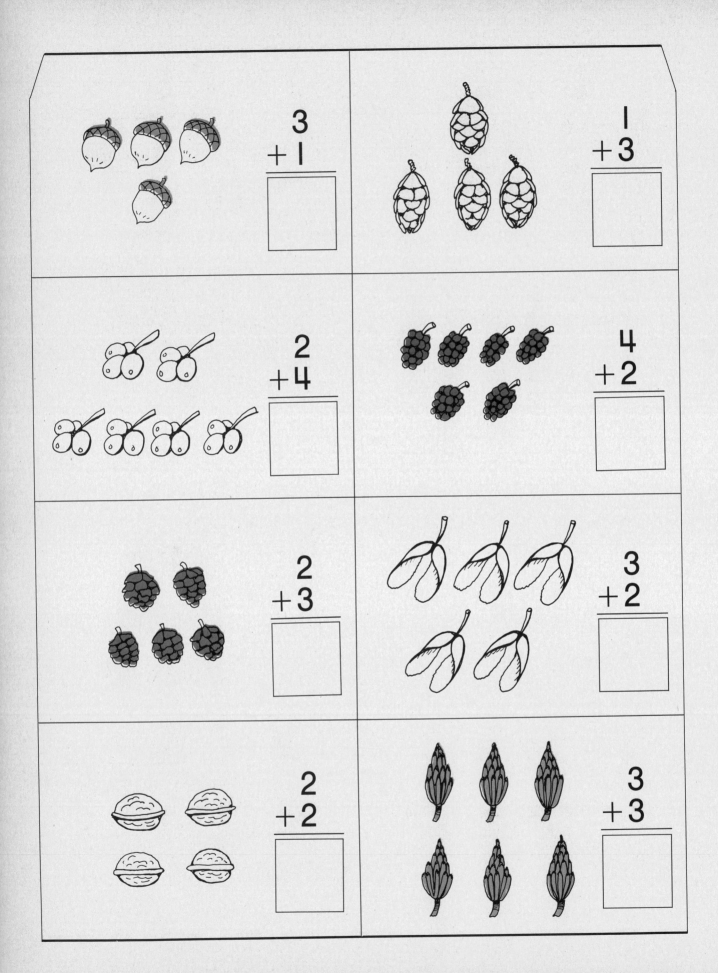

$$\begin{array}{r} 3 \\ +1 \\ \hline \end{array}$$

$$\begin{array}{r} 1 \\ +3 \\ \hline \end{array}$$

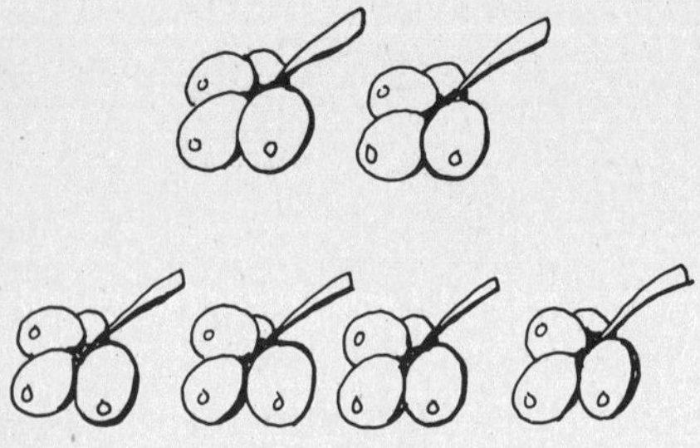

$$\begin{array}{r} 2 \\ +4 \\ \hline \end{array}$$

$$\begin{array}{r} 4 \\ +2 \\ \hline \end{array}$$

$$\begin{array}{r} 2 \\ +3 \\ \hline \end{array}$$

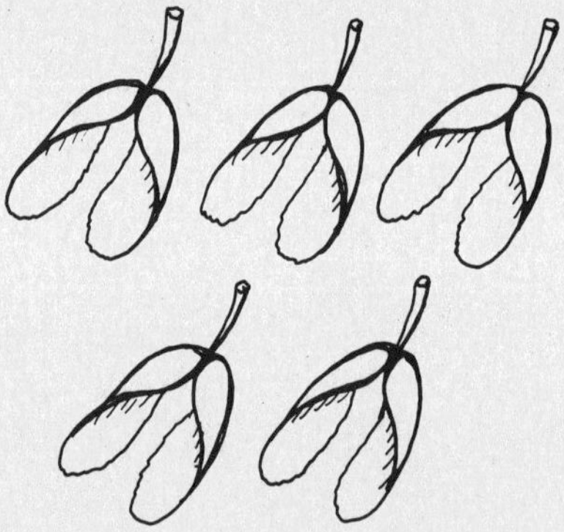

$$\begin{array}{r} 3 \\ +2 \\ \hline \end{array}$$

$$\begin{array}{r} 2 \\ +2 \\ \hline \end{array}$$

$$\begin{array}{r} 3 \\ +3 \\ \hline \end{array}$$

Use the objects to help find how many in all. Write the number.

4 and 1 more is 5.

$4 + 1 =$ 5

$1 + 3 =$

$2 + 2 =$

$2 + 3 =$

$1 + 5 =$

$1 + 4 =$

$3 + 3 =$

$4 + 2 =$

$5 + 1 =$

$3 + 2 =$

$2 + 4 =$

Use the objects to help find how many in all. Write the number.

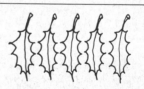

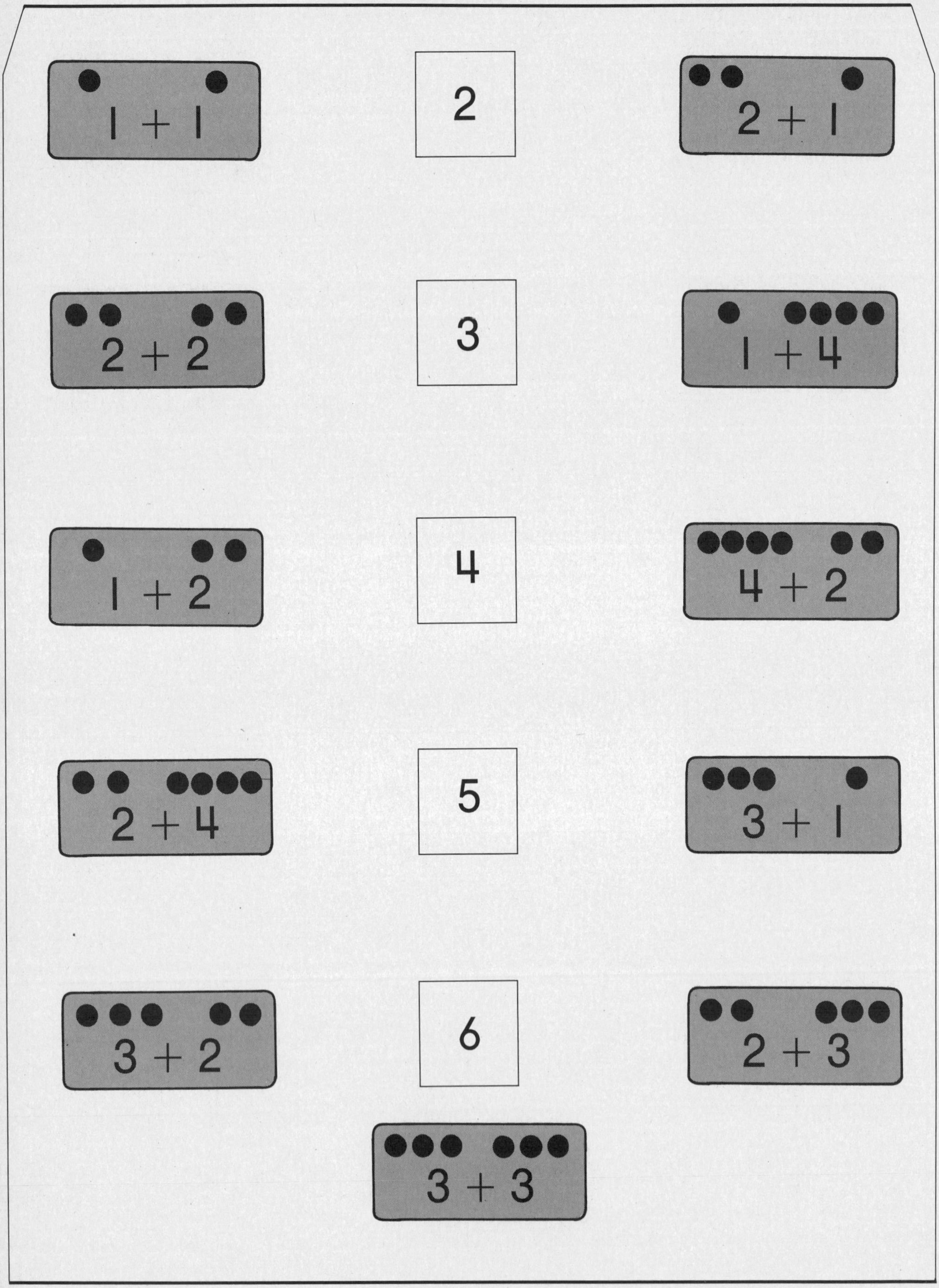

Draw a line from the domino to the number that tells how many dots in all.

Name ____

2 ¢ + 3 ¢ = 5 ¢

☐ ¢ + ☐ ¢ = ☐ ¢

☐ ¢ + ☐ ¢ = ☐ ¢

☐ ¢ + ☐ ¢ = ☐ ¢

Count the pennies. Write how much money in each set and how much money in all.

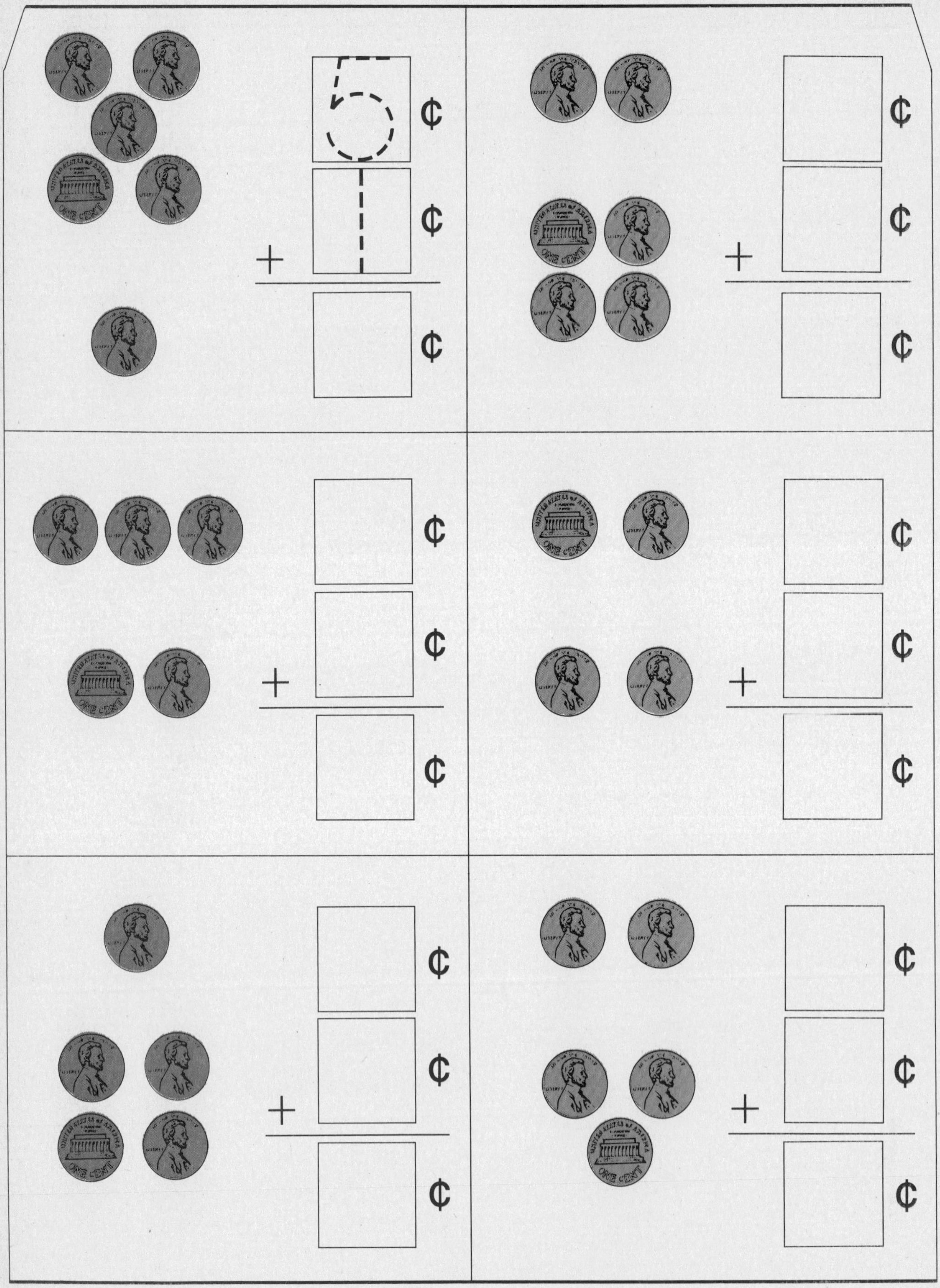

Count the pennies. Write how much money in each set and how much money in all.

Name ______________________________

2 ¢

\+ 2 ¢

______ ¢

¢

\+ ¢

______ ¢

¢

\+ ¢

______ ¢

¢

\+ ¢

______ ¢

¢

\+ ¢

______ ¢

¢

\+ ¢

______ ¢

Write the cost of each toy and how much money both toys cost together.

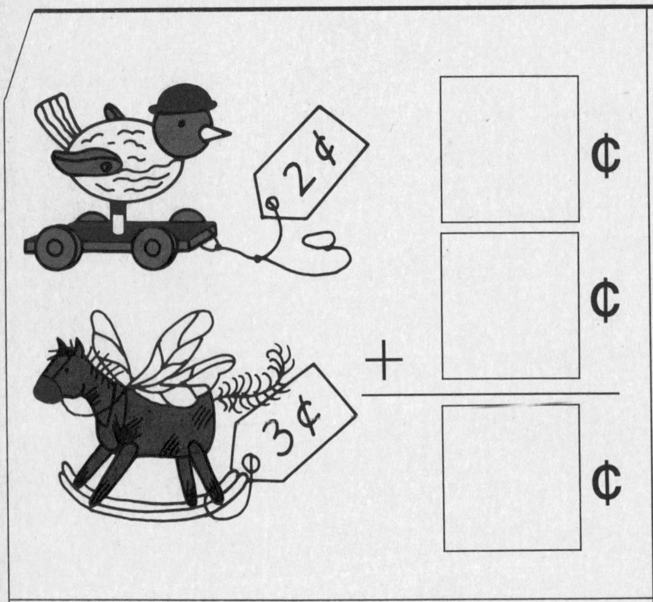

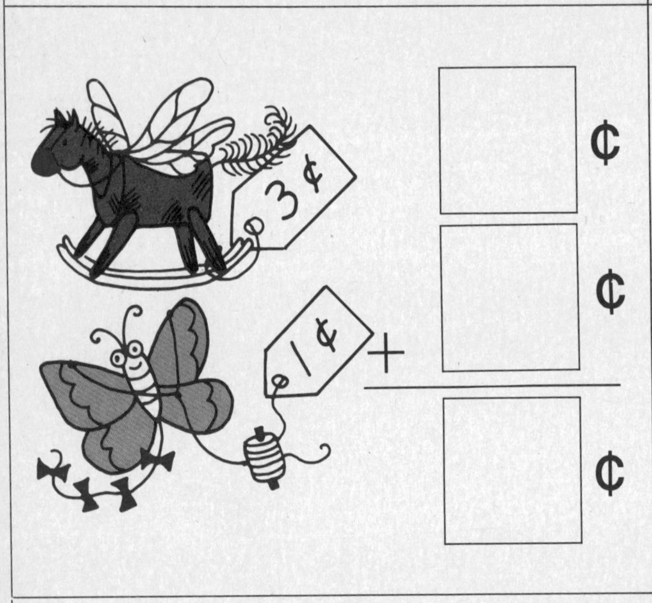

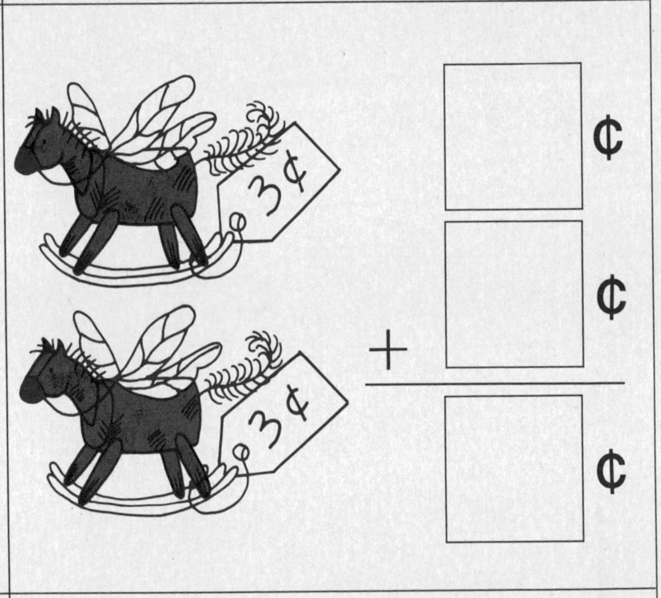

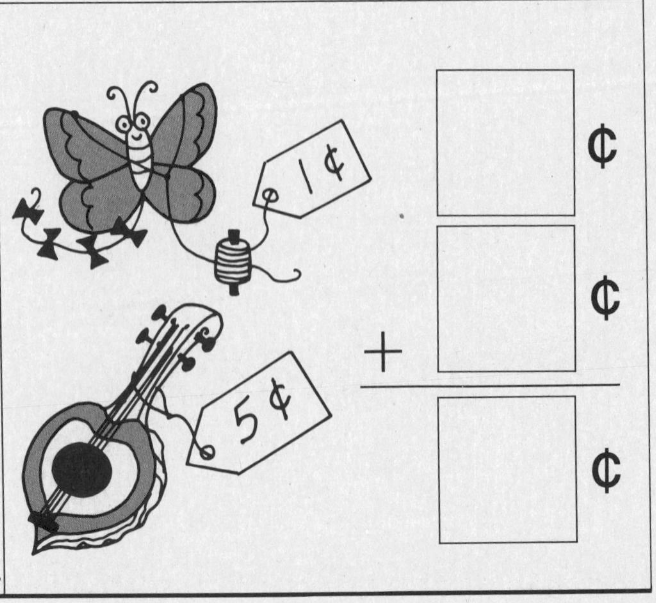

Write the cost of each toy and how much money both toys cost together.

Name ______________________________

☐ + ☐ = ☐

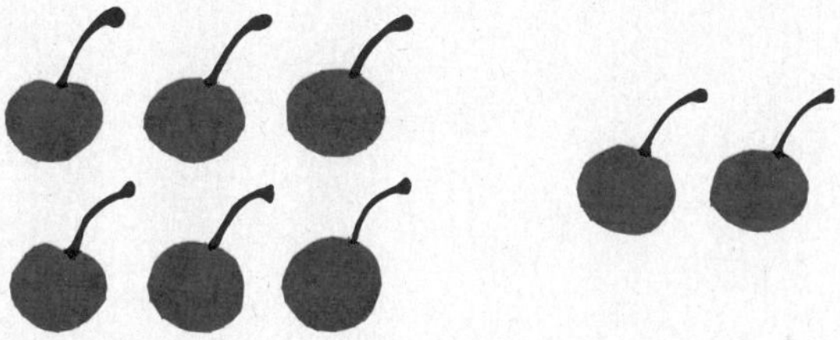

☐ + ☐ = ☐

☐ + ☐ = ☐

☐ + ☐ = ☐

Write the number of objects in each set and the number that tells how many in all.

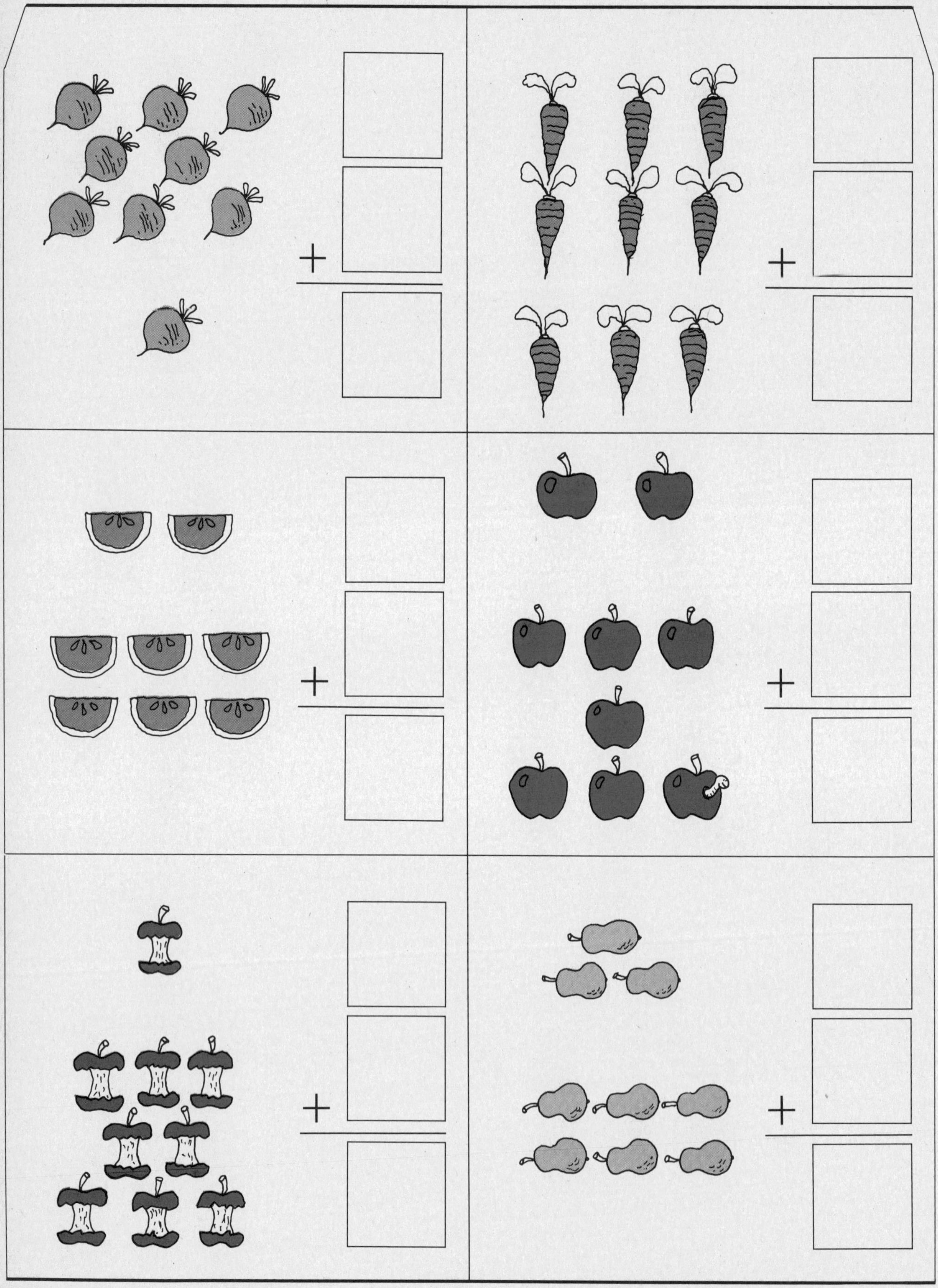

Write the number of objects in each set and the number that tells how many in all.

Name ______________________________

$3 + 1 = \square$

$\square + \square = \square$

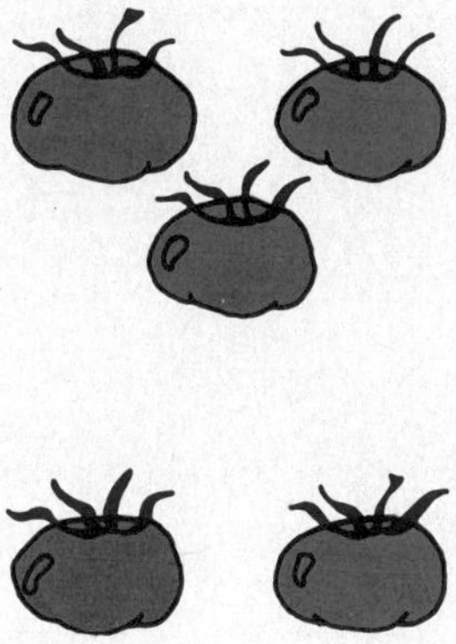

$$\begin{array}{r} 3 \\ +2 \\ \hline \square \end{array}$$

$$\begin{array}{r} \square \\ +\square \\ \hline \square \end{array}$$

$\square$¢ + $\square$¢ = $\square$¢

Chapter Checkup Write the number that tells how many objects, how many in each set or how much in all.

3 Yellow

4 Orange

5 Red

6 Brown

$$\begin{array}{r} 4 \\ +\ 1 \\ \hline \end{array}$$

$$\begin{array}{r} 2 \\ +\ 2 \\ \hline \end{array}$$

$$\begin{array}{r} 2 \\ +\ 1 \\ \hline \end{array}$$

$$\begin{array}{r} 3 \\ +\ 3 \\ \hline \end{array}$$

$$\begin{array}{r} 1 \\ +\ 3 \\ \hline \end{array}$$

$$\begin{array}{r} 3 \\ +\ 2 \\ \hline \end{array}$$

$$\begin{array}{r} 2 \\ +\ 4 \\ \hline \end{array}$$

$$\begin{array}{r} 1 \\ +\ 2 \\ \hline \end{array}$$

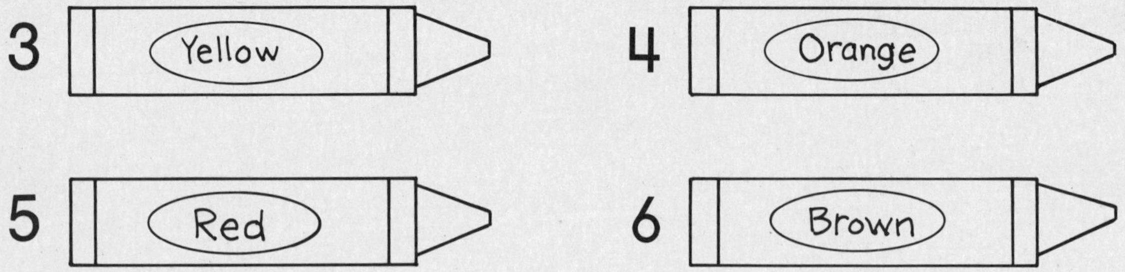

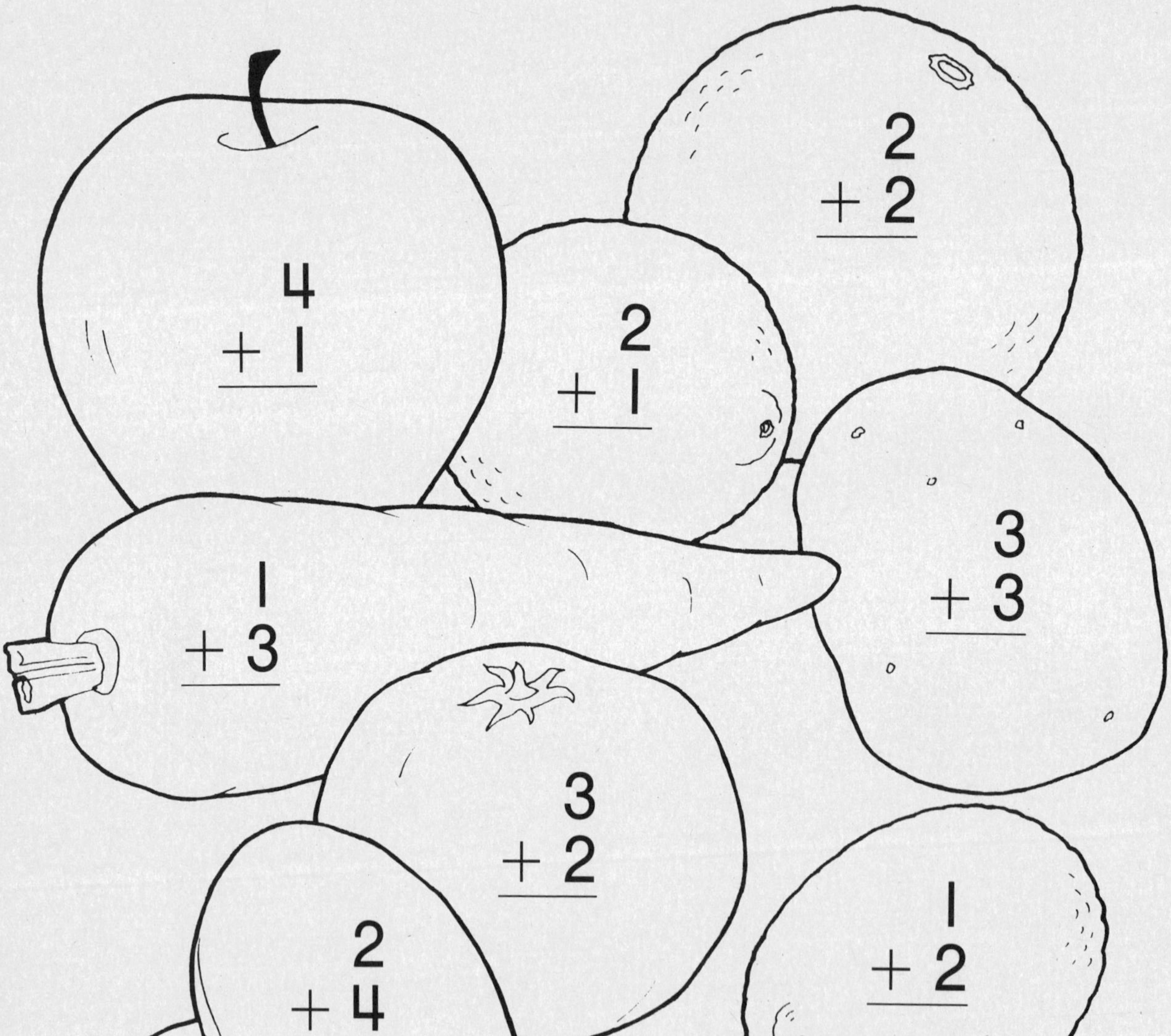

Field Trip   Color all areas yellow where 3 tells how many in all. Color the areas orange where 4 tells how many in all. Color the areas red where 5 tells how many in all. Color the areas brown where 6 tells how many in all.

Name _____

SUBTRACTION

10

3 minus 1 are ⟦2⟧

4 minus 2 are ☐

4 minus 1 are ☐

5 minus 1 are ☐

Write the number that tells how many are left.

4 minus 3 are

5 minus 1 are

6 minus 2 are

3 minus 2 are

Write the number that tells how many are left.

$$\boxed{2} \text{ minus } \boxed{1} \text{ are } \boxed{1}$$

$$\boxed{} \text{ minus } \boxed{} \text{ are } \boxed{}$$

$$\boxed{} \text{ minus } \boxed{} \text{ are } \boxed{}$$

$$\boxed{} \text{ minus } \boxed{} \text{ are } \boxed{}$$

Write the number that tells how many there are in all, how many are
leaving and how many are left.

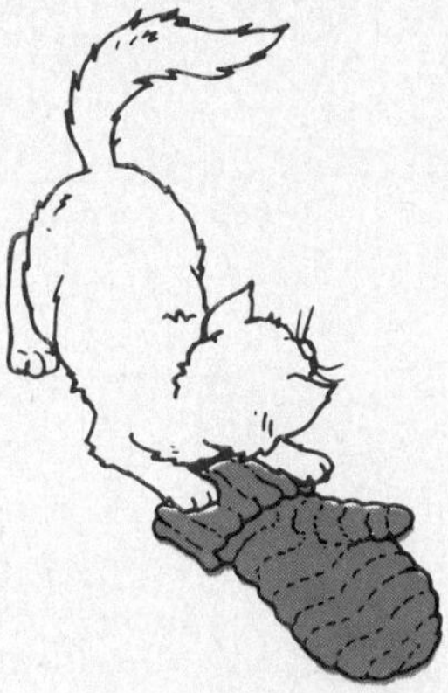

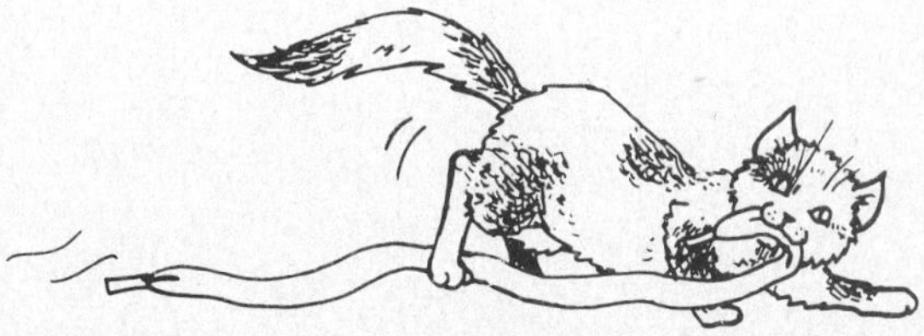

minus are

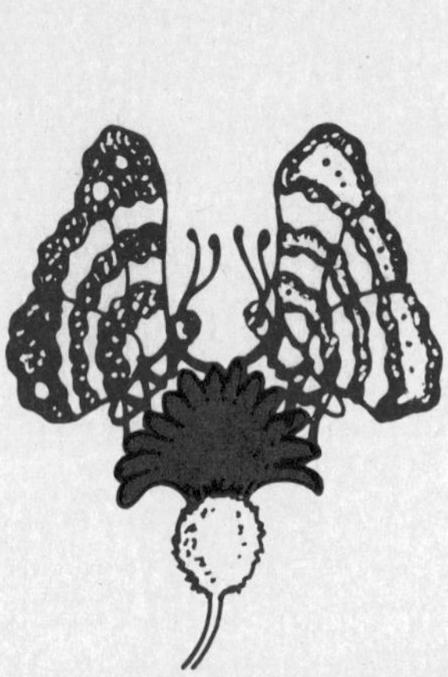

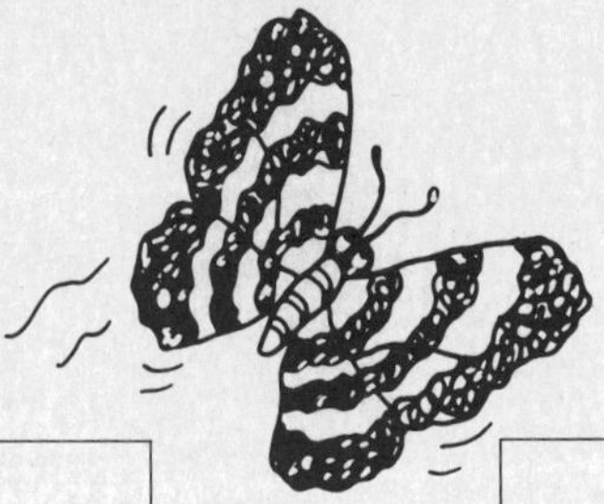

minus are

minus are

minus are

Write the number that tells how many there are in all, how many are leaving and how many are left.

Name ____________________

3 − 2 = 1

☐ − ☐ = ☐

☐ − ☐ = ☐

☐ − ☐ = ☐

Write the number that tells how many there are in all, how many are leaving and how many are left.

☐ − ☐ = ☐

☐ − ☐ = ☐

☐ − ☐ = ☐

☐ − ☐ = ☐

Write the number that tells how many there are in all, how many are leaving and how many are left.

Name ______________________________

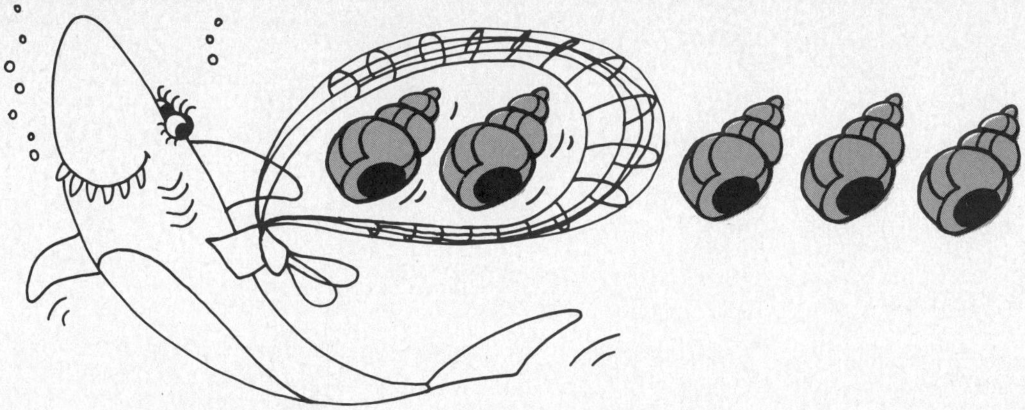

$$5 - 2 = 3$$

$$5 - 4 = \square$$

$$6 - 3 = \square$$

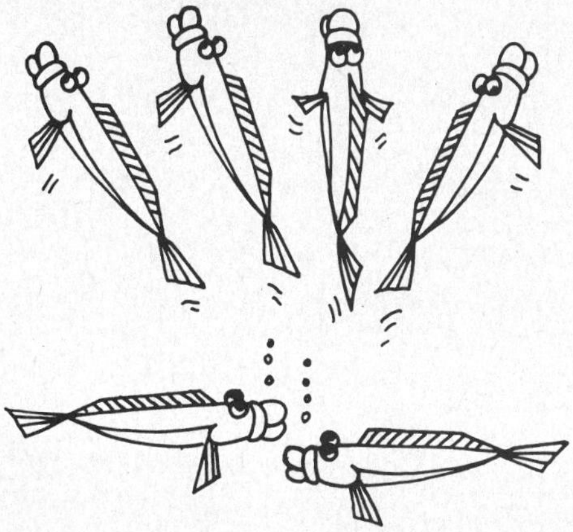

$$6 - 4 = \square$$

$$4 - 3 = \square$$

$$5 - 3 = \square$$

$$6 - 5 = \square$$

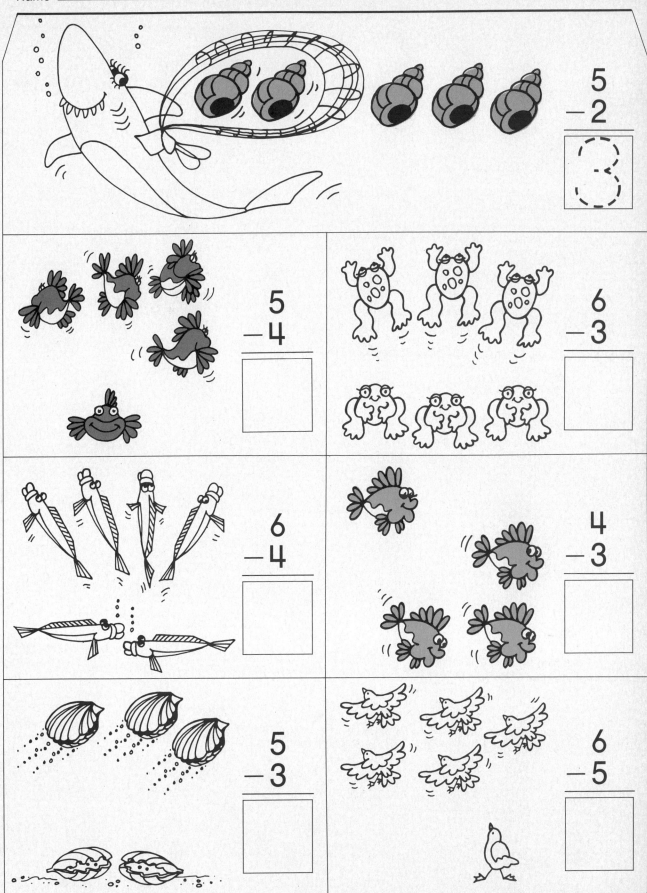

Write the number that tells how many are left.

$$\begin{array}{r} 4 \\ -\ 1 \\ \hline \square \end{array}$$

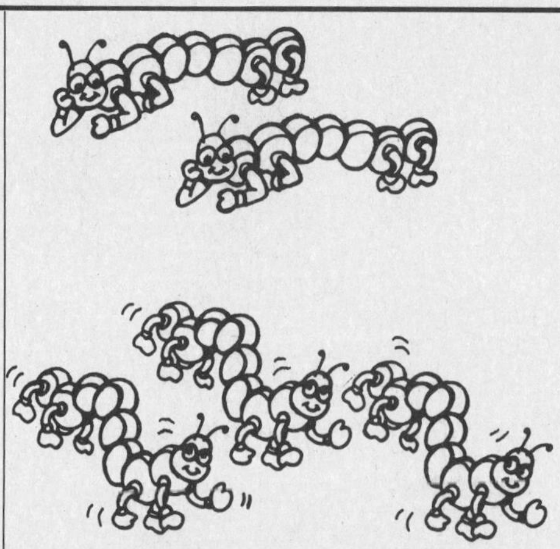

$$\begin{array}{r} 5 \\ -\ 3 \\ \hline \square \end{array}$$

$$\begin{array}{r} 6 \\ -\ 2 \\ \hline \square \end{array}$$

$$\begin{array}{r} 3 \\ -\ 1 \\ \hline \square \end{array}$$

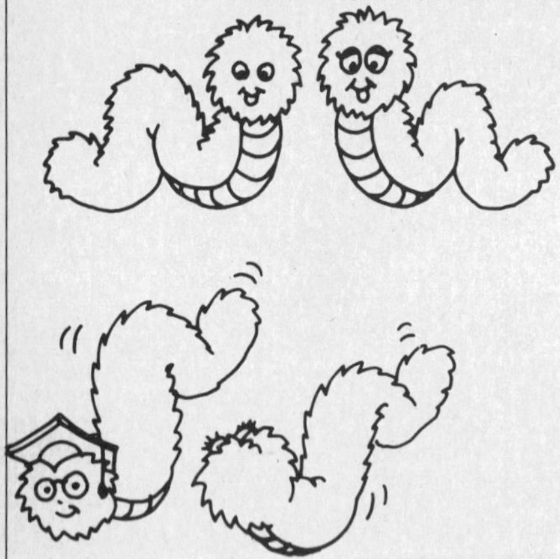

$$\begin{array}{r} 4 \\ -\ 2 \\ \hline \square \end{array}$$

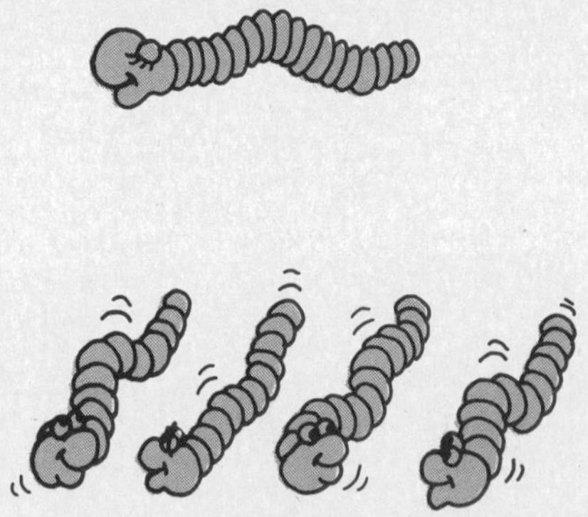

$$\begin{array}{r} 5 \\ -\ 4 \\ \hline \square \end{array}$$

$$\begin{array}{r} 6 \\ -\ 3 \\ \hline \square \end{array}$$

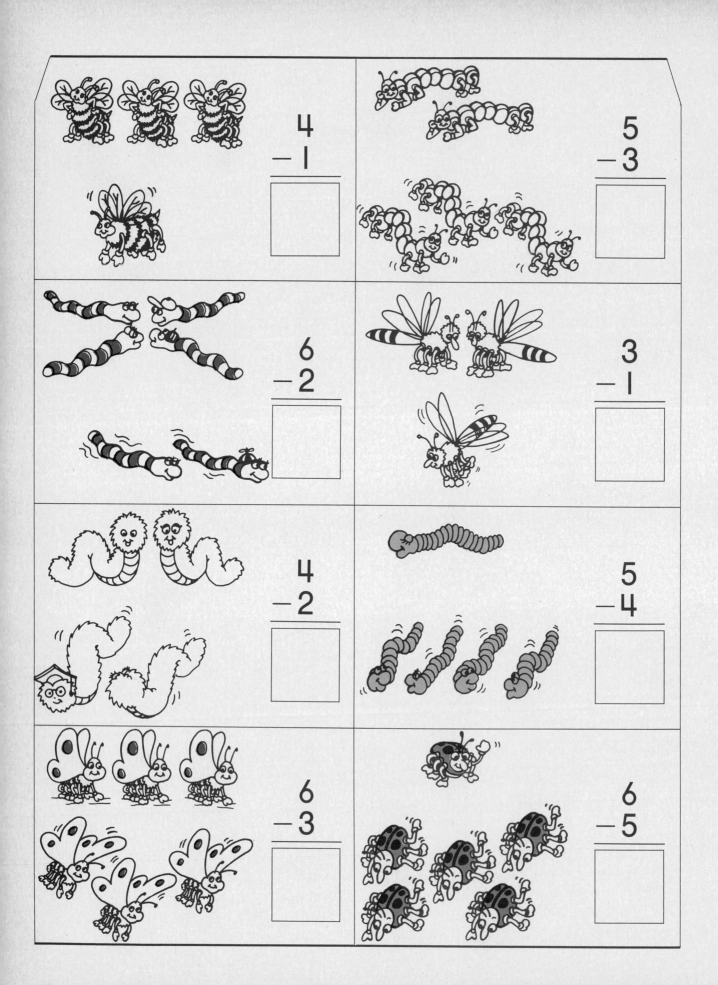

$$\begin{array}{r} 6 \\ -\ 5 \\ \hline \square \end{array}$$

Write the number that tells how many are left.

Name ______________________________

$$\begin{array}{r} 4 \\ -2 \\ \hline 2 \end{array}$$

$$\begin{array}{r} 3 \\ -2 \\ \hline \square \end{array}$$

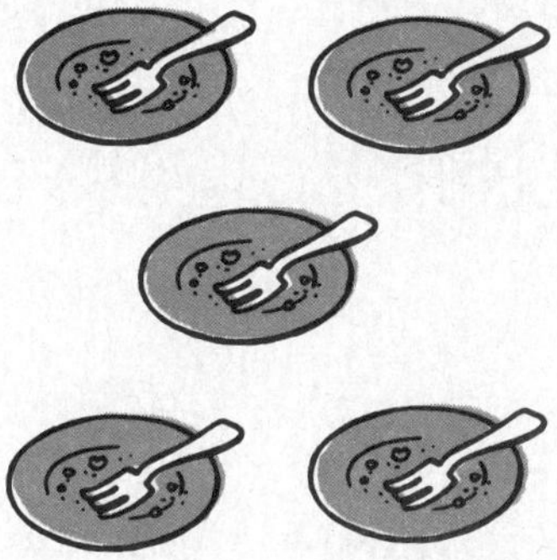

$$\begin{array}{r} 5 \\ -3 \\ \hline \square \end{array}$$

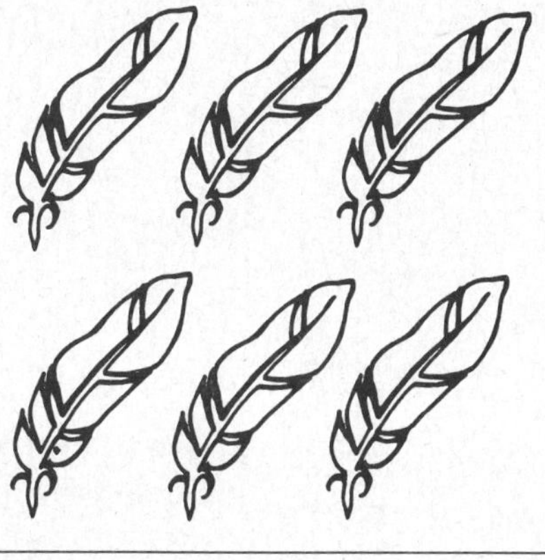

$$\begin{array}{r} 6 \\ -5 \\ \hline \square \end{array}$$

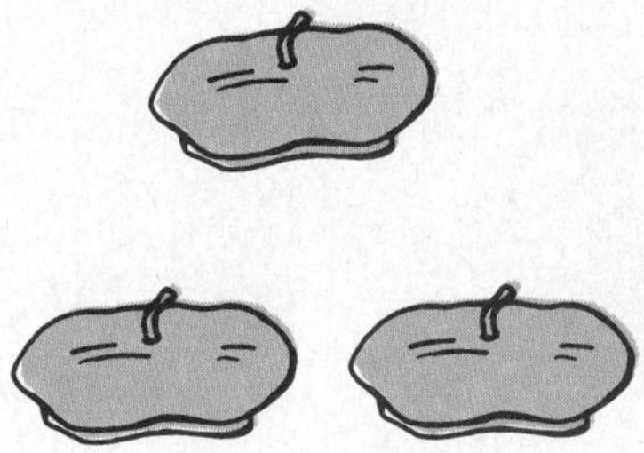

$$\begin{array}{r} 3 \\ -1 \\ \hline \square \end{array}$$

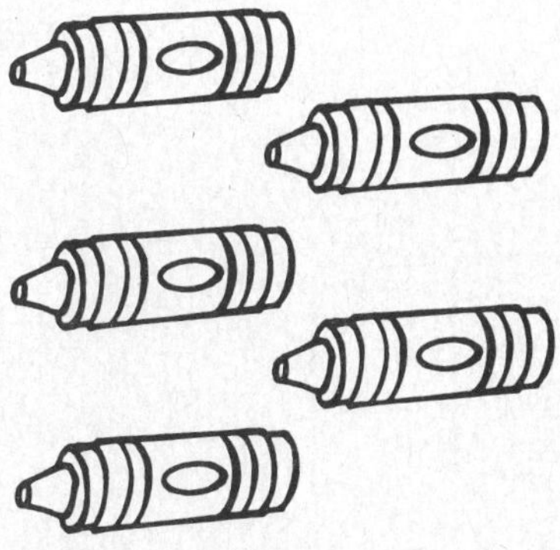

$$\begin{array}{r} 5 \\ -2 \\ \hline \square \end{array}$$

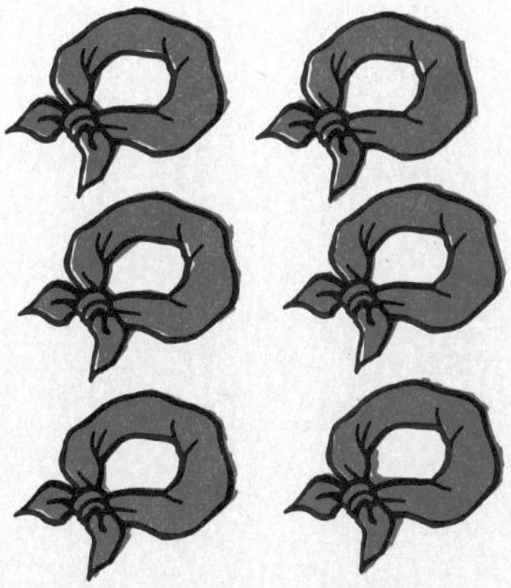

$$\begin{array}{r} 6 \\ -4 \\ \hline \square \end{array}$$

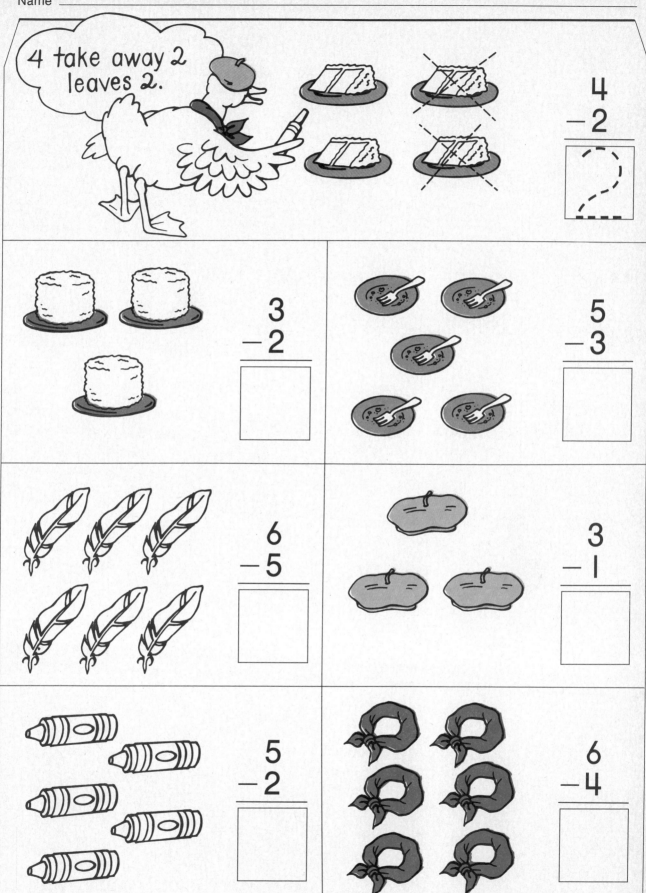

Cross out the objects to be taken away. Write the number that are left.

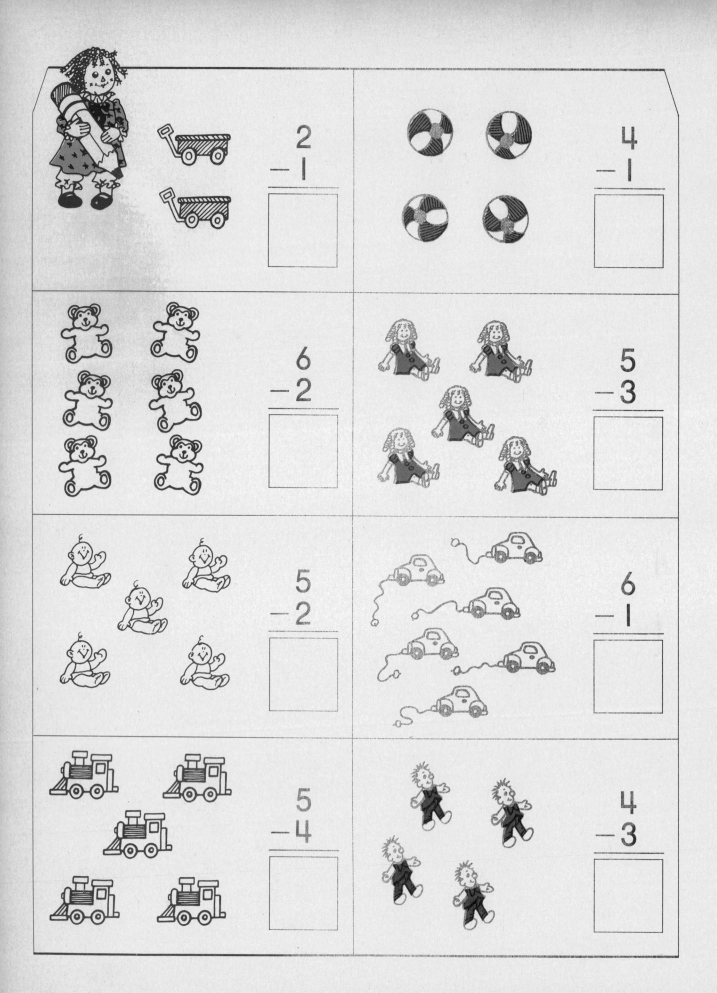

$$\begin{array}{r} 2 \\ -1 \\ \hline \end{array}$$

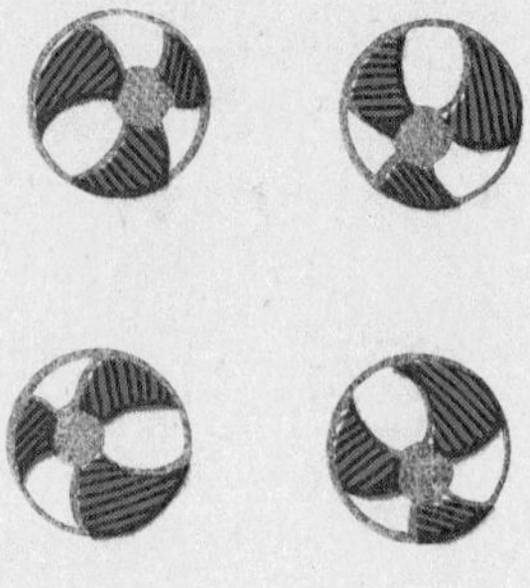

$$\begin{array}{r} 4 \\ -1 \\ \hline \end{array}$$

$$\begin{array}{r} 6 \\ -2 \\ \hline \end{array}$$

$$\begin{array}{r} 5 \\ -3 \\ \hline \end{array}$$

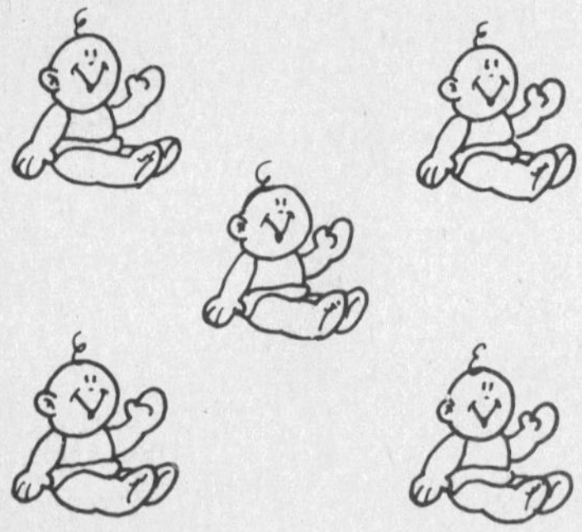

$$\begin{array}{r} 5 \\ -2 \\ \hline \end{array}$$

$$\begin{array}{r} 6 \\ -1 \\ \hline \end{array}$$

$$\begin{array}{r} 5 \\ -4 \\ \hline \end{array}$$

$$\begin{array}{r} 4 \\ -3 \\ \hline \end{array}$$

Cross out the objects to be taken away. Write the number that are left.

Name ____________________

$5 - 2 = 3$

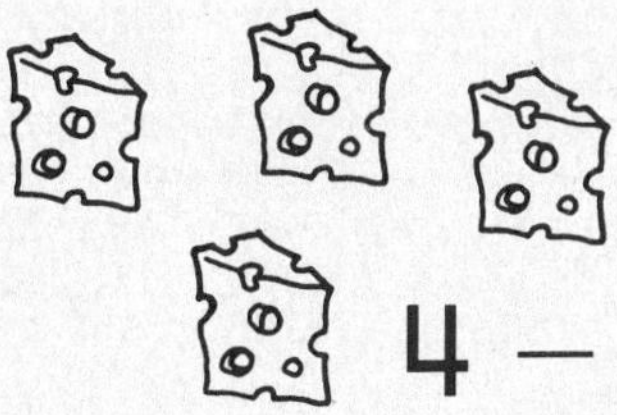

$4 - 3 = \square$

$3 - 1 = \square$

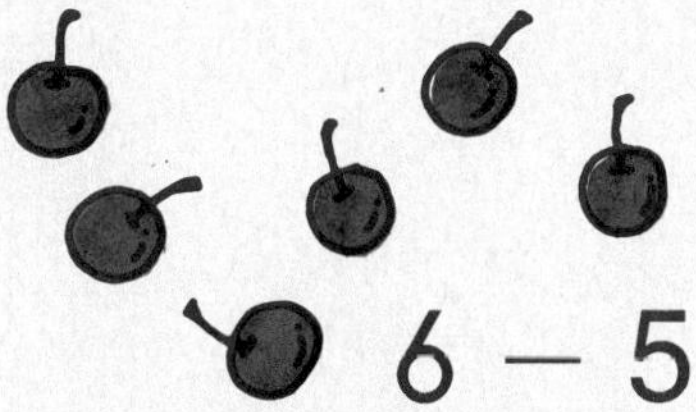

$6 - 5 = \square$

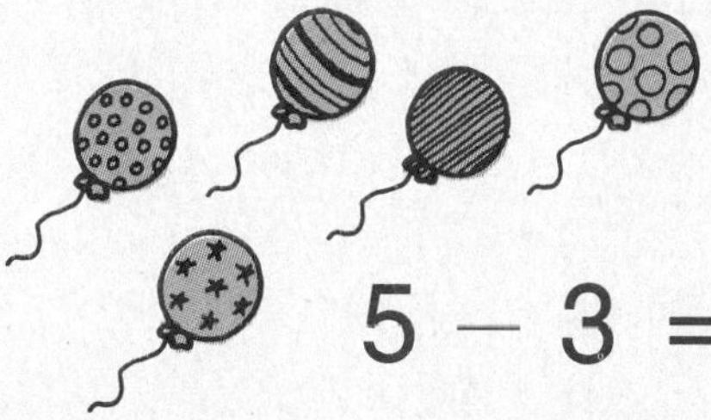

$5 - 3 = \square$

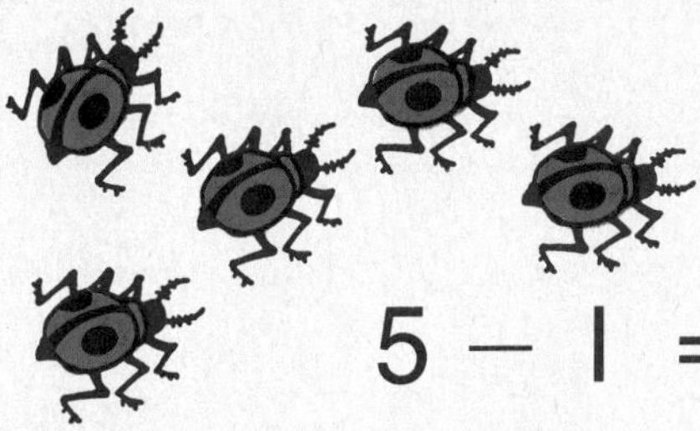

$5 - 1 = \square$

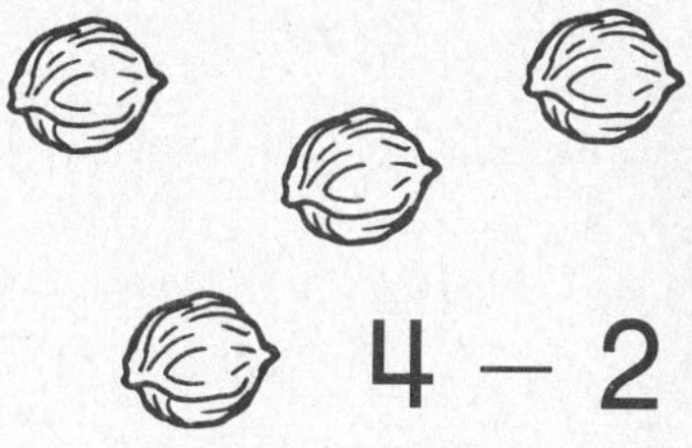

$4 - 2 = \square$

$6 - 3 = \square$

$5 - 4 = \square$

$3 - 2 = \square$

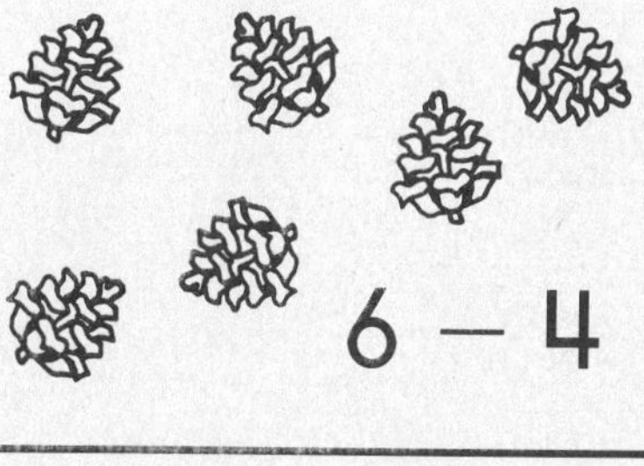

$6 - 4 = \square$

Cross out the objects to be taken away. Write the number that are left.

4 − 3   1   3 − 1

2   5 − 4

5 − 3

3   4 − 2

4 − 1

4

5 − 1   5 − 2

5

6 − 3   6 − 2

6 − 1

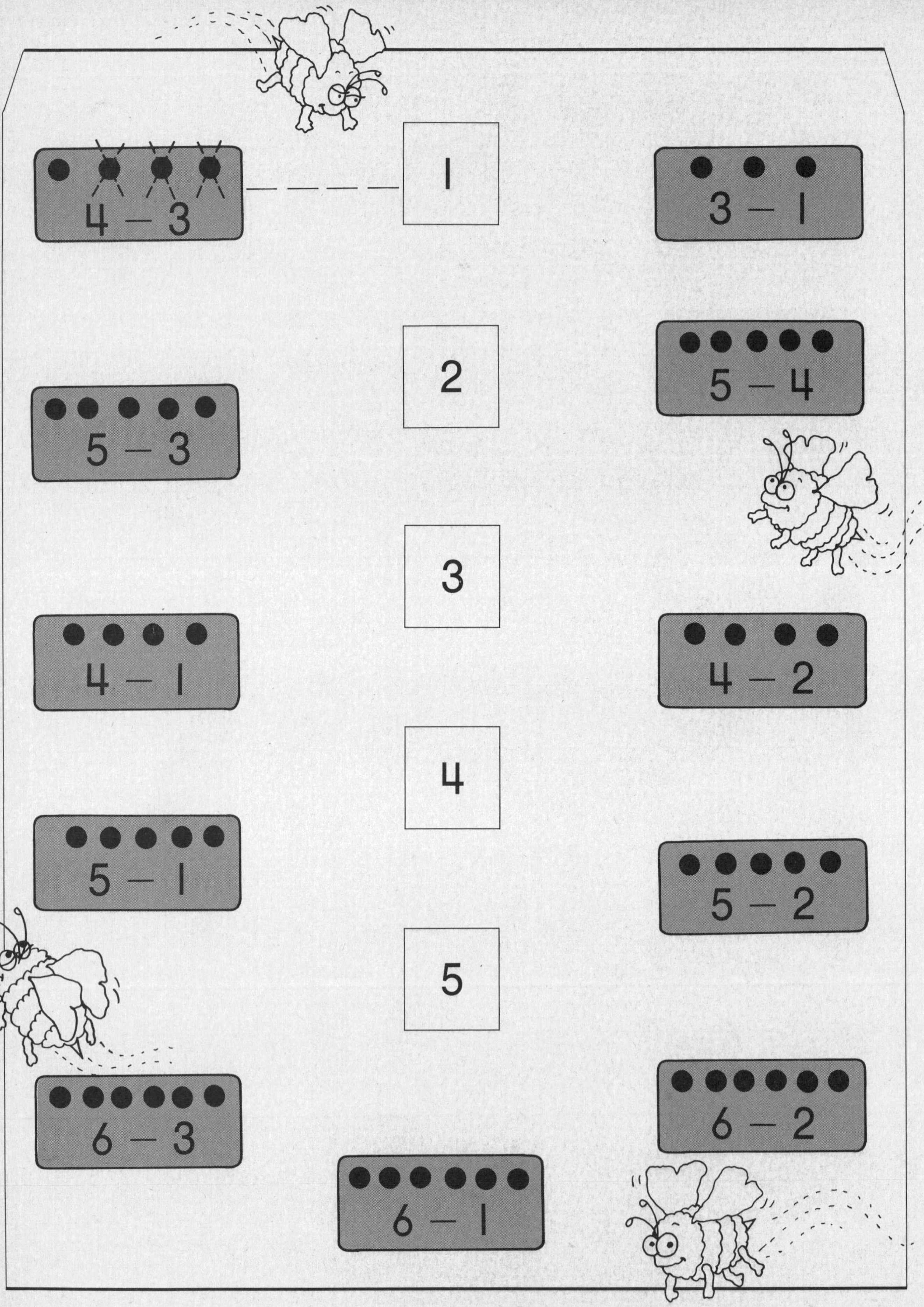

Draw a line from the domino to the number that tells how many dots are left.

Name ______________________________

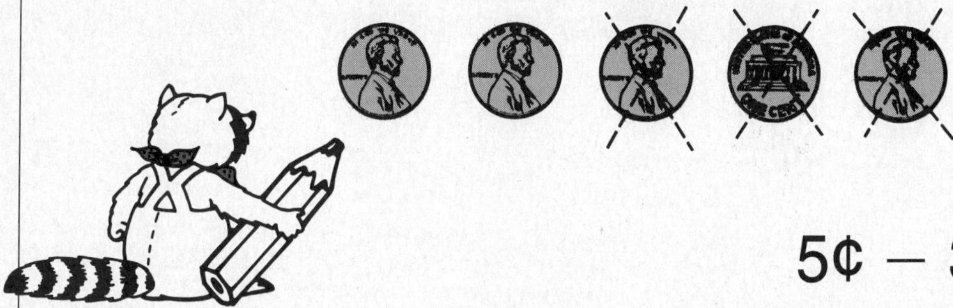

5¢ – 3¢ = 2 ¢

4¢ – 1¢ = ☐ ¢

4¢ – 2¢ = ☐ ¢

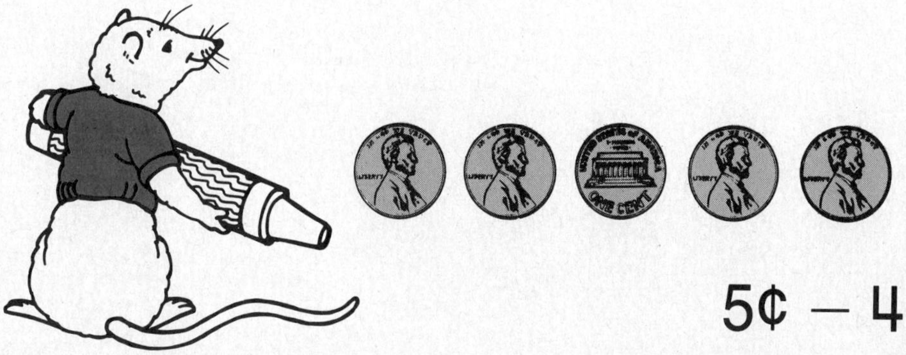

5¢ – 4¢ = ☐ ¢

Cross out the pennies to be taken away. Write how many cents are left.

4¢
− 3¢
☐ ¢

6¢
− 4¢
☐ ¢

5¢
− 2¢
☐ ¢

3¢
− 1¢
☐ ¢

6¢
− 3¢
☐ ¢

4¢
− 2¢
☐ ¢

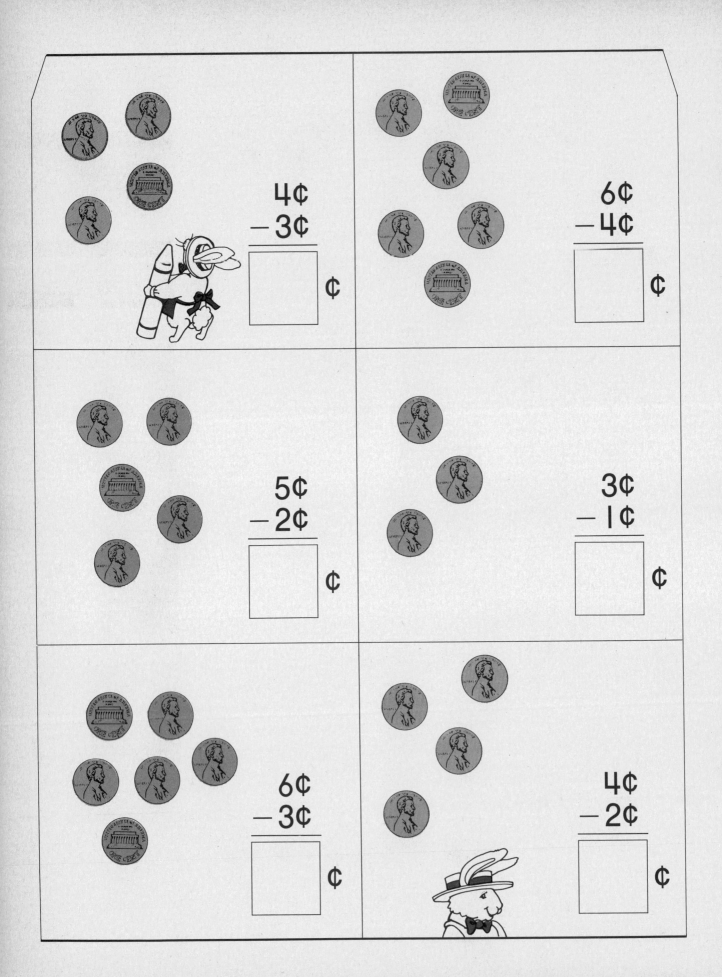

Cross out the pennies to be taken away. Write how many cents are left.

Name ____________________

3

4

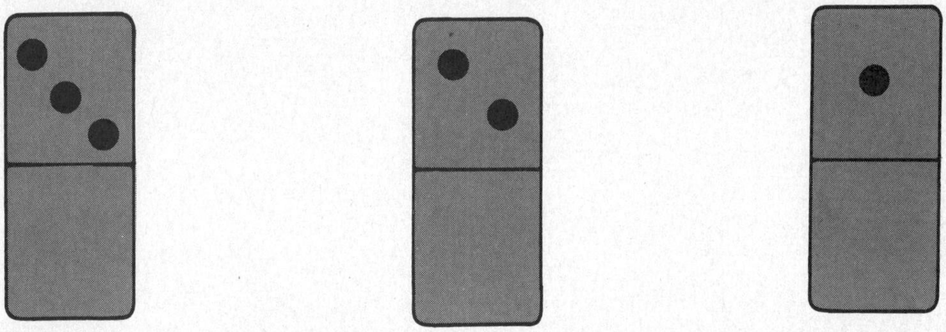

5

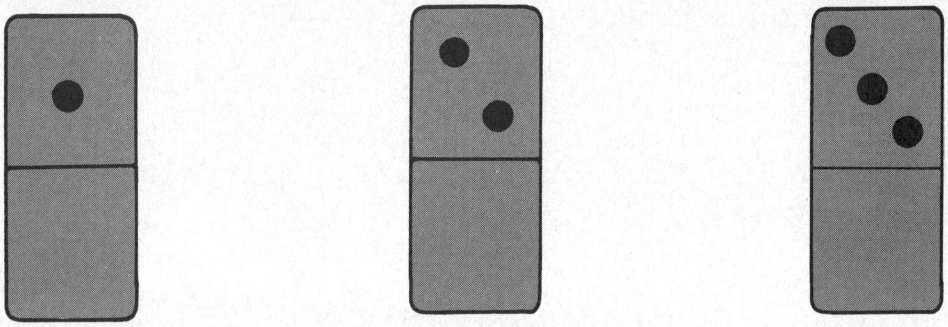

6

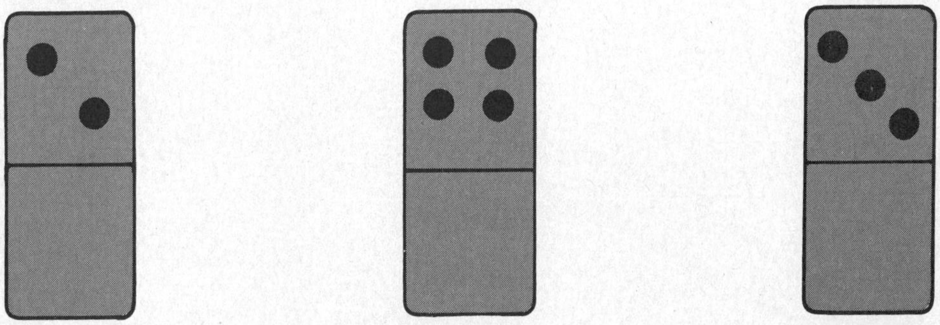

Draw enough dots on each domino to match the number on the left.

2
⊕ 1

3

4
○ 2

2

4
○ 1

3

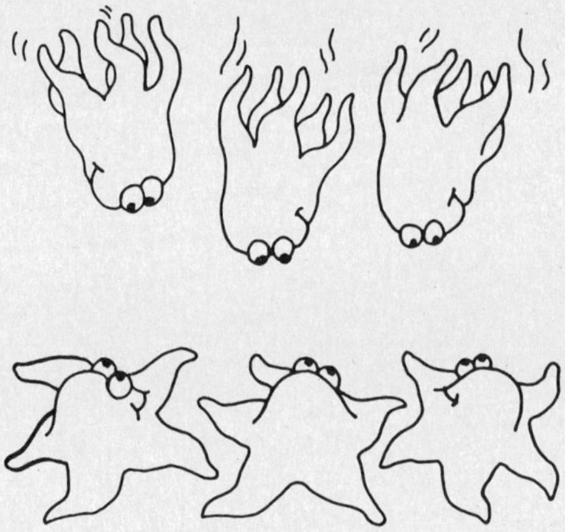

3
○ 3

6

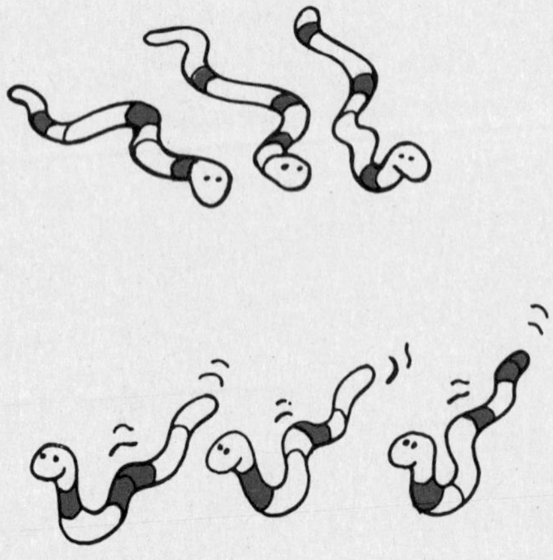

6
○ 3

3

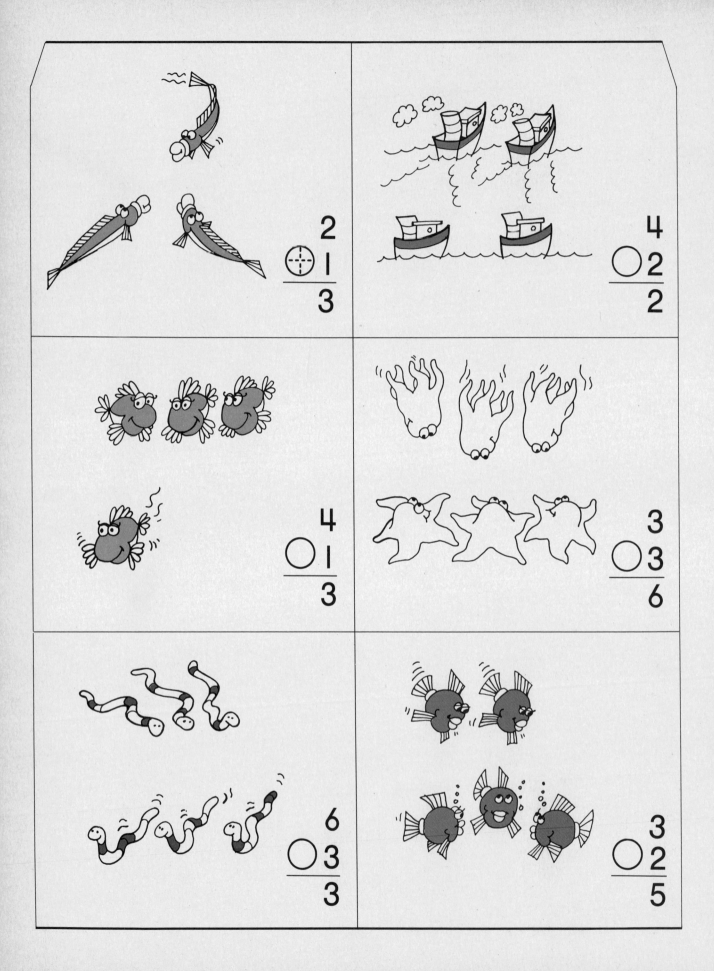

3
○ 2

5

Choose the correct operation. Write the + or − sign in the circle.

Name ____________________

$2 + 2 = 4$	$1 + 3 =$ ☐	$3 + 1 =$ ☐	$2 + 3 =$ ☐	$3 + 2 =$ ☐
$3 + 3 =$ ☐	$5 + 1 =$ ☐	$1 + 5 =$ ☐	$2 + 4 =$ ☐	$4 + 2 =$ ☐
$3 - 1 = 2$	$4 - 1 =$ ☐	$6 - 2 =$ ☐	$5 - 2 =$ ☐	$4 - 2 =$ ☐
$4 - 3 =$ ☐	$5 - 3 =$ ☐	$6 - 3 =$ ☐	$6 - 4 =$ ☐	$6 - 5 =$ ☐

Write the number that tells how many in all and how many are left.

$$\begin{array}{r} 3 \\ +2 \\ \hline \end{array}$$
$$\begin{array}{r} 5 \\ +1 \\ \hline \end{array}$$
$$\begin{array}{r} 2 \\ +4 \\ \hline \end{array}$$
$$\begin{array}{r} 3 \\ +1 \\ \hline \end{array}$$
$$\begin{array}{r} 4 \\ -2 \\ \hline \end{array}$$

$$\begin{array}{r} 6 \\ -3 \\ \hline \end{array}$$
$$\begin{array}{r} 5 \\ -1 \\ \hline \end{array}$$
$$\begin{array}{r} 3 \\ -2 \\ \hline \end{array}$$
$$\begin{array}{r} 1 \\ +5 \\ \hline \end{array}$$
$$\begin{array}{r} 2 \\ +3 \\ \hline \end{array}$$

$$\begin{array}{r} 4 \\ -3 \\ \hline \end{array}$$
$$\begin{array}{r} 3 \\ -1 \\ \hline \end{array}$$
$$\begin{array}{r} 2 \\ +2 \\ \hline \end{array}$$
$$\begin{array}{r} 6 \\ -4 \\ \hline \end{array}$$
$$\begin{array}{r} 4 \\ +2 \\ \hline \end{array}$$

$$\begin{array}{r} 5 \\ -3 \\ \hline \end{array}$$
$$\begin{array}{r} 3 \\ +3 \\ \hline \end{array}$$
$$\begin{array}{r} 5 \\ -2 \\ \hline \end{array}$$
$$\begin{array}{r} 6 \\ -1 \\ \hline \end{array}$$
$$\begin{array}{r} 1 \\ +4 \\ \hline \end{array}$$

Write the number that tells how many in all or how many are left.

Name ____________________

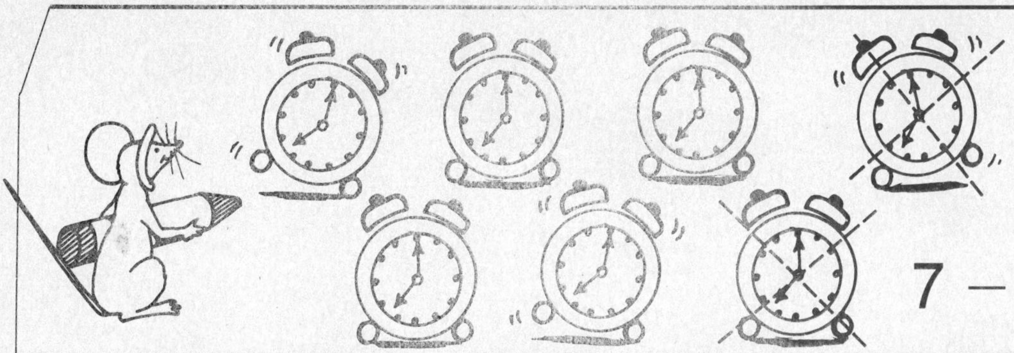

7 − 2 = 5

8 − 1 = ☐

9 − 2 = ☐

7 − 1 = ☐

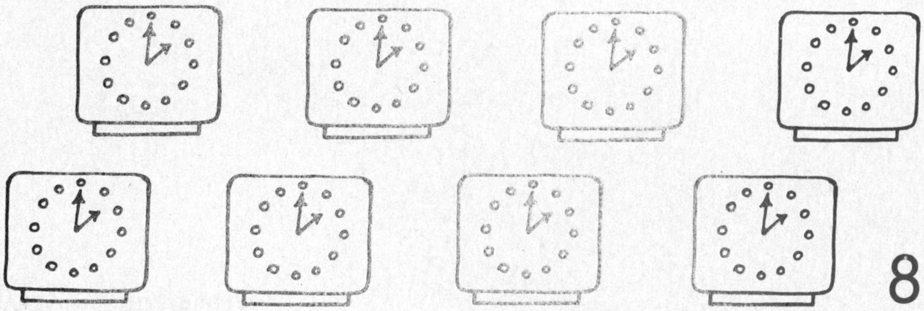

8 − 2 = ☐

Cross out the objects to be subtracted. Write the number left.

$$\begin{array}{r} 6 \\ -1 \\ \hline \end{array}$$

$$\begin{array}{r} 7 \\ -1 \\ \hline \end{array}$$

$$\begin{array}{r} 8 \\ -2 \\ \hline \end{array}$$

$$\begin{array}{r} 6 \\ -2 \\ \hline \end{array}$$

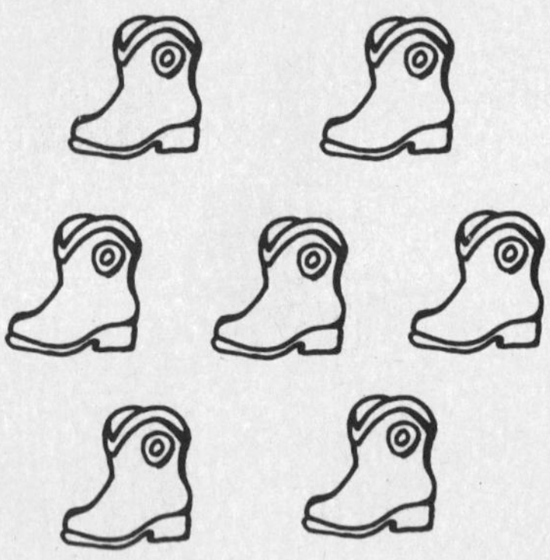

$$\begin{array}{r} 7 \\ -2 \\ \hline \end{array}$$

$$\begin{array}{r} 9 \\ -1 \\ \hline \end{array}$$

$$\begin{array}{r} 9 \\ -2 \\ \hline \end{array}$$

$$\begin{array}{r} 8 \\ -1 \\ \hline \end{array}$$

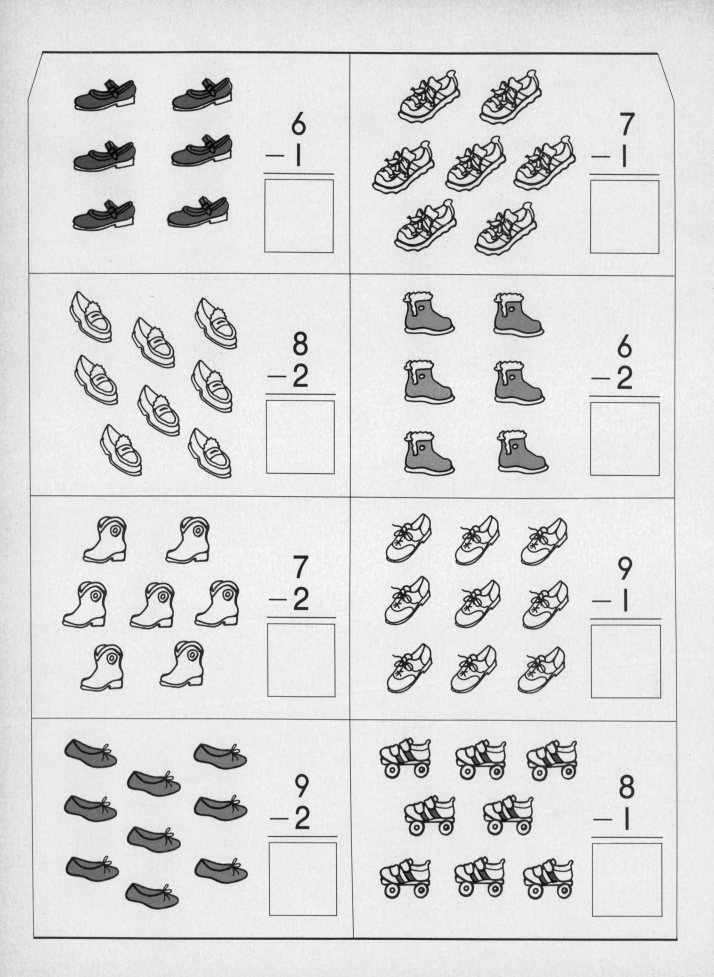

Cross out the objects to be taken away. Write the number left.

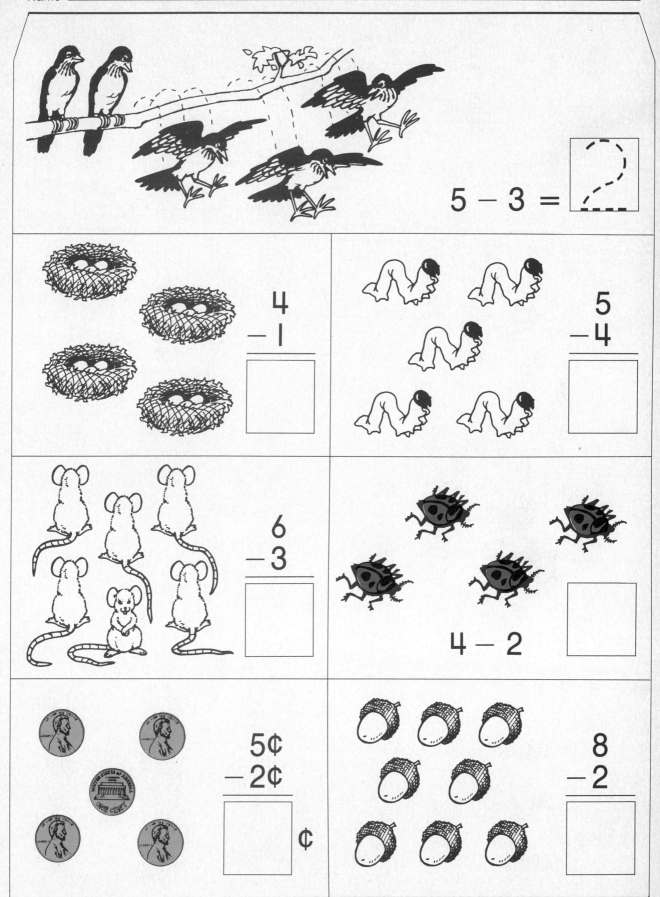

Name ____________________

$5 - 3 = 2$

$$\begin{array}{r} 4 \\ -1 \\ \hline \square \end{array}$$

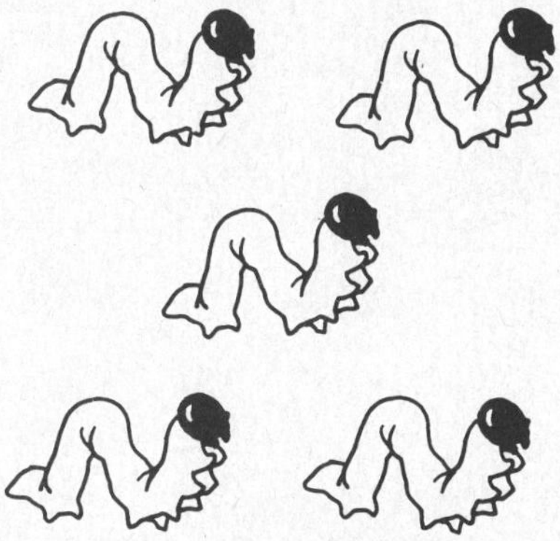

$$\begin{array}{r} 5 \\ -4 \\ \hline \square \end{array}$$

$$\begin{array}{r} 6 \\ -3 \\ \hline \square \end{array}$$

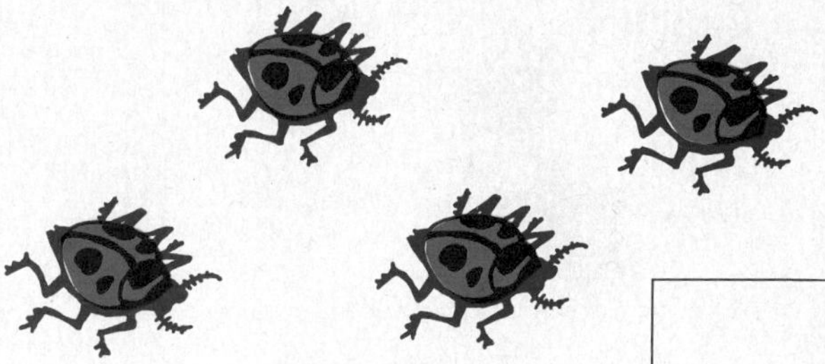

$4 - 2$ $\square$

$$\begin{array}{r} 5¢ \\ -2¢ \\ \hline \square ¢ \end{array}$$

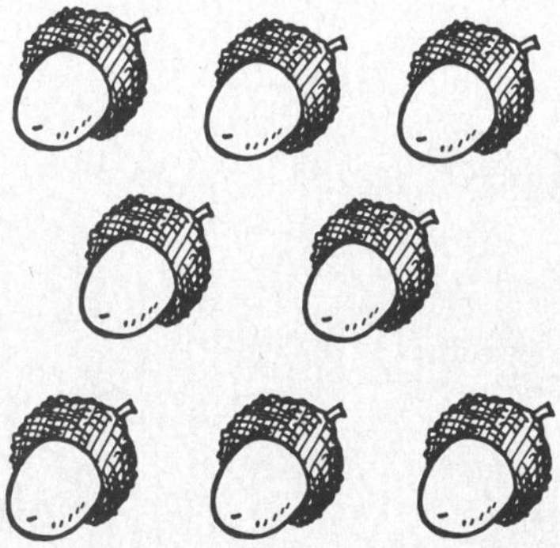

$$\begin{array}{r} 8 \\ -2 \\ \hline \square \end{array}$$

Chapter Checkup Cross out the objects to be taken away. Write the number left.

- 2 Brown
- 3 Purple
- 4 Red
- 5 Blue

Field Trip Write the answers. Color the picture using the number code.